MANY VOICES LITERATURE SERIES

AMERICAN SHORT STORIES

1920 TO THE PRESENT

Perfection Learning

★★

EDITORIAL DIRECTOR	Julie A. Schumacher
SENIOR EDITORS	Rebecca Christian, Terry Ofner
EDITORIAL ASSISTANTS	Suzanne Foggia, Megan Snyder
PERMISSIONS	Meghan Schumacher
DESIGN	William Seabright and Associates, Glencoe, Illinois
TEACHER REVIEWERS	LoAnn Campbell, Retired Teacher of English, Ames High School, Ames, Iowa
	Eric D. Turley, Teacher of English, Johnsburg High School, Johnsburg, Illinois
STUDENT REVIEWERS	Luke Scheele, Hermann High School, Hermann, Missouri
	George Thompson, Hoover High School, Des Moines, Iowa

Dr. Neil E. Nakadate, consultant for this book, is a Professor of English at Iowa State University, Ames, Iowa. A recipient of the Iowa State University Foundation Award for Career Achievement in Teaching, Dr. Nakadate earned a Ph.D. in English from Indiana University and specializes in contemporary American fiction. He is the author of several books and articles, including *Understanding Jane Smiley*. Dr. Nakadate reviewed selections for this volume and helped to shape the table of contents. His work also includes the essay "On Style" and the essays that introduce each unit. In addition, he wrote The Author's Style feature, which appears before each story.

Copyright © 2003 by Perfection Learning Corporation
1000 North Second Avenue
P.O. Box 500, Logan, Iowa 51546-0500
Tel: 1-800-831-4190 • Fax: 1-800-543-2745

Printed in the United States of America

6 7 8 9 10 11 RD 12 11 10 09 08 07

Paperback ISBN-10: 0-7891-5940-6   ISBN-13: 978-0-7891-5940-3
Hardback ISBN-10: 0-7569-9950-2   ISBN-13: 978-0-7569-9950-6

MANY VOICES LITERATURE SERIES

AMERICAN SHORT STORIES
1920 TO THE PRESENT

Perfection Learning

TO THE READER   8

ON STYLE   10

LITERARY ELEMENTS OF THE SHORT STORY   13

UNIT ONE

Literature from the 1920s to the 1940s

IN ANOTHER COUNTRY (1927)   ERNEST HEMINGWAY   21

HE (1930)   KATHERINE ANNE PORTER   29

BABYLON REVISITED (1931)   F. SCOTT FITZGERALD   43

THE FAR AND THE NEAR (1935)   THOMAS WOLFE   67

SUCKER (1936)   CARSON MCCULLERS   73

THE CHRYSANTHEMUMS (1937)   JOHN STEINBECK   85

WHY I LIVE AT THE P.O. (1941)   EUDORA WELTY   99

THE BLACK BALL (ca. 1941)   RALPH ELLISON   115

THE SECRET LIFE OF WALTER MITTY (1942)   JAMES THURBER   127

THE LOTTERY (1944)   SHIRLEY JACKSON   135

MIRIAM (1945)   TRUMAN CAPOTE   147

Responding to Unit One   162

UNIT TWO

Literature from the 1950s and 1960s

THE VELDT (1950) RAY BRADBURY   169

BARN BURNING (1950) WILLIAM FAULKNER   185

ANGEL LEVINE (1955) BERNARD MALAMUD   207

THE WRYSONS (1958) JOHN CHEEVER   221

HARRISON BERGERON (1961) KURT VONNEGUT   231

EVERYTHING THAT RISES MUST CONVERGE (1961)
        FLANNERY O'CONNOR   241

A & P (1961) JOHN UPDIKE   259

THE SKY IS GRAY (1963) ERNEST J. GAINES   269

THE WOOING OF ARIADNE (1965) HARRY MARK PETRAKIS   299

Responding to Unit Two   314

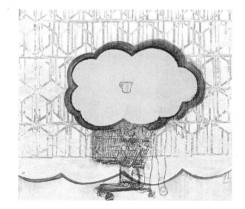

UNIT THREE

Literature from the 1970s and 1980s

THE KEY (1970) ISAAC BASHEVIS SINGER 321

THE FLOWERS (1973) ALICE WALKER 333

WHERE HAVE YOU GONE, CHARMING BILLY? (1975) TIM O'BRIEN 337

EVERYTHING STUCK TO HIM (1981) RAYMOND CARVER 349

DETROIT SKYLINE, 1949 (1982) BOBBIE ANN MASON 357

AMERICAN HORSE (1983) LOUISE ERDRICH 377

THE WRITER IN THE FAMILY (1984) E.L. DOCTOROW 391

THE FISH (1986) RUSSELL BANKS 407

TRUCKSTOP (1987) GARRISON KEILLOR 417

RULES OF THE GAME (1989) AMY TAN 425

Responding to Unit Three 438

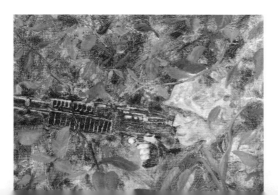

★★★

UNIT FOUR

Literature from the 1990s

LADIES AND GENTLEMEN: (1990)   JOYCE CAROL OATES   445

FAULT LINES (1992)   BARBARA KINGSOLVER   455

TOP OF THE FOOD CHAIN (1992)   T. CORAGHESSAN BOYLE   467

LETTERS FROM MY FATHER (1992)   ROBERT OLEN BUTLER   475

THIS IS WHAT IT MEANS TO SAY PHOENIX, ARIZONA (1993)
    SHERMAN ALEXIE   485

THE INTRUDER (1995)   ANDRE DUBUS   499

MORTALS (1996)   TOBIAS WOLFF   513

CHARLIE HOGLE'S EARRING (1997)   PAUL THEROUX   525

Responding to Unit Four   540

GLOSSARY OF LITERARY TERMS   542

INDEX OF TITLES AND AUTHORS   546

TO THE READER

An American father in search of his daughter in France. A ranch woman in the Salinas Valley who yearns for companionship and a sense of self-worth. A postmistress in Mississippi who decides to live at the post office after feuding with her eccentric family. A terrified soldier in Vietnam who longs for his Minnesota home.

These are some of the characters and situations you will encounter in *American Short Stories: 1920 to the Present*. They are as varied as the geography of the U.S. itself. Yet their common denominator is that each is part of a short story, a form—like jazz or baseball—that some claim is uniquely American.

Of course, thousands of American short stories have been written, and collections of them abound. What sets this volume apart is its emphasis on the authors' writing styles. By examining approaches as diverse as the spare, understated prose of Ernest Hemingway and the dazzling imagery of Louise Erdrich, you will come to recognize many elements of style. It has been said that style is comprised of the fingerprints an author leaves on a story, making it so unmistakably his or hers that a careful reader can tell who has written it without the byline.

As many of the writers in this volume have remarked, good reading comes before good writing. Reading this book and completing the activities will help you shape your own writing style.

Aside from what you will learn about style, this volume provides an overview of the American short story's development over the last century. Many literary historians credit Edgar Allan Poe, the master of horror, with inventing, or at least refining, the short story form in the mid-19th century. He saw the short story as different from the novel not only in length but also in intention and form. Writing when Americans were still trying to create a distinct literature for their country, Poe developed highly atmospheric, tightly constructed stories in which brevity and unity contributed to a single, focused effect.

Other American writers followed Poe's example by developing their own subjects and methods. From the beginning, a particular focus of the American short story has been the theme of personal identity, often explored in stories of personal quests that determine an individual's sense of self and relationship to others and the world.

During the 19th century, nearly all of the basic themes and issues of the American short story were introduced and developed by writers such as Nathaniel Hawthorne, Herman Melville, Mark Twain, and Kate Chopin. These and other writers focused on specifically American locations, subjects, and problems, developing a wide range of styles for storytelling. Their stories arose from local history, moral fables, character studies, and the dilemmas posed by race and class.

Against the backdrop of westward expansion, the effects of the Industrial Revolution, and the impact of wave after wave of immigration, American writers explored crucial moments of insight in response to conflicts and dilemmas. The short story—with its limited cast of characters, few scenes or episodes, and focus on a single effect—provided a good forum for such explorations. It was practical, besides. With Americans spread out across a continent, ten cent magazines delivered nationwide by mail gave the country a sense of having its own literature. It also provided a mass market for short story writers.

Change was even more rapid in the 20th century, when the stories in this volume begin. Social, political, and cultural developments included the building of transcontinental highways, the Constitutional amendment allowing women to vote, and broad recognition that World War I had introduced a new era of fears and possibilities. American stories since 1920 frequently focus on the relationships of individuals to the changing times, other people, and locations both familiar and new.

Many 20th-century writers whose works are represented in this book convey a firm sense of regional identity. Others focus on the lives of people in the city and the suburbs. Still others explore ethnic identity. The approaches of these writers range from the use of straightforward plots with conventional language to the creation of quirky plot lines, points of view, and narrative voices. The tone ranges from assertive pride to playful irony to sympathy for suffering and loss.

Since the United States is constantly changing, no single story could appropriately be called the American story. America is a complex whole, comprised of countless individual experiences. To read this collection of short stories is not to define the American experience so much as to learn from various pieces of it. It is to find yourself—in a phrase borrowed from John Steinbeck—in search of America.

ON STYLE

As you study this collection of American short stories, you will be introduced to some of the 20th century's most important writers. Almost certainly you won't "like" every one, but each author has a unique message to send and a distinctive way of sending it. The way a writer conveys a message is called his or her style. Whether in clothing, music, visual art, or literature, style is easy to see but hard to define. You might think of style in writing as the way thoughts are *dressed*. While reading this collection of the greatest short stories from the 20th century, you will be able to explore the authors' styles. Analyzing style will make you a more perceptive reader and help you develop your own writer's voice. A good definition of style for this book is that it is *the author's distinctive manner of expression.*

As in most arts, it takes time and familiarity to recognize distinctions among literary styles. Perhaps an analogy will help here. To the untrained eye, a forest is just a collection of indistinct trees. To the trained eye, however, the forest is composed of a grove of white oaks on the hillside, a stand of willows by the stream, and thorn-bearing hawthorn trees along its edges. As you read, follow the Literary Lens prompts and pay close attention to the information about the author's life and style that precedes each selection. Before long, clear distinctions will emerge.

In fact, some writers have such distinctive styles that they have spawned imitators. The works of authors who follow paths blazed by Ernest Hemingway and William Faulkner are sometimes called "Hemingwayesque" or "Faulknerian." Hemingway probably would have been startled by such praise. He once wrote, "In stating as fully as I could how things were, it was often very difficult and I wrote awkwardly and the awkwardness is what they called my style."

Hemingway is not alone in implying that he never deliberately set out to create a style, but only wrote as well as he could instinctively. Katherine Anne Porter once complained, "I've been called a stylist until I really could tear my hair out. And I simply don't believe in style. Style is you."

Style is hard to describe because part of it is a certain indefinable uniqueness. Some aspects of style are easier to pin down, however. That's because style includes the set of choices and techniques that enable a writer to tell a story. Choices regarding **characterization**, **setting**, and **tone**—to name a few—impact the style of a story. But there are other sources of style, such as the author's background, whether that author is a man or a woman, and the author's race or ethnicity.

For example, F. Scott Fitzgerald grew up in modest circumstances in St. Paul, Minnesota. He later left the Midwest and became fascinated with the flamboyant rich of the East Coast. Fitzgerald's descriptions often mix criticism, sympathy, and awe for the rich lifestyle, as in this one-line character sketch in his novel *The Great Gatsby*: "Her voice is full of money." The stories of Alice Walker, on the other hand, come out of her experience as a woman of color growing up in the United States. Her fiction often depicts a female character finding her way in an environment of oppression.

Personal **values** also determine writers' attitudes toward their characters. John Steinbeck's sympathies for those who fled the Oklahoma Dust Bowl of the 1930s went into his writing about the struggle of common people for economic justice. Flannery O'Connor's fiction reflects her devout Catholicism; her grotesque characters and often violent story lines express her belief in the need for salvation. The combination of background, gender, ethnicity, and values makes up the author's **world view**.

Style also develops from writers' responses to earlier writers they have read. Some choose to work within a **stylistic tradition**, such as **social realism**, in which the everyday lives of characters are depicted against a social, political, and economic background that is presented as a matter of fact. John Steinbeck, Katherine Anne Porter, John Updike, and Russell Banks are among the American writers in this tradition. Other writers rebel against tradition or find it necessary to innovate. They develop new styles to convey a particular point of view. For example, William Faulkner uses **internal monologue** to narrate stories through characters whose limitations would make it impossible for them to tell their stories in the usual way. Ray Bradbury and Kurt Vonnegut use futuristic settings in order to question and probe current attitudes and trends.

Another aspect of style is **tone**, or the author's attitude toward his or her subject. Words such as "sympathetic," "comic," "passionate," or "harsh" can be used to describe the attitude of the writer. The tone helps determine the story's intellectual and emotional impact on the reader. One of the dominant tones of fiction in the 20th century is **irony**. Irony reflects the sadness or humor resulting from the gap between life as it is idealized, and life as it really is. Generally irony is used to criticize some aspect of society or to reveal the silliness of people's behavior. Irony also results from unusual or unexpected points of view, oddly humorous situations, and shocking revelations or sudden turns of event. Sherman Alexie uses ironic humor to reveal the sad realities of Native American life on and off the reservation. Flannery O'Connor, Kurt Vonnegut, John Cheever, Joyce Carol Oates, and T. Coraghessan Boyle are among many whose stories use irony that is sometimes comic and sometimes bitingly satirical.

Finally, style includes the way a writer uses language. Some writers, like Thomas Wolfe, are said to be **lyrical**—that is, expressing intense personal emotions in much the same way as a songwriter or poet. Some, like Raymond Carver, are considered **minimalists**—that is, they let the events of the story speak for themselves without much interpretation from the author. Others, like Harry Mark Petrakis, are described as **colorful**, meaning full of variety and interest. Still others, such as T. Coraghessan Boyle, are labeled **energetic**, writing in a way that is so highly charged the reader has little choice but to go along for the ride.

Other contributions to style include: language used by the story's narrator and in the dialogue of characters; variations in **dialect** and usage that are tied to particular groups of people or regions of the country; repetitions of key words and phrases; and even the length and structure of individual sentences. Truman Capote once wrote, "I think of myself as a stylist, and stylists can become notoriously obsessed with the placing of a comma, the weight of a semicolon."

Faulkner's long, sometimes convoluted sentences convey the dynamic intensity of his characters' thoughts and emotions while the dialogue of his characters is written in the rural **vernacular** of his native Mississippi. The rhythm of Yiddish storytelling is reflected in the prose of Isaac Bashevis Singer. The speech of Katherine Anne Porter's characters often reflects her roots in rural Texas and the languages of Mexico and other countries in which she lived. The dialogue of the American-born daughters and native Chinese mothers in Amy Tan's stories reveal the barriers that language differences can create within a family as well as within a society.

Ultimately, how you respond to the author's style contributes greatly to the pleasure of reading. As American poet Robert Frost put it, "All the fun's in how you say a thing."

LITERARY ELEMENTS OF THE SHORT STORY

Once upon a time" is a phrase that beckons young and old alike because it lets readers or listeners know that a story is coming. Whether it unfolds through the oral tradition, on the screen of a television, or in the pages of a book like this one, a story takes us out of our lives and helps us make sense of them at the same time.

A story can be defined simply as a telling of incidents or events. A useful definition for this book is that a story is *a fictional narrative shorter than a novel*. Whatever the definition, a story contains the following basic elements.

Plot

Simply put, the plot of a story is what happens in it. As one old saying has it, the writer gets the hero up a tree and then gets him back down again. Also known as narrative structure, a plot usually includes causality: one event causes another, which causes another, and so on until the story ends. There are a variety of ways that stories move from beginning to end. The most common plot structure moves from **exposition** through **rising action** to a **climax**, followed by the resolution.

In the exposition we are introduced to the main character, or **protagonist**, in his or her familiar **setting**—be that a neighborhood in New York City or a farm in the Salinas Valley of California. If the narrative continued describing this "normal" life, there would be no story. A problem or **conflict** is needed to move the story forward. The conflict may be **external**—perhaps between the protagonist and a family member or between the protagonist and nature; or the problem may be **internal**—between the protagonist's sense of duty and her desire for freedom, for example. Complex stories often have both external and internal conflicts. As the conflict deepens, the story is propelled through the rising action to the climax, or high point. Here that bully of an aunt is confronted, the life-saving fire is started, or the inner demon is discovered. The tension of the climax is released in the **resolution**, or as it sometimes called, the *dénouement*, a French word that literally means "untying." In the resolution, the knot of the conflict is untied and everyone that is still alive goes on to a new "normal" existence.

Of course, not all stories conform to the above plot structure. Some stories start at a high point in the action, employing a technique known as *in media res,* which means "in the midst of things." Such stories will fill in the exposition along the way through **dialogue** or embedded stories. Another approach is to tell the ending first and fill in the rest through **flashbacks**, one effect of which is to make the reader pay close attention to motives and causes. Whatever the plot structure, you can be sure that there will be a problem and a character to confront it.

Character

Readers keep turning the pages of stories mainly because they are interested in what happens to the characters. Called characterization, the development of believable characters is perhaps the most basic task of the author. But writers have many tools at their disposal. Besides direct description of a character's traits, the author can also reveal character through actions, speeches, thoughts, feelings, and interactions with others. Depending on the type of story being told and the stylistic tradition the author is working in, characters may be fully drawn and realistic or they may be representative character types. How important they are to the story determines whether they are main or primary characters, secondary characters, or minor characters. The more crucial the character is to the plot, the more he or she will be developed by the author. Even in stories that stress realism, some minor characters might only be present as types rather than as individuals.

Another important part of characterization is **point of view**, or the eyes through which the story is told. This is determined through the author's choice of narrator. There are three main narrative points of view: **first person**, **third person limited**, and **third person omniscient**. In the first person or "I" point of view, the narrator tells his or her own story as Huck does in *The Adventures of Huckleberry Finn.* The third person limited narrator is a character in the story and only sees, hears, and knows what that character could see, hear, and know. This means that he or she might only have partial knowledge and understanding of the events and other characters. Doctor Watson of the Sherlock Holmes tales is a good example of this type of narrator. Often this limited point of view is that of the major character or protagonist, but sometimes the author chooses to tell the story from the limited point of view of a secondary character.

The third person omniscient narrator sees all and is able to comment on any aspect of the story because the narrator is an outsider, not a character in the story. Readers often like to equate the omniscient narrator with the author, but it is good to remember that any narrator or point of view is a carefully developed tool and not simply the author's voice. Some stories switch back and forth between various points of view.

Setting

A **setting** is where and when a story takes place. It is important because environment has a strong impact on what happens in a story. In this book, for example, some stories are set in Harlem, New York; a ranching area of California; and a sleepy town in the Deep South. These environments influence not only the action but also the characters' attitudes. Setting can also help to shape how characters speak and behave. Sometimes the setting of a story assumes almost as much importance in the reader's imagination as memorable characters do.

Theme

The **theme** is the underlying meaning or message of a story. A story may evoke more than one theme, depending upon your interpretation of the narrative. For example, a story in which a character struggles with a decision to lead a conventional life or seek freedom and adventure could be interpreted several ways. One person might summarize the theme of the story as "rash behavior leads to ruin" whereas another might say "it is better to have tried and failed than to have never tried at all." Whatever theme you might come up with for a story, it is important to realize that the theme statement is not the story. Authors usually don't write stories with a theme in mind. They might get an idea from a news item which gives them an idea for a character. Once the character is alive on the page, the character may take the story into places the author never dreamed. And that is the point, after all. We read stories so that they will take us to places we have never been before. Have a good trip.

For a full list of literary terms, see the *Glossary of Literary Terms* on pages 542–545.

UNIT ONE

Literature from the 1920s to the 1940s

Literature from the 1920s to the 1940s

top to bottom: 1930: *Couple Descending a Staircase* by J.C. Leyendecker illustrates the indulgent pursuit of pleasure and wealth during the 1920s. ★ 1933: *The White Angel Breadline* by Dorothea Lange. This and other Lange photos put a face on the devastation of the Great Depression. ★ 1945: *The Liberation of Buchenwald* by Margaret Bourke-White showed the world the horror of the WWII Nazi concentration camps.

The years between 1920 and 1950 were ones of tumult and growth for the United States. This was reflected in the literature of the period as the country recovered from the trauma of World War I and then reveled in the energetic social and cultural ferment of the "Roaring Twenties." The exuberance of the twenties was stilled in the thirties as the country grappled with economic disaster, which began with the stock market crash of 1929. The crash, which was followed by a long-term depression and a terrible drought in the country's heartland, led to quiet despair for many Americans. Ironically, it took World War II to restore the economy as the country's factories began to produce the material needed to allow the U.S. to take a leading role in stopping fascism and imperialism in Europe.

The thirties and forties were major decades in the era referred to as modern. In this period, much of the writing reflected a national mood of sober reality rather than the earlier optimism of the beginning of the century. A sense of separation, deprivation, and loss was prevalent. This is reflected in many of the stories and novels of the era, such as Ernest Hemingway's war stories and F. Scott Fitzgerald's tales of The Jazz Age and the "crack-up" that followed it. Meanwhile, John Steinbeck contributed gritty stories of working-class struggle. In many of the short stories from the period, dreaming, healing, and survival are prominent themes. Also notable is a tone of wistfulness for something better—more money and security, more excitement or love, peace in the family and the world.

American literature of this era also reflected the beginnings of numerous migrations. African Americans were drawn from the South by promises of more freedom and economic opportunity up North. The artistic flowering of the Harlem

Renaissance was one reflection of this trend. At the same time, there was a nationwide migration from the country to the cities, giving rise to new possibilities as well as new problems. A strain of nostalgia for simpler or more innocent times can be heard in the stories of Wolfe and Fitzgerald. And finally, tens of thousands were drawn toward the "golden" West, a migration chronicled in the fiction of John Steinbeck.

Many of the stories of this period focus less on historical or public events than on the specific places and families in which individuals made their lives. In his novels and stories, Thomas Wolfe wrote poignantly about what it means to long for home, and James Thurber's cartoons and stories provided readers with a humorous view of their own silliness. Regional writers from the Midwest (including Hemingway and Fitzgerald) and from the South (Wolfe, William Faulkner, Carson McCullers, Eudora Welty, and Truman Capote) gained a national readership.

The styles of this period range from the pared-down sentences of Hemingway to the brilliantly descriptive writing of Fitzgerald and the emotional prose of Wolfe. Katherine Anne

Porter developed sensitive and complex character studies. Faulkner experimented with internal monologue and stream-of-consciousness. The basic tone of literature of the era was ironic—one that called attention to the gap between what people believed and wanted, and what their lives were really like.

top to bottom: 1930: Adolph Hitler at a Nazi rally in Dortmund, Germany. ★ 1936: *Death of a Loyalist Soldier* by Robert Capa, taken during the Spanish Civil War (1936–1939). Almost 3,000 American volunteers formed the Abe Lincoln Brigade in a losing cause to defend Spain against a military takeover led by General Francisco Franco. ★ 1936: *Dust Bowl* by Arthur Rothstein. Severe drought caused the collapse of farming in the Midwest at a time when America was already suffering from the Depression. ★ 1940: *St. Paul's Cathedral* was photographed by John Topham during a WWII firebomb attack on London. ★ 1945: *Iwo Jima* by Joe Rosenthal. Marines raise the flag at the top of Mt. Suribachi on the Japanese island of Iwo Jima. A fierce battle for the island raged for 36 days and resulted in over 23,000 U.S. casualties, including three of the flag raisers in the picture.

Ernest Hemingway
1899–1961

About the Author

An innovative writing style and an adventurous, much-publicized life made Ernest Hemingway not only one of the most influential writers of the 20th century but also a cultural icon. A leader of the post-World War I group of artists known as "The Lost Generation," Hemingway was a big game hunter and fisherman, world traveler, and war correspondent. These pursuits influenced his work, which is often set in Africa or Europe.

Born to a doctor's family in Oak Park, Illinois, Hemingway edited his high school newspaper and worked as a reporter at *The Kansas City Star*. He served as an ambulance driver during World War I and was seriously wounded at the age of eighteen.

Like the heroes of his fiction, the author courted danger to prove his courage. Two plane crashes late in life left him in a state of chronic pain that some say prompted his suicide. Like his father before him, he died of a self-inflicted gunshot wound. Among his best-known works are the novels *A Farewell to Arms* and *The Old Man and the Sea*, the latter of which earned the Pulitzer Prize.

* * * * * * * * * * *

The Author's Style

Many of Hemingway's stories involve initiations or tests, both of which stress codes of conduct that typically require courage and endurance. His characters are involved in violent activities such as boxing, hunting, bullfighting, and combat, where they are in a position to suffer both physical and psychological wounds.

Spare, understated prose is a hallmark of the Hemingway style. It emphasizes carefully pared-down declarative sentences based on simple syntax, strategic repetition, and a minimum of explanatory material. This style nevertheless conveys his characters' situations and feelings. It is considered by many to be his most important contribution to 20th-century American fiction.

Hemingway mistrusted flowery and official-sounding language, preferring to use much simpler, concrete language in both narration and dialogue.

The ironic tone of Hemingway's storytelling is also crucial. In his war stories, it reflects his cynicism about authorities who use notions such as duty in pushing naïve soldiers to sacrifice themselves. Sometimes a Hemingway character uses irony to protect himself from fully acknowledging the depth of his pain. So it is particularly important whenever a Hemingway character does make a direct statement about his feelings or his situation. The story you are about to read owes its insight to the author's personal war experiences.

LITERARY LENS Pay attention to the mood of this story.

In Another Country

ERNEST HEMINGWAY

In the fall the war was always there, but we did not go to it any more. It was cold in the fall in Milan[1] and the dark came very early. Then the electric lights came on, and it was pleasant along the streets looking in the windows. There was much game hanging outside the shops, and the snow powdered in the fur of the foxes and the wind blew their tails. The deer hung stiff and heavy and empty, and small birds blew in the wind and the wind turned their feathers. It was a cold fall and the wind came down from the mountains.

We were all at the hospital every afternoon, and there were different ways of walking across the town through the dusk to the hospital. Two of the ways were alongside canals, but they were long. Always, though, you crossed a bridge across a canal to enter the

---

1 **Milan:** a large city in northern Italy

hospital. There was a choice of three bridges. On one of them a woman sold roasted chestnuts. It was warm, standing in front of her charcoal fire, and the chestnuts were warm afterward in your pocket. The hospital was very old and very beautiful, and you entered through a gate and walked across a courtyard and out a gate on the other side. There were usually funerals starting from the courtyard. Beyond the old hospital were the new brick **pavilions**, and there we met every afternoon and were all very polite and interested in what was the matter, and sat in the machines that were to make so much difference.

pavilions:
annexes;
outbuildings

The doctor came up to the machine where I was sitting and said: "What did you like best to do before the war? Did you practice a sport?"

I said: "Yes, football."

"Good," he said. "You will be able to play football again better than ever."

My knee did not bend and the leg dropped straight from the knee to the ankle without a calf, and the machine was to bend the knee and make it move as in riding a tricycle. But it did not bend yet, and instead the machine lurched when it came to the bending part. The doctor said: "That will all pass. You are a fortunate young man. You will play football again like a champion."

In the next machine was a major who had a little hand like a baby's. He winked at me when the doctor examined his hand, which was between two leather straps that bounced up and down and flapped the stiff fingers, and said: "And will I too play football, captain-doctor?" He had been a very great fencer, and before the war the greatest fencer in Italy.

The doctor went to his office in a back room and brought a photograph which showed a hand that had been withered almost as small as the major's, before it had taken a machine course, and after was a little larger. The major held the photograph with his good hand and looked at it very carefully. "A wound?" he asked.

"An industrial accident," the doctor said.

"Very interesting, very interesting," the major said, and handed it back to the doctor.

"You have confidence?"

"No," said the major.

There were three boys who came each day who were about the same age I was. They were all three from Milan, and one of them was to be a lawyer, and one was to be a painter, and one had intended to be a soldier, and after we were finished with the machines, sometimes we walked back together to the Café Cova, which was next door to the Scala.[2] We walked the short way through the communist quarter because we were four together. The people hated us because we were officers, and from a wine-shop someone would call out, "*A basso gli ufficiali!*"[3] as we passed. Another boy who walked with us sometimes and made us five wore a black silk handkerchief across his face because he had no nose then and his face was to be rebuilt. He had gone out to the front from the military academy and been wounded within an hour after he had gone into the front line for the first time. They rebuilt his face, but he came from a very old family and they could never get the nose exactly right. He went to South America and worked in a bank. But this was a long time ago, and then we did not any of us know how it was going to be afterward. We only knew then that there was always the war, but that we were not going to it any more.

We all had the same medals, except the boy with the black silk bandage across his face, and he had not been at the front long enough to get any medals. The tall boy with the very pale face who was to be a lawyer had been lieutenant of *Arditi*[4] and had three medals of the sort we each had only one of. He had lived a very long time with death and was a little detached. We were all a little detached, and there was nothing that held us together except that we met every

ERNEST HEMINGWAY RECOVERING FROM WWI WOUNDS, ITALY, 1919

afternoon at the hospital. Although, as we walked to the Cova through the tough part of town, walking in the dark, with light and singing coming out of the wine-shops, and sometimes having to walk into the street when the

---

2 **Scala:** La Scala, a famous opera house in Milan

3 **"A basso gli ufficiali!":** Italian for "Down with the officers!"

4 **Arditi:** heavily armed and highly trained soldiers who were given the most dangerous combat assignments

The boys at first were very polite about my medals and asked me what I had done to get them.

men and women would crowd together on the sidewalk so that we would have had to jostle them to get by, we felt held together by there being something that had happened that they, the people who disliked us, did not understand.

We ourselves all understood the Cova, where it was rich and warm and not too brightly lighted, and noisy and smoky at certain hours, and there were always girls at the tables and the illustrated papers on a rack on the wall. The girls at the Cova were very patriotic, and I found that the most patriotic people in Italy were the café girls—and I believe they are still patriotic.

The boys at first were very polite about my medals and asked me what I had done to get them. I showed them the papers, which were written in very beautiful language and full of *fratellanza*[5] and *abnegazione*,[6] but which really said, with the adjectives removed, that I had been given the medals because I was an American. After that their manner changed a little toward me, although I was their friend against outsiders. I was a friend, but I was never really one of them after they had read the citations, because it had been different with them and they had done very different things to get their medals. I had been wounded, it was true; but we all knew that being wounded, after all, was really an accident. I was never ashamed of the ribbons, though, and sometimes, after the cocktail hour, I would imagine myself having done all the things they had done to get their medals; but walking home at night through the empty streets with the cold wind and all the shops closed, trying to keep near the street lights, I knew that I would never have done such things, and I was very much afraid to die, and often lay in bed at night by myself, afraid to die and wondering how I would be when I went back to the front again.

The three with the medals were like hunting-hawks;[7] and I was not a hawk, although I might seem a hawk to those who had never hunted; they, the three, knew better and so we drifted apart. But I stayed good friends with

---

5 *fratellanza:* brotherhood

6 *abnegazione:* sacrifice

7 **hunting-hawks:** Literally, hunting hawks are birds trained to hunt and kill prey; with reference to war, "hawks" are people who are pro-military.

the boy who had been wounded his first day at the front, because he would never know now how he would have turned out; so he could never be accepted either, and I liked him because I thought perhaps he would not have turned out to be a hawk either.

The major, who had been the great fencer, did not believe in bravery, and spent much time while we sat in the machines correcting my grammar. He had complimented me on how I spoke Italian, and we talked together very easily. One day I had said that Italian seemed such an easy language to me that I could not take a great interest in it; everything was so easy to say. "Ah, yes," the major said. "Why, then, do you not take up the use of grammar?" So we took up the use of grammar, and soon Italian was such a difficult language that I was afraid to talk to him until I had the grammar straight in my mind.

The major came very regularly to the hospital. I do not think he ever missed a day, although I am sure he did not believe in the machines. There was a time when none of us believed in the machines, and one day the major said it was all nonsense. The machines were new then and it was we who were to prove them. It was an idiotic idea, he said, "a theory, like another." I had not learned my grammar, and he said I was a stupid impossible disgrace, and he was a fool to have bothered with me. He was a small man and he sat straight up in his chair with his right hand thrust into the machine and looked straight ahead at the wall while the straps thumped up and down with his fingers in them.

"What will you do when the war is over if it is over?" he asked me. "Speak grammatically!"

"I will go to the States."

"Are you married?"

"No, but I hope to be."

"The more of a fool you are," he said. He seemed very angry. "A man must not marry."

"Why, Signor Maggiore?"

"Don't call me 'Signor Maggiore.'"

"Why must not a man marry?"

"He cannot marry. He cannot marry," he said angrily. "If he is to lose everything, he should not place himself in a position to lose that. He should not place himself in a position to lose. He should find things he cannot lose."

He spoke very angrily and bitterly, and looked straight ahead while he talked.

"But why should he necessarily lose it?"

"He'll lose it," the major said. He was looking at the wall. Then he looked down at the machine and jerked his little hand out from between the straps and slapped it hard against his thigh. "He'll lose it," he almost shouted. "Don't argue with me!" Then he called to the attendant who ran the machines. "Come and turn this damned thing off."

He went back into the other room for the light treatment and the massage. Then I heard him ask the doctor if he might use his telephone and he shut the door. When he came back into the room, I was sitting in another machine. He was wearing his cape and had his cap on, and he came directly toward my machine and put his arm on my shoulder.

"I am sorry," he said, and patted me on the shoulder with his good hand. "I would not be rude. My wife has just died. You must forgive me."

"Oh—" I said, feeling sick for him. "I am *so* sorry."

He stood there biting his lower lip. "It is very difficult," he said. "I cannot resign myself."

He looked straight past me and out through the window. Then he began to cry. "I am utterly unable to resign myself," he said and choked. And then crying, his head up looking at nothing, carrying himself straight and soldierly, with tears on both cheeks and biting his lips, he walked past the machines and out the door.

The doctor told me that the major's wife, who was very young and whom he had not married until he was definitely invalided out of the war,[8] had died of pneumonia. She had been sick only a few days. No one expected her to die. The major did not come to the hospital for three days. Then he came at the usual hour, wearing a black band on the sleeve of his uniform. When he came back, there were large framed photographs around the wall, of all sorts of wounds before and after they had been cured by the machines. In front of the machine the major used were three photographs of hands like his that were completely restored. I do not know where the doctor got them. I always understood we were the first to use the machines. The photographs did not make much difference to the major because he only looked out of the window.

---

8 **invalided out of the war:** meaning that the major was injured and could no longer fight in the war

Ernest Hemingway

Responding to the Story

1. **LITERARY LENS** Mood is conveyed through descriptions of the setting, the author's (or narrator's) attitude toward the story, and through imagery. Select one of the images in the story and describe how it influences the mood of the story.

2. Hemingway once defined courage as "grace under pressure." In what way, if at all, is this idea demonstrated in "In Another Country"?

3. Hemingway is known as an "existentialist" writer. Existentialism is the belief that humans exist in an empty universe that does not care about human existence. In the face of this nothingness and loneliness, humans must create their own meaning and purpose. In what ways does "In Another Country" reflect the idea of existentialism?

4. What do you think the view of the narrator is toward war and the military establishment? Support your answer with evidence from the text.

5. **THE AUTHOR'S STYLE** After reading the quotation below, locate two sentences in the story that seem to fit his description of the "true simple declarative sentence."

One True Sentence

Sometimes when I was starting a new story and I could not get it going . . . I would stand and look out over the roofs of Paris and think, "Do not worry. You have always written before and you will write now. All you have to do is write one true sentence. Write the truest sentence that you know." So finally I would write one true sentence, and then go on from there . . . If I started to write elaborately, or like someone introducing or presenting something, I found that I could cut that scrollwork or ornament out and throw it away and start with the first true simple declarative sentence I had written.

—Ernest Hemingway, *A Moveable Feast*

Katherine Anne Porter
1890–1980

About the Author

Born in Indian Creek, Texas, Katherine Anne Porter led a long and full life. The glamorous blonde author married for the first of four times at 16. A world traveler, she acted in two movies and moved frequently, both within the States and overseas. She also enjoyed a long writing career, living to the age of 90 and thus outlasting most of her contemporaries.

Because her mother died when Porter was two, the author was reared afterward by her beloved grandmother. It amused Porter that although she was to teach at many prestigious universities, she never went to college herself.

She began her career as a theatre and music critic, publishing her first story in 1922.

Porter was known mostly for her short stories and was awarded the National Book Award and the Pulitzer Prize for *Collected Short Stories*, published in 1965. While travelling to Germany in 1931 for a fellowship, Porter was horrified by the rise of the Nazis to power. This trip provided her with the background for her only novel, *Ship of Fools*, which was published 31 years later and made into a popular film.

****

The Author's Style

Katherine Anne Porter's stories always convey a strong sense of place, revealing her understanding of the practical impact of social and economic conditions on people's lives. Her primary focus, however, is on the hidden motives and emotions of her characters.

Porter understood that everyday people and uncomplicated events can still provide powerful stories of individual personality, character, and moral choice. Her often simple characters are typified by conflicted feelings and unexpressed tensions. She brings their perspectives out by clarifying and respecting their points of view. Many of Porter's most memorable characters are women.

Known as a careful planner of her novel and stories, the author revised each one many times in order to produce precise phrasing, concentrated action, and emotional focus. Her stories also reflect her careful attention to the idioms and dialects of particular times and places, making her writing representative of what came to be known as "the local color movement." A native Texan, Porter eventually lived and worked in Dallas, Denver, Chicago, and New York, and she traveled and lived for extended periods in Mexico and in Europe, including several years in Paris.

LITERARY LENS Watch for internal as well as external conflicts in this family drama.

He

Katherine Anne Porter

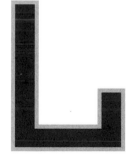ife was very hard for the Whipples. It was hard to feed all the hungry mouths, it was hard to keep the children in flannels[1] during the winter, short as it was: "God knows what would become of us if we lived north," they would say: keeping them decently clean was hard. "It looks like our luck won't never let up on us," said Mr. Whipple, but Mrs. Whipple was all for taking what was sent and calling it good, anyhow when the neighbors were in earshot. "Don't ever let a soul hear us complain," she kept saying to her husband. She couldn't stand to be pitied. "No, not if it comes to it that

---

1 **flannels:** underwear made of soft cloth

we have to live in a wagon and pick cotton around the country," she said, "nobody's going to get a chance to look down on us."

Mrs. Whipple loved her second son, the simple-minded one, better than she loved the other two children put together. She was forever saying so, and when she talked with certain of her neighbors, she would even throw in her husband and her mother for good measure.

FARMER'S WIFE, Horace Bristol, 1939

"You needn't keep on saying it around," said Mr. Whipple, "you'll make people think nobody else has any feelings about Him but you."

"It's natural for a mother," Mrs. Whipple would remind him. "You know yourself it's more natural for a mother to be that way. People don't expect so much of fathers, some way."

This didn't keep the neighbors from talking plainly among themselves. "A Lord's pure mercy if He should die," they said. "It's the sins of the fathers," they agreed among themselves. "There's bad blood and bad doings somewhere, you can bet on that." This behind the Whipples' backs. To their faces everybody said, "He's not so bad off. He'll be all right yet. Look how He grows!"

Mrs. Whipple hated to talk about it, she tried to keep her mind off it, but every time anybody set foot in the house, the subject always came up, and she had to talk about Him first, before she could get on to anything else. It seemed to ease her mind. "I wouldn't have anything happen to Him for all the world, but it just looks like I can't keep Him out of mischief. He's so strong and active, He's always into everything; He was like that since He could walk. It's actually funny sometimes, the way He can do anything; it's laughable to see Him up to His tricks. Emly has more accidents; I'm forever tying up her bruises, and Adna can't fall a foot without cracking a bone. But

He can do anything and not get a scratch. The preacher said such a nice thing once when he was here. He said, and I'll remember it to my dying day, 'The innocent walk with God— that's why He don't get hurt.'" Whenever Mrs. Whipple repeated these words, she always felt a warm pool spread in her breast, and the tears would fill her eyes, and then she could talk about something else.

He did grow and He never got hurt. A plank blew off the chicken house and struck Him on the head and He never seemed to know it. He had learned a few words, and after this He forgot them. He didn't whine for food as the other children did, but waited until it was given Him. He ate squatting in the corner, smacking and mumbling. Rolls of fat covered Him like an overcoat, and He could carry twice as much wood and water as Adna. Emly had a cold in the head most of the time—"she takes that after me," said Mrs. Whipple—so in bad weather they gave her the extra blanket off His cot. He never seemed to mind the cold.

Just the same, Mrs. Whipple's life was a torment for fear something might happen to Him. He climbed the peach trees much better than Adna and went skittering along the branches like a monkey, just a regular monkey. "Oh, Mrs. Whipple, you hadn't ought to let Him do that. He'll lose His balance sometime. He can't rightly know what He's doing."

Mrs. Whipple almost screamed out at the neighbor. "He *does* know what He's doing! He's as able as any other child! Come down out of there, you!" When He finally reached the ground she could hardly keep her hands off Him for acting like that before people, a grin all over His face and her worried sick about Him all the time.

"It's the neighbors," said Mrs. Whipple to her husband. "Oh, I do **mortally** wish they would keep out of our business. I can't afford to let Him do anything for fear they'll come nosing around about it. Look at the bees, now. Adna can't handle them, they sting him up so; I haven't got time to do everything, and now I don't dare let Him. But if He gets a sting He don't really mind."

"It's just because He ain't got sense enough to be scared of anything," said Mr. Whipple.

> *I*t's the neighbors," said Mrs. Whipple to her husband. "Oh, I do mortally wish they would keep out of our business."

mortally: intensely; unremittingly

"You ought to be ashamed of yourself," said Mrs. Whipple, "talking that way about your own child. Who's to take up for Him if we don't, I'd like to know? He sees a lot that goes on, He listens to things all the time. And anything I tell Him to do He does it. Don't never let anybody hear you say such things. They'd think you favored the other children over Him."

"Well, now I don't, and you know it, and what's the use of getting all worked up about it? You always think the worst of everything. Just let Him alone, He'll get along somehow. He gets plenty to eat and wear, don't He?" Mr. Whipple suddenly felt tired out. "Anyhow, it can't be helped now."

> *I*t's a waste and I don't hold with waste the way we are now," said Mr. Whipple. "That pig'll be worth money by Christmas."

Mrs. Whipple felt tired too, she complained in a tired voice. "What's done can't never be undone, I know that good as anybody; but He's my child, and I'm not going to have people say anything. I get sick of people coming around saying things all the time."

In the early fall Mrs. Whipple got a letter from her brother saying he and his wife and two children were coming over for a little visit next Sunday week.[2] "Put the big pot in the little one," he wrote at the end. Mrs. Whipple read this part out loud twice, she was so pleased. Her brother was a great one for saying funny things. "We'll just show him that's no joke," she said, "we'll just butcher one of the sucking pigs."

"It's a waste and I don't hold with waste the way we are now," said Mr. Whipple. "That pig'll be worth money by Christmas."

vittles:
food

"It's a shame and a pity we can't have a decent meal's **vittles** once in a while when my own family comes to see us," said Mrs. Whipple. "I'd hate for his wife to go back and say there wasn't a thing in the house to eat. My God, it's better than buying up a great chance of meat in town. There's where you'd spend the money!"

"All right, do it yourself then," said Mr. Whipple. "Christamighty, no wonder we can't get ahead!"

The question was how to get the little pig away from his ma, a great fighter, worse than a Jersey cow. Adna wouldn't try it: "That sow'd rip my insides out all over the pen." "All right, old fraidy," said Mrs. Whipple, "*He's* not scared. Watch *Him* do it." And she laughed as though it was all a good joke and gave

---

2 **Sunday week:** the Sunday of the following week

Him a little push towards the pen. He sneaked up and snatched the pig right away from the teat and galloped back and was over the fence with the sow raging at His heels. The little black squirming thing was screeching like a baby in a tantrum, stiffening its back and stretching its mouth to the ears. Mrs. Whipple took the pig with her face stiff and sliced its throat with one stroke. When He saw the blood He gave a great jolting breath and ran away. "But He'll forget and eat plenty, just the same," thought Mrs. Whipple. Whenever she was thinking, her lips moved making words. "He'd eat it all if I didn't stop Him. He'd eat up every mouthful from the other two if I'd let Him."

And she boxed Him on the ears, hard. He blinked and blinked and rubbed His head, and His face hurt Mrs. Whipple's feelings.

She felt badly about it. He was ten years old now and a third again as large as Adna, who was going on fourteen. "It's a shame, a shame," she kept saying under her breath, "and Adna with so much brains!"

She kept on feeling badly about all sorts of things. In the first place it was the man's work to butcher; the sight of the pig scraped pink and naked made her sick. He was too fat and soft and pitiful-looking. It was simply a shame the way things had to happen. By the time she had finished it up, she almost wished her brother would stay at home.

Early Sunday morning Mrs. Whipple dropped everything to get Him all cleaned up. In an hour He was dirty again, with crawling under fences after a possum, and straddling along the rafters of the barn looking for eggs in the hayloft. "My Lord, look at you now after all my trying! And here's Adna and Emly staying so quiet. I get tired trying to keep you decent. Get off that shirt and put on another, people will say I don't half dress you!" And she boxed Him on the ears, hard. He blinked and blinked and rubbed His head, and His face hurt Mrs. Whipple's feelings. Her knees began to tremble, she had to sit down while she buttoned His shirt. "I'm just all gone before the day starts."

The brother came with his plump healthy wife and two great roaring hungry boys. They had a grand dinner, with the pig roasted to a crackling in the middle of the table, full of dressing, a pickled peach in his mouth and plenty of gravy for the sweet potatoes.

"This looks like prosperity all right," said the brother; "you're going to have to roll me home like I was a barrel when I'm done."

So that was over, and Mrs. Whipple loaded up a big plate for Him first, before everybody. "I always say He ain't to be slighted, no matter who else goes without," she said, and carried it to Him herself.

Everybody laughed out loud; it was fine to hear them laughing all at once around the table. Mrs. Whipple felt warm and good about it. "Oh, we've got six more of these; I say it's as little as we can do when you come to see us so seldom." He wouldn't come into the dining room, and Mrs. Whipple passed it off very well. "He's timider than my other two," she said, "He'll just have to get used to you. There isn't everybody He'll make up with, you know how it is with some children, even cousins." Nobody said anything out of the way.

"Just like my Alfy here," said the brother's wife. "I sometimes got to lick him to make him shake hands with his own grand-mammy."

So that was over, and Mrs. Whipple loaded up a big plate for Him first, before everybody. "I always say He ain't to be slighted, no matter who else goes without," she said, and carried it to Him herself.

"He can chin Himself on the top of the door," said Emly, helping along.

"That's fine, He's getting along fine," said the brother.

They went away after supper. Mrs. Whipple rounded up the dishes, and sent the children to bed and sat down and unlaced her shoes. "You see?" she said to Mr. Whipple. "That's the way my whole family is. Nice and considerate about everything. No out-of-the-way remarks—they *have* got refinement. I get awfully sick of people's remarks. Wasn't that pig good?"

Mr. Whipple said, "Yes, we're out three hundred pounds of pork, that's all. It's easy to be polite when you come to eat. Who knows what they had in their minds all along?"

"Yes, that's like you," said Mrs. Whipple. "I don't expect anything else from you. You'll be telling me next that my own brother will be saying around that we made Him eat in the kitchen! Oh, my God!" She rocked her head in her hands, a hard pain started in the very middle of her forehead. "Now it's all spoiled, and everything was so nice and easy. All right, you don't like them and you never did—all right, they'll not come here again soon, never you mind! But they *can't* say He wasn't dressed every lick as good as Adna—oh, honest, sometimes I wish I was dead!"

"I wish you'd let up," said Mr. Whipple. "It's bad enough as it is."

I t was a hard winter. It seemed to Mrs. Whipple that they hadn't ever known anything but hard times, and now to cap it all a winter like this. The crops were about half of what they had a right to expect; after the cotton was in it didn't do much more than cover the grocery bill. They swapped off one of the plow horses, and got cheated, for the new one died of the heaves.[3] Mrs. Whipple kept thinking all the time it was terrible to have a man you couldn't depend on not to get cheated. They cut down on everything, but Mrs. Whipple kept saying there are things you can't cut down on, and they cost money. It took a lot of warm clothes for Adna and Emly, who walked four miles to school during the three-months session. "He sets around the fire a lot, He won't need so much," said Mr. Whipple. "That's so," said Mrs. Whipple, "and when He does the outdoor chores He can wear your tarpaullion[4] coat. I can't do no better, that's all."

In February He was taken sick, and lay curled up under His blanket looking very blue in the face and acting as if He would choke. Mr. and Mrs. Whipple did everything they could for Him for two days, and then they were scared and sent for the doctor. The doctor told them they must keep Him warm and give Him plenty of milk and eggs. "He isn't as stout as He looks, I'm afraid," said the doctor. "You've got to watch them when they're like that. You must put more cover onto Him, too."

"I just took off His big blanket to wash," said Mrs. Whipple, ashamed. "I can't stand dirt."

"Well, you'd better put it back on the minute it's dry," said the doctor, "or He'll have pneumonia."

Mr. and Mrs. Whipple took a blanket off their own bed and put His cot in by the fire. "They can't say we didn't do everything for Him," she said, "even to sleeping cold ourselves on His account."

When the winter broke He seemed to be well again, but He walked as if His feet hurt Him. He was able to run a cotton planter during the season.

"I got it all fixed up with Jim Ferguson about breeding the cow next time," said Mr. Whipple. "I'll pasture the bull this summer and give Jim some fodder in the fall. That's better than paying out money when you haven't got it."

"I hope you didn't say such a thing before Jim Ferguson," said Mrs. Whipple. "You oughtn't to let him know we're so down as all that."

---

3 **heaves:** a type of emphysema that causes difficulty breathing and a persistent cough

4 **tarpaullion:** a durable, heavy material

"Godamighty, that ain't saying we're down. A man is got to look ahead sometimes. *He* can lead the bull over today. I need Adna on the place."

At first Mrs. Whipple felt easy in her mind about sending Him for the bull. Adna was too jumpy and couldn't be trusted. You've got to be steady around animals. After He was gone she started thinking, and after a while she could hardly bear it any longer. She stood in the lane and watched for Him. It was nearly three miles to go and a hot day, but He oughtn't to be so long about it. She shaded her eyes and stared until colored bubbles floated in her eyeballs. It was just like everything else in life, she must always worry and never know a moment's peace about anything. After a long time she saw Him turn into the side lane, limping. He came on very slowly, leading the big hulk of an animal by a ring in the nose, twirling a little stick in His hand, never looking back or sideways, but coming on like a sleepwalker with His eyes half shut.

Mrs. Whipple was scared sick of bulls; she had heard awful stories about how they followed on quietly enough, and then suddenly pitched on with a bellow and pawed and gored a body to pieces. Any second now that black monster would come down on Him, my God, He'd never have sense enough to run.

She mustn't make a sound nor a move; she mustn't get the bull started. The bull heaved his head aside and horned the air at a fly. Her voice burst out of her in a shriek, and she screamed at Him to come on, for God's sake. He didn't seem to hear her clamor, but kept on twirling His switch and limping on, and the bull lumbered along behind him as gently as a calf. Mrs. Whipple stopped calling and ran towards the house, praying under her breath: "Lord, don't let anything happen to Him. Lord, you *know* people will say we oughtn't to have sent Him. You *know* they'll say we didn't take care of Him. Oh, get Him home, safe home, safe home, and I'll look out for Him better! Amen."

She watched from the window while He led the beast in, and tied him up in the barn. It was no use trying to keep up, Mrs. Whipple couldn't bear another thing. She sat down and rocked and cried with her apron over her head.

> *I*t was no use trying to keep up, Mrs. Whipple couldn't bear another thing. She sat down and rocked and cried with her apron over her head.

From year to year the Whipples were growing poorer and poorer. The place just seemed to run down of itself, no matter how hard they worked. "We're losing our hold," said Mrs. Whipple. "Why can't we do like other people and watch for our best chances? They'll be calling us poor white trash next."

"When I get to be sixteen I'm going to leave," said Adna. "I'm going to get a job in Powell's grocery store. There's money in that. No more farm for me."

"I'm going to be a schoolteacher," said Emly. "But I've got to finish the eighth grade, anyhow. Then I can live in town. I don't see any chances here."

"Emly takes after my family," said Mrs. Whipple. "Ambitious every last one of them, and they don't take second place for anybody."

When fall came Emly got a chance to wait on table in the railroad eating-house in the town near by, and it seemed such a shame not to take it when the wages were good and she could get her food too, that Mrs. Whipple decided to let her take it, and not bother with school until the next session. "You've got plenty of time," she said. "You're young and smart as a whip."

With Adna gone too, Mr. Whipple tried to run the farm with just Him to help. He seemed to get along fine, doing His work and part of Adna's without noticing it. They did well enough until Christmas time, when one morning He slipped on the ice coming up from the barn. Instead of getting up He thrashed round and round, and when Mr. Whipple got to Him, He was having some sort of fit.

They did well enough until Christmas time, when one morning He slipped on the ice coming up from the barn. Instead of getting up He thrashed round and round, and when Mr. Whipple got to Him, He was having some sort of fit.

They brought Him inside and tried to make Him sit up, but He blubbered and rolled, so they put Him to bed and Mr. Whipple rode to town for the doctor. All the way there and back he worried about where the money was to come from: it sure did look like he had about all the troubles he could carry.

PUBLIC SALE
1943
Andrew Wyeth
The Philadelphia Museum of Art

From then on He stayed in bed. His legs swelled up double their size, and the fits kept coming back. After four months, the doctor said, "It's no use, I think you'd better put Him in the County Home for treatment right away. I'll see about it for you. He'll have good care there and be off your hands."

"We don't begrudge Him any care, and I won't let Him out of my sight," said Mrs. Whipple. "I won't have it said I sent my sick child off among strangers."

"I know how you feel," said the doctor. "You can't tell me anything about that, Mrs. Whipple. I've got a boy of my own. But you'd better listen to me. I can't do anything more for Him, that's the truth."

Mr. and Mrs. Whipple talked it over a long time that night after they went to bed. "It's just charity," said Mrs. Whipple, "that's what we've come to, charity! I certainly never looked for this."

"We pay taxes to help support the place just like everybody else," said Mr. Whipple, "and I don't call that taking charity. I think it would be fine to have Him where He'd get the best of everything . . . and besides, I can't keep up with these doctor bills any longer."

"Maybe that's why the doctor wants us to send Him—he's scared he won't get his money," said Mrs. Whipple.

"Don't talk like that," said Mr. Whipple, feeling pretty sick, "or we won't be able to send Him."

"Oh, but we won't keep Him there long," said Mrs. Whipple. "Soon's He's better, we'll bring Him right back home."

"The doctor has told you and told you time and again He can't ever get better, and you might as well stop talking," said Mr. Whipple.

"Doctors don't know everything," said Mrs. Whipple, feeling almost happy. "But anyhow, in the summer Emly can come home for a vacation, and Adna can get down for Sundays: we'll all work together and get on our feet again, and the children will feel they've got a place to come to."

All at once she saw it full summer again, with the garden going fine, and new white roller shades up all over the house, and Adna and Emly home, so full of life, all of them happy together. Oh, it could happen, things would ease up on them.

They didn't talk before Him much, but they never knew just how much He understood. Finally the doctor set the day and a neighbor who owned a double-seated carryall[5] offered to drive them over. The hospital would have

---

5 **carryall:** a covered carriage for four people

sent an ambulance, but Mrs. Whipple couldn't stand to see Him going away looking so sick as all that. They wrapped Him in blankets, and the neighbor and Mr. Whipple lifted Him into the back seat of the carryall beside Mrs. Whipple, who had on her black shirtwaist.[6] She couldn't stand to go looking like charity.

"You'll be all right, I guess I'll stay behind," said Mr. Whipple. "It don't look like everybody ought to leave the place at once."

"Besides, it ain't as if He was going to stay forever," said Mrs. Whipple to the neighbor. "This is only for a little while."

They started away, Mrs. Whipple holding to the edges of the blankets to keep Him from sagging sideways. He sat there blinking and blinking. He worked His hands out and began rubbing His nose with His knuckles, and then with the end of the blanket. Mrs. Whipple couldn't believe what she saw; He was scrubbing away big tears that rolled out of the corners of His eyes. He sniveled and made a gulping noise. Mrs. Whipple kept saying, "Oh, honey, you don't feel so bad, do you? You don't feel so bad, do you?" for He seemed to be accusing her of something. Maybe He remembered that time she boxed His ears, maybe He had been scared that day with the bull, maybe He had slept cold and couldn't tell her about it; maybe He knew they were sending Him away for good and all because they were too poor to keep Him. Whatever it was, Mrs. Whipple couldn't bear to think of it. She began to cry, frightfully, and wrapped her arms tight around Him. His head rolled on her shoulder: she had loved Him as much as she possibly could, there were Adna and Emly who had to be thought of too, there was nothing she could do to make up to Him for His life. Oh, what a mortal pity He was ever born.

They came in sight of the hospital, with the neighbor driving very fast, not daring to look behind him.

---

6 **shirtwaist:** a tailored blouse or dress

Responding to the Story

1. **LITERARY LENS** Define what you think the major conflict is in this short story.

2. Why do you think the other members of the family in this story refer to the mentally disabled boy as "He"?

3. Do you think Mrs. Whipple failed her son in any way? If so, what could she have done differently?

4. Do you think that attitudes toward mentally disabled people have changed very much since this story was written? Explain.

5. **THE AUTHOR'S STYLE** Porter is known for her ability to bring complex characters to life. Select a passage that you think demonstrates Porter's skill at characterization. Be prepared to explain your choice.

F. Scott Fitzgerald
1896–1940

About the Author

One of the most important writers of his generation, F. Scott Fitzgerald coined the term The Jazz Age for the prosperous twenties. He was born in St. Paul, Minnesota, to an established family, and named for Francis Scott Key Fitzgerald, author of "The Star-Spangled Banner" and an ancestor of his father. In 1913, he went east to prestigious Princeton University, later dropping out of college to join the army. He never saw combat, and instead spent most of his army time writing a spectacularly successful first novel, *This Side of Paradise*, published in 1920.

That same year Fitzgerald married a temperamental Southern belle, Zelda Sayre. The couple's sophisticated, globetrotting life became the backdrop for his work as the Fitzgeralds flitted from the Riviera to Paris and New York. By 1930, however, too much of everything took its toll; Fitzgerald had become an alcoholic and his wife was mentally ill. Afterward, when Fitzgerald was struggling to recover, he became known as the spokesman for "The Lost Generation." This was a group of artists who rode the roller coaster of the times and reflected on its aftermath in their work. One of his best-known works is his novel *The Great Gatsby*.

The Author's Style

F. Scott Fitzgerald's fiction conveys the contrasts and extremes of The Jazz Age of the twenties. He was equally adept at chronicling the period of deflation and regret that followed it after the stock market crash of 1929. Fitzgerald, like many of his protagonists, was a participant in a wild culture that led to excesses of many kinds. His prose is both subtle and richly descriptive. Through the precise rendering of dialogue, gesture, metaphor, and crucial detail, his style captures the subtle distinctions of setting, character, and tone. Fitzgerald was particularly good at rendering the glossy social lives of the affluent. He also revealed how the close attention rich people pay to manners and customs can mask their moral inadequacies. Often his characters are both shaped by wealth and injured by its loss.

The mood of many Fitzgerald stories is one of tragic regret—not only for fortunes squandered, but for bad behavior, opportunities lost, and nagging reminders of past mistakes that follow people into the future.

LITERARY LENS Watch for Fitzgerald's use of *in medias res* in this story. Literally meaning "in the midst of things," *in medias res* refers to the technique of opening a story in the middle of the action, without letting the reader know who the main character is or where and when the story is taking place.

Babylon Revisited

F. Scott Fitzgerald

1

And where's Mr. Campbell?"Charlie asked.

"Gone to Switzerland. Mr. Campbell's a pretty sick man, Mr. Wales."

"I'm sorry to hear that. And George Hardt?" Charlie inquired.

"Back in America, gone to work."

"And where is the Snow Bird?"

"He was in here last week. Anyway, his friend, Mr. Schaeffer, is in Paris."

Two familiar names from the long list of a year and a half ago. Charlie scribbled an address in his notebook and tore out the page.

"If you see Mr. Schaeffer, give him this," he said. "It's my brother-in-law's address. I haven't settled on a hotel yet."

portentous:
ominous; full of
meaning

He was not really disappointed to find Paris was so empty. But the stillness in the Ritz bar was strange and **portentous**. It was not an American bar
any more—he felt polite in it, and not as if he owned it. It had gone back
into France. He felt the stillness from the moment he got out of the taxi and
saw the doorman, usually in a frenzy of activity at this hour, gossiping with
a *chasseur*[1] by the servants' entrance.

Passing through the corridor, he heard only a single, bored voice in the
once-clamorous women's room. When he turned into the bar he traveled the
twenty feet of green carpet with his eyes fixed straight ahead by old habit; and
then, with his foot firmly on the rail, he turned and surveyed the room,
encountering only a single pair of eyes that fluttered up from a newspaper in
the corner. Charlie asked for the head barman, Paul, who in the latter days
of the bull market[2] had come to work in his own custom-built car—disem-

nicety:
correctness;
propriety

barking, however, with due **nicety** at the nearest corner. But Paul was at his
country house today and Alix giving him information.

"No, no more," Charlie said. "I'm going slow these days."

Alix congratulated him: "You were going pretty strong a couple of years ago."

"I'll stick to it all right," Charlie assured him. "I've stuck to it for over a
year and a half now."

"How do you find conditions in America?"

"I haven't been to America for months. I'm in business in Prague, representing a couple of concerns there. They don't know about me down there."

Alix smiled.

"Remember the night of George Hardt's bachelor dinner here?" said
Charlie. "By the way, what's become of Claude Fessenden?"

Alix lowered his voice confidentially: "He's in Paris, but he doesn't come
here any more. Paul doesn't allow it. He ran up a bill of thirty thousand
francs, charging all his drinks and his lunches, and usually his dinner, for
more than a year. And when Paul finally told him he had to pay, he gave him
a bad check."

Alix shook his head sadly.

"I don't understand it, such a dandy fellow. Now he's all bloated up—"
he made a plump apple of his hands.

strident:
commanding
attention

Charlie watched a group of **strident** queens installing themselves in a
corner.

---

1 *chasseur:* French for "messenger boy"

2 **bull market:** a period when the stock market is rising

F. Scott Fitzgerald

"Nothing affects them," he thought. "Stocks rise and fall, people loaf or work, but they go on forever." The place oppressed him. He called for the dice and shook with Alix for the drink.

"Here for long, Mr. Wales?"

"I'm here for four or five days to see my little girl."

"Oh-h! You have a little girl?"

Outside, the fire-red, gas-blue, ghost-green signs shone smokily through the tranquil rain. It was late afternoon and the streets were in movement; the *bistros*[3] gleamed. At the corner of the Boulevard des Capucines he took a taxi. The Place de la Concorde moved by in pink majesty; they crossed the logical Seine,[4] and Charlie felt the sudden provincial[5] quality of the Left Bank.[6]

> They were closing the iron grill in front of Brentano's Bookstore, and people were already at dinner behind the trim little bourgeois hedge of Duval's.

Charlie directed his taxi to the Avenue de l'Opéra, which was out of his way. But he wanted to see the blue hour spread over the magnificent façade, and imagine that the cab horns, playing endlessly the first few bars of *Le Plus que Lente*,[7] were the trumpets of the Second Empire.[8] They were closing the iron grill in front of Brentano's Bookstore, and people were already at dinner behind the trim little **bourgeois** hedge of Duval's. He had never eaten at a really cheap restaurant in Paris. Five-course dinner, four francs fifty, eighteen cents, wine included. For some odd reason he wished that he had.

bourgeois: middle-class; conventional

As they rolled on to the Left Bank and he felt its sudden provincialism, he thought, "I spoiled this city for myself. I didn't realize it, but the days came along one after another, and then two years were gone, and everything was gone, and I was gone."

He was thirty-five, and good to look at. The Irish mobility of his face was sobered by a deep wrinkle between his eyes. As he rang his brother-in-law's bell in the Rue Palatine, the wrinkle deepened till it pulled down his brows;

---

3 *bistros:* French for "taverns"

4 **Seine:** a river in France

5 **provincial:** regional; in this case, rural or small-town

6 **Left Bank:** the southern shore of the Seine in Paris, less stylish than the Right Bank

7 *Le Plus que Lente:* a waltz by Claude Debussy

8 **Second Empire:** refers to the reign of Napoleon III from 1852 until 1871

he felt a cramping sensation in his belly. From behind the maid who opened the door darted a lovely little girl of nine, who shrieked "Daddy!" and flew up, struggling like a fish, into his arms. She pulled his head around by one ear and set her cheek against his.

"My old pie," he said.

"Oh, daddy, daddy, daddy, daddy, dads, dads, dads!"

She drew him into the salon, where the family waited, a boy and girl his daughter's age, his sister-in-law and her husband. He greeted Marion with his voice pitched carefully to avoid either **feigned** enthusiasm or dislike, but her response was more frankly **tepid**, though she minimized her expression of unalterable distrust by directing her regard toward his child. The two men clasped hands in a friendly way and Lincoln Peters rested his for a moment on Charlie's shoulder.

The room was warm and comfortably American. The three children moved intimately about, playing through the yellow oblongs that led to other rooms; the cheer of six o'clock spoke in the eager smacks of the fire and the sounds of French activity in the kitchen. But Charlie did not relax; his heart sat up rigidly in his body and he drew confidence from his daughter, who from time to time came close to him, holding in her arms the doll he had brought.

"Really extremely well," he declared in answer to Lincoln's question. "There's a lot of business there that isn't moving at all, but we're doing even better than ever. In fact, damn well. I'm bringing my sister over from America next month to keep house for me. My income last year was bigger than it was when I had money. You see, the Czechs—"

His boasting was for a specific purpose; but after a moment, seeing a faint **restiveness** in Lincoln's eye, he changed the subject:

"Those are fine children of yours, well brought up, good manners."

"We think Honoria's a great little girl too."

Marion Peters came back from the kitchen. She was a tall woman with worried eyes, who had once possessed a fresh American loveliness. Charlie had never been sensitive to it and was always surprised when people spoke of how pretty she had been. From the first there had been an instinctive **antipathy** between them.

"Well, how do you find Honoria?" she asked.

"Wonderful. I was astonished how much she's grown in ten months. All the children are looking well."

feigned:
pretended

tepid:
lukewarm;
unenthusiastic

restiveness:
uneasiness

antipathy:
intense dislike

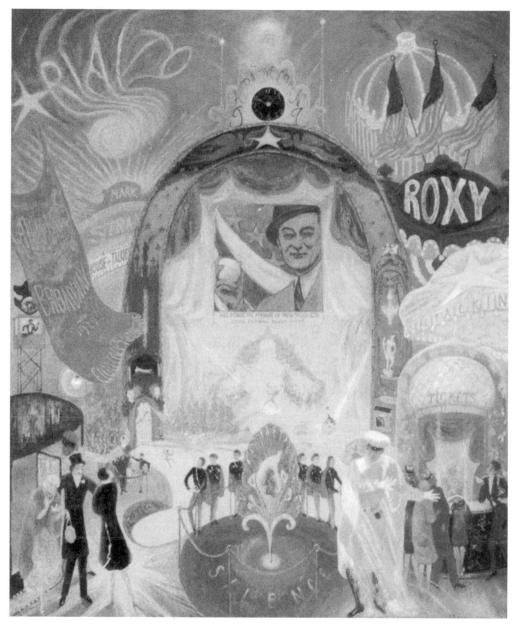

THE CATHEDRALS OF BROADWAY, Florine Stettheimer, 1929, The Metropolitan Museum of Art

"We haven't had a doctor for a year. How do you like being back in Paris?"

"It seems very funny to see so few Americans around."

vehemently: forcefully; with conviction

"I'm delighted," Marion said **vehemently**. "Now at least you can go into a store without their assuming you're a millionaire. We've suffered like everybody, but on the whole it's a good deal pleasanter."

"But it was nice while it lasted," said Charlie. "We were a sort of royalty, almost infallible, with a sort of magic around us. In the bar this afternoon"— he stumbled, seeing his mistake—"there wasn't a man I knew."

She looked at him keenly. "I should think you'd have had enough of bars."

"I only stayed a minute. I take one drink every afternoon, and no more."

"Don't you want a cocktail before dinner?" Lincoln asked.

"I take only one drink every afternoon, and I've had that."

"I hope you keep to it," said Marion.

Her dislike was evident in the coldness with which she spoke, but Charlie only smiled; he had larger plans. Her very aggressiveness gave him an advantage, and he knew enough to wait. He wanted them to initiate the discussion of what they knew had brought him to Paris.

At dinner he couldn't decide whether Honoria was most like him or her mother. Fortunate if she didn't combine the traits of both that had brought them to disaster. A great wave of protectiveness went over him. He thought he knew what to do for her. He believed in character; he wanted to jump back a whole generation and trust in character again as the eternally valuable element. Everything else wore out.

He left soon after dinner, but not to go home. He was curious to see Paris by night with clearer and more judicious eyes than those of other days. He bought a *strapontin*[9] for the Casino and watched Josephine Baker[10] go through her chocolate arabesques.[11]

After an hour he left and strolled toward Montmartre,[12] up the Rue Pigalle[13] into the Place Blanche.[14] The rain had stopped and there were a few people in

---

9 ***strapontin:*** French for "cheap seat"

10 **Josephine Baker:** popular African American dancer in Paris in the 1920s

11 **arabesques:** ballet moves

12 **Montmartre:** a hill in northern Paris known for its artists and breathtaking view of the city

13 **Rue Pigalle:** French for "Pigalle Street"

14 **Place Blanche:** French for "White Square"

evening clothes disembarking from taxis in front of cabarets, and *cocottes*[15] prowling singly or in pairs, and many Negroes. He passed a lighted door from which issued music, and stopped with the sense of familiarity; it was Bricktop's, where he had parted with so many hours and so much money. A few doors farther on he found another ancient rendezvous and incautiously put his head inside. Immediately an eager orchestra burst into sound, a pair of professional dancers leaped to their feet and a maître d'hôtel swooped toward him, crying, "Crowd just arriving, sir!" But he withdrew quickly.

"You have to be damn drunk," he thought.

Zelli's was closed, the bleak and **sinister** cheap hotels surrounding it were dark; up in the Rue Blanche there was more light and a local, **colloquial** French crowd. The Poet's Cave had disappeared, but the two great mouths of the Café of Heaven and the Café of Hell still yawned—even devoured, as he watched, the meager contents of a tourist bus—a German, a Japanese, and an American couple who glanced at him with frightened eyes.

sinister: dangerous looking

colloquial: familiar; ordinary

So much for the effort and ingenuity of Montmartre. All the catering to vice and waste was on an utterly childish scale, and he suddenly realized the meaning of the word "dissipate"—to dissipate into thin air; to make nothing out of something. In the little hours of the night every move from place to place was an enormous human jump, an increase of paying for the privilege of slower and slower motion.

He remembered thousand-franc notes given to an orchestra for playing a single number, hundred-franc notes tossed to a doorman for calling a cab.

> *He* remembered thousand-franc notes given to an orchestra for playing a single number, hundred-franc notes tossed to a doorman for calling a cab.

But it hadn't been given for nothing.

It had been given, even the most wildly squandered sum, as an offering to destiny that he might not remember the things most worth remembering, the things that now he would always remember—his child taken from his control, his wife escaped to a grave in Vermont.

In the glare of a *brasserie*[16] a woman spoke to him. He bought her some eggs and coffee, and then, eluding her encouraging stare, gave her a twenty-franc note and took a taxi to his hotel.

---

15 **cocottes:** French for "tarts," meaning "prostitutes"

16 **brasserie:** French for a tavern that also serves as a restaurant

II

He woke up on a fine fall day—football weather. The depression of yesterday was gone and he liked the people on the streets. At noon he sat opposite Honoria at Le Grand Vatel, the only restaurant he could think of not reminiscent of champagne dinners and long luncheons that began at two and ended in a blurred and vague twilight.

"Now, how about vegetables? Oughtn't you to have some vegetables?"

"Well, yes."

"Here's *épinards* and *chou-fleur* and carrots and *haricots*."[17]

"I'd like chou-fleur."

"Wouldn't you like to have two vegetables?"

"I usually have only one at lunch."

The waiter was pretending to be inordinately fond of children. *"Qu'elle est mignonne, la petite! Elle parle exactement comme une française."*[18]

"How about dessert? Shall we wait and see?"

The waiter disappeared. Honoria looked at her father expectantly.

"What are we going to do?"

"First, we're going to that toy store in the Rue Saint-Honoré and buy you anything you like. And then we're going to the vaudeville at the Empire."

She hesitated. "I like it about the vaudeville, but not the toy store."

"Why not?"

"Well, you brought me this doll." She had it with her. "And I've got lots of things. And we're not rich any more, are we?"

"We never were. But today you are to have anything you want."

"All right," she agreed resignedly.

When there had been her mother and a French nurse he had been inclined to be strict; now he extended himself, reached out for a new tolerance; he must be both parents to her and not shut any of her out of communication.

"I want to get to know you," he said gravely. "First let me introduce myself. My name is Charles J. Wales, of Prague."

"Oh, daddy!" her voice cracked with laughter.

"And who are you, please?" he persisted, and she accepted a rôle immediately: "Honoria Wales, Rue Palatine, Paris."

"Married or single?"

"No, not married. Single."

---

17 *épinards ... chou-fleur ... haricots:* French for "spinach," "cauliflower," "beans"

18 *"Qu'elle ... française.":* French for "She is charming, the little one! She speaks exactly like a French girl."

He indicated the doll. "But I see you have a child, madame."

Unwilling to disinherit it, she took it to her heart and thought quickly: "Yes, I've been married, but I'm not married now. My husband is dead."

He went on quickly, "And the child's name?"

"Simone. That's after my best friend at school."

"I'm very pleased that you're doing so well at school."

"I'm third this month," she boasted. "Elsie"—that was her cousin—"is only about eighteenth, and Richard is about at the bottom."

"You like Richard and Elsie, don't you?"

"Oh, yes. I like them all right."

Cautiously and casually he asked: "And Aunt Marion and Uncle Lincoln—which do you like best?"

"Oh, Uncle Lincoln, I guess."

He was increasingly aware of her presence. As they came in, a murmur of " . . . adorable" followed them, and now the people at the next table bent all their silences upon her, staring as if she were something no more conscious than a flower.

"Why don't I live with you?" she asked suddenly. "Because mamma's dead?"

"You must stay here and learn more French. It would have been hard for daddy to take care of you so well."

"I don't really need much taking care of any more. I do everything for myself."

Going out of the restaurant, a man and a woman unexpectedly hailed him.

"Well, the old Wales!"

"Hello there, Lorraine . . . Dunc."

Sudden ghosts out of the past: Duncan Schaeffer, a friend from college. Lorraine Quarles, a lovely, pale blonde of thirty; one of a crowd who had helped them make months into days in the lavish times of three years ago.

"My husband couldn't come this year," she said, in answer to his question. "We're poor as hell. So he gave me two hundred a month, and told me I could do my worst on that. . . . This your little girl?"

"What about coming back and sitting down?" Duncan asked.

"Can't do it." He was glad for an excuse. As always, he felt Lorraine's passionate, **provocative** attraction, but his own rhythm was different now.

"Well, how about dinner?" she asked.

provocative:
suggestive;
exciting

"I'm not free. Give me your address and let me call you."

"Charlie, I believe you're sober," she said **judicially**. "I honestly believe he's sober, Dunc. Pinch him and see if he's sober."

judicially: critically; with judgement

Charlie indicated Honoria with his head. They both laughed.

"What's your address?" said Duncan skeptically.

He hesitated, unwilling to give the name of his hotel.

"I'm not settled yet. I'd better call you. We're going to see the vaudeville at the Empire."

"There! That's what I want to do," Lorraine said. "I want to see some clowns and acrobats and jugglers. That's just what we'll do, Dunc."

"We've got to do an errand first," said Charlie. "Perhaps we'll see you there."

"All right, you snob. . . . Good-by, beautiful little girl."

"Good-by."

She was already an individual with a code of her own, and Charlie was more and more absorbed by the desire of putting a little of himself into her before she crystallized utterly.

Honoria bobbed politely.

Somehow, an unwelcome encounter. They liked him because he was functioning, because he was serious; they wanted to see him, because he was stronger than they were now, because they wanted to draw a certain **sustenance** from his strength.

sustenance: nourishment; support

At the Empire, Honoria proudly refused to sit upon her father's folded coat. She was already an individual with a code of her own, and Charlie was more and more absorbed by the desire of putting a little of himself into her before she crystallized utterly. It was hopeless to try to know her in so short a time.

Between the acts they came upon Duncan and Lorraine in the lobby where the band was playing.

"Have a drink?"

"All right; but not up at the bar. We'll take a table."

"The perfect father."

Listening abstractedly to Lorraine, Charlie watched Honoria's eyes leave their table, and he followed them wistfully about the room, wondering what they saw. He met her glance and she smiled.

"I liked that lemonade," she said.

What had she said? What had he expected? Going home in a taxi afterward, he pulled her over until her head rested against his chest.

"Darling, do you ever think about your mother?"

"Yes, sometimes," she answered vaguely.

"I don't want you to forget her. Have you got a picture of her?"

"Yes, I think so. Anyhow, Aunt Marion has. Why don't you want me to forget her?"

"She loved you very much."

"I loved her too."

They were silent for a moment.

"Daddy, I want to come and live with you," she said suddenly.

His heart leaped; he had wanted it to come like this.

"Aren't you perfectly happy?"

"Yes, but I love you better than anybody. And you love me better than anybody, don't you, now that mummy's dead?"

"Of course I do. But you won't always like me best, honey. You'll grow up and meet somebody your own age and go marry him and forget you ever had a daddy."

"Yes, that's true," she agreed **tranquilly**.

He didn't go in. He was coming back at nine o'clock and he wanted to keep himself fresh and new for the thing he must say then.

"When you're safe inside, just show yourself in that window."

"All right. Good-by, dads, dads, dads, dads."

He waited in the dark street until she appeared, all warm and glowing, in the window above and kissed her fingers out into the night.

III

They were waiting: Marion sat behind the coffee service in a dignified black dinner dress that just faintly suggested mourning. Lincoln was walking up and down with the animation of one who had already been talking. They were as anxious as he was to get into the question. He opened it almost immediately:

"I suppose you know what I want to see you about—why I really came to Paris."

Marion played with the black stars on her necklace and frowned.

"I'm awfully anxious to have a home," he continued. "And I'm awfully anxious to have Honoria in it. I appreciate your taking in Honoria for her

tranquilly: calmly

mother's sake, but things have changed now"—he hesitated and then continued more forcibly—"changed radically with me, and I want to ask you to reconsider the matter. It would be silly for me to deny that about three years ago I was acting badly—"

Marion looked up at him with hard eyes.

"—But all that's over. As I told you, I haven't had more than a drink a day for over a year, and I take that drink deliberately, so that the idea of alcohol won't get too big in my imagination. You see the idea?"

"No," said Marion succinctly.

"It's a sort of stunt I set myself. It keeps the matter in proportion."

"I get you," said Lincoln. "You don't want to admit it's got any attraction for you."

"Something like that. Sometimes I forget and don't take it. But I try to take it. Anyhow, I couldn't afford to drink in my position. The people I represent are more than satisfied with what I've done, and I'm bringing my sister over from Burlington to keep house for me, and I want awfully to have Honoria too. You know that even when her mother and I weren't getting along well we never let anything that happened touch Honoria. I know she's fond of me and I know I'm able to take care of her—well, there you are. How do you feel about it?"

He knew that now he would have to take a beating. It would last an hour or two hours, and it would be difficult, but if he **modulated** his inevitable resentment to the **chastened** attitude of the reformed sinner, he might win his point in the end.

Keep your temper, he told himself. You don't want to be justified. You want Honoria.

Lincoln spoke first: "We've been talking it over ever since we got your letter last month. We're happy to have Honoria here. She's a dear little thing, and we're glad to be able to help her, but of course that isn't the question—"

Marion interrupted suddenly. "How long are you going to stay sober, Charlie?" she asked.

"Permanently, I hope."

"How can anybody count on that?"

"You know I never did drink heavily until I gave up business and came over here with nothing to do. Then Helen and I began to run around with—"

"Please leave Helen out of it. I can't bear to hear you talk about her like that."

modulated:
adjusted; modified

chastened:
humble; disciplined

He stared at her grimly; he had never been certain how fond of each other the sisters were in life.

"My drinking only lasted about a year and a half—from the time we came over until I—collapsed."

"It was time enough—"

"It was time enough," he agreed.

"My duty is entirely to Helen," she said. "I try to think what she would have wanted me to do. Frankly, from the night you did that terrible thing you haven't really existed for me. I can't help that. She was my sister."

"Yes."

"When she was dying she asked me to look out for Honoria. If you hadn't been in a sanitarium then, it might have helped matters."

He had no answer.

*H*e shook his head. "I'll simply lose her, don't you see?"

"I'll never in my life be able to forget the morning when Helen knocked at my door, soaked to the skin and shivering, and said you'd locked her out."

Charlie gripped the sides of the chair. This was more difficult than he expected: he wanted to launch out into a long **expostulation** and explanation, but he only said: "The night I locked her out—" and she interrupted, "I don't feel up to going over that again."

expostulation: justification

After a moment's silence Lincoln said: "We're getting off the subject. You want Marion to set aside her legal guardianship and give you Honoria. I think the main point for her is whether she has confidence in you or not."

"I don't blame Marion," Charlie said slowly, "but I think she can have entire confidence in me. I had a good record up to three years ago. Of course, it's within human possibilities I may go wrong again. But if we wait much longer I'll lose Honoria's childhood and my chance for a home." He shook his head. "I'll simply lose her, don't you see?"

"Yes, I see," said Lincoln.

"Why didn't you think of all this before?" Marion asked.

"I suppose I did, from time to time, but Helen and I were getting along badly. When I consented to the guardianship, I was flat on my back in a sanitarium, and the market had cleaned me out. I knew I'd acted badly, and I thought if it would bring any peace to Helen, I'd agree to anything. But now it's different. I'm functioning, I'm behaving damn well, so far as—"

"Please don't swear at me," Marion said.

He looked at her, startled. With each remark the force of her dislike became more and more apparent. She had built up all her fear of life into one wall and faced it toward him. This trivial **reproof** was possibly the result of some trouble with the cook several hours before. Charlie became increasingly alarmed at leaving Honoria in this atmosphere of hostility against himself; sooner or later it would come out, in a word here, a shake of the head there, and some of that distrust would be **irrevocably** implanted in Honoria. But he pulled his temper down out of his face and shut it up inside him; he had won a point, for Lincoln realized the absurdity of Marion's remark, and asked her lightly since when she had objected to the word "damn."

"Another thing," Charlie said: "I'm able to give her certain advantages now. I'm going to take a French governess to Prague with me. I've got a lease on a new apartment—"

He stopped, realizing that he was blundering. They couldn't be expected to accept with **equanimity** the fact that his income was again twice as large as their own.

"I suppose you can give her more luxuries than we can," said Marion. "When you were throwing away money we were living along watching every ten francs. . . . I suppose you'll start doing it again."

"Oh, no," he said. "I've learned. I worked hard for ten years, you know— until I got lucky in the market, like so many people. Terribly lucky. It didn't seem any use working any more, so I quit. It won't happen again."

There was a long silence. All of them felt their nerves straining, and for the first time in a year Charlie wanted a drink. He was sure now that Lincoln Peters wanted him to have his child.

Marion shuddered suddenly; part of her saw that Charlie's feet were planted on the earth now, and her own maternal feeling recognized the naturalness of his desire; but she had lived for a long time with a prejudice—a prejudice founded on a curious disbelief in her sister's happiness, which, in the shock of one terrible night, had turned to hatred for him. It had all happened at a point in her life where the discouragement of ill health and adverse circumstances made it necessary for her to believe in tangible villainy and a tangible villain.

"I can't help what I think!" she cried out suddenly. "How much you were responsible for Helen's death, I don't know. It's something you'll have to square with your own conscience."

reproof:
criticism;
reprimand

irrevocably:
permanently;
unchangeably

equanimity:
pleasant calmness

An electric current of agony surged through him; for a moment he was almost on his feet, an unuttered sound echoing in his throat.

He hung on to himself for a moment, another moment.

"Hold on there," said Lincoln uncomfortably. "I never thought you were responsible for that."

"Helen died of heart trouble," Charlie said dully.

"Yes, heart trouble." Marion spoke as if the phrase had another meaning for her.

Then, in the flatness that followed her outburst, she saw him plainly and she knew he had somehow arrived at control over the situation. Glancing at her husband, she found no help from him, and as abruptly as if it were a matter of no importance, she threw up the sponge.

"Do what you like!" she cried, springing up from her chair. "She's your child. I'm not the person to stand in your way. I think if it were my child I'd rather see her—" She managed to check herself. "You two decide it. I can't stand this. I'm sick. I'm going to bed."

She hurried from the room; after a moment Lincoln said:

"This has been a hard day for her. You know how strongly she feels—" His voice was almost apologetic: "When a woman gets an idea in her head."

"Of course."

"It's going to be all right. I think she sees now that you—can provide for the child, and so we can't very well stand in your way or Honoria's way."

"Thank you, Lincoln."

"I'd better go along and see how she is."

"I'm going."

He was still trembling when he reached the street, but a walk down the Rue Bonaparte to the quais[19] set him up, and as he crossed the Seine, fresh and new by the quai lamps, he felt exultant. But back in his room he couldn't sleep. The image of Helen haunted him. Helen whom he had loved so until they had senselessly begun to abuse each other's love, tear it into shreds. On that terrible February night that Marion remembered so vividly, a slow quarrel had gone on for hours. There was a scene at the Florida, and then he attempted to take her home, and then she kissed young Webb at a table; after that there was what she had hysterically said. When he arrived home alone he turned the key in the lock in wild anger. How could he know she would arrive an hour later alone, that there would be a snowstorm in which she

---

19 **quais:** French for "shores"

wandered about in slippers, too confused to find a taxi? Then the aftermath, her escaping pneumonia by a miracle, and all the attendant horror. They were "reconciled," but that was the beginning of the end, and Marion, who had seen with her own eyes and who imagined it to be one of many scenes from her sister's martyrdom, never forgot.

Going over it again brought Helen nearer, and in the white, soft light that steals upon half sleep near morning he found himself talking to her again. She said that he was perfectly right about Honoria and that she wanted Honoria to be with him. She said she was glad he was being good and doing better. She said a lot of other things—very friendly things—but she was in a swing in a white dress, and swinging faster and faster all the time, so that at the end he could not hear clearly all that she said.

IV

He woke up feeling happy. The door of the world was open again. He made plans, vistas, futures for Honoria and himself, but suddenly he grew sad, remembering all the plans he and Helen had made. She had not planned to die. The present was the thing—work to do, and some one to love. But not to love too much, for he knew the injury that a father can do to a daughter or a mother to a son by attaching them too closely; afterward, out in the world, the child would seek in the marriage partner the same blind tenderness and, failing probably to find it, turn against love and life.

It was another bright, crisp day. He called Lincoln Peters at the bank where he worked and asked if he could count on taking Honoria when he left for Prague. Lincoln agreed that there was no reason for delay. One thing—the legal guardianship. Marion wanted to retain that a while longer. She was upset by the whole matter, and it would oil things if she felt that the situation was still in her control for another year. Charlie agreed, wanting only the tangible, visible child.

Then the question of a governess. Charlie sat in a gloomy agency and talked to a cross Bernaise and to a **buxom** Breton[20] peasant neither of whom he could have endured. There were others whom he would see tomorrow.

He lunched with Lincoln Peters at Griffons, trying to keep down his exultation.

"There's nothing quite like your own child," Lincoln said. "But you understand how Marion feels too."

buxom:
full-figured

---

20 **Bernaise ... Breton:** persons from the French regions Béarn and Brittany, respectively

"She's forgotten how hard I worked for seven years there," Charlie said. "She just remembers one night."

"There's another thing," Lincoln hesitated. "While you and Helen were tearing around Europe throwing money away, we were just getting along. I didn't touch any of the prosperity because I never got ahead enough to carry anything but my insurance. I think Marion felt there was some kind of injustice in it—you not even working toward the end, and getting richer and richer."

"It went just as quick as it came," said Charlie.

"Yes, a lot of it stayed in the hands of chasseurs and saxophone players and maîtres d'hôtel—well, the big party's over now. I just said that to explain Marion's feeling about those crazy years. If you drop in about six o'clock tonight before Marion's too tired, we'll settle the details on the spot."

Back at his hotel, Charlie found a *pneumatique*[21] that had been redirected from the Ritz bar where Charlie had left his address for the purpose of finding a certain man.

> DEAR CHARLIE:
>
> You were so strange when we saw you the other day that I wondered if I did something to offend you. If so, I'm not conscious of it. In fact, I have thought about you too much for the last year, and it's always been in the back of my mind that I might see you if I came over here. We *did* have such good times that crazy spring, like the night you and I stole the butcher's tricycle, and the time we tried to call on the president and you had the old derby rim[22] and the wire cane. Everybody seems so old lately, but I don't feel old a bit. Couldn't we get together some time today for old time's sake? I've got a vile hang-over for the moment, but will be feeling better this afternoon and will look for you about five in the sweetshop at the Ritz.
>
> Always devotedly,
> LORRAINE.

His first feeling was one of awe that he had actually, in his mature years, stolen a tricycle and pedaled Lorraine all over the Étoile[23] between the small hours and dawn. In retrospect it was a nightmare. Locking out Helen didn't fit in with any other act of his life, but the tricycle incident did—it was one

---

21 *pneumatique:* French for "message"

22 **derby rim:** rim of a stiff felt cap called a derby

23 **Étoile:** the square in Paris where the Arc de Triomphe is located

of many. How many weeks or months of dissipation to arrive at that condition of utter irresponsibility?

He tried to picture how Lorraine had appeared to him then—very attractive; Helen was unhappy about it, though she said nothing. Yesterday, in the restaurant, Lorraine had seemed trite, blurred, worn away. He emphatically did not want to see her, and he was glad Alix had not given away his hotel address. It was a relief to think, instead, of Honoria, to think of Sundays spent with her and of saying good morning to her and of knowing she was there in his house at night, drawing her breath in the darkness.

At five he took a taxi and bought presents for all the Peters—a **piquant** cloth doll, a box of Roman soldiers, flowers for Marion, big linen handkerchiefs for Lincoln.

He saw, when he arrived in the apartment, that Marion had accepted the inevitable. She greeted him now as though he were a **recalcitrant** member of the family, rather than a menacing outsider. Honoria had been told she was going; Charlie was glad to see that her tact made her conceal her excessive happiness. Only on his lap did she whisper her delight and the question "When?" before she slipped away with the other children.

He and Marion were alone for a minute in the room, and on an impulse he spoke out boldly:

"Family quarrels are bitter things. They don't go according to any rules. They're not like aches or wounds; they're more like splits in the skin that won't heal because there's not enough material. I wish you and I could be on better terms."

"Some things are hard to forget," she answered. "It's a question of confidence." There was no answer to this and presently she asked, "When do you propose to take her?"

"As soon as I can get a governess. I hoped the day after tomorrow."

"That's impossible. I've got to get her things in shape. Not before Saturday."

He yielded. Coming back into the room, Lincoln offered him a drink.

"I'll take my daily whisky," he said.

It was warm here, it was a home, people together by a fire. The children felt very safe and important; the mother and father were serious, watchful. They had things to do for the children more important than his visit here. A spoonful of medicine was, after all, more important than the strained relations between Marion and himself. They were not dull people, but they were very much in the grip of life and circumstances. He wondered if he couldn't do something to get Lincoln out of his rut at the bank.

piquant:
charming

recalcitrant:
difficult to manage

A long peal at the door-bell; the *bonne à tout faire*[24] passed through and went down the corridor. The door opened upon another long ring, and then voices, and the three in the salon looked up expectantly; Richard moved to bring the corridor within his range of vision, and Marion rose. Then the maid came back along the corridor, closely followed by the voices, which developed under the light into Duncan Schaeffer and Lorraine Quarles.

They were gay, they were hilarious, they were roaring with laughter. For a moment Charlie was astounded; unable to understand how they had **ferreted** out the Peters' address.

ferreted: searched

"Ah-h-h!" Duncan wagged his finger **roguishly** at Charlie. "Ah-h-h!"

roguishly: mischievously

They both slid down another cascade of laughter. Anxious and at a loss, Charlie shook hands with them quickly and presented them to Lincoln and Marion. Marion nodded, scarcely speaking. She had drawn back a step toward the fire; her little girl stood beside her, and Marion put an arm about her shoulder.

With growing annoyance at the intrusion, Charlie waited for them to explain themselves. After some concentration Duncan said:

"We came to invite you out to dinner. Lorraine and I insist that all this shishi business 'bout your address got to stop."

Charlie came closer to them, as if to force them backward down the corridor.

"Sorry, but I can't. Tell me where you'll be and I'll phone you in half an hour."

This made no impression. Lorraine sat down suddenly on the side of a chair, and focussing her eyes on Richard, cried, "Oh, what a nice little boy! Come here, little boy." Richard glanced at his mother, but did not move. With a perceptible shrug of her shoulders, Lorraine turned back to Charlie.

"Come and dine. Sure your cousins won' mine. See you so sel'om. Or solemn."

"I can't," said Charlie sharply. "You two have dinner and I'll phone you."

Her voice became suddenly unpleasant. "All right, we'll go. But I remember once when you hammered on my door at four A.M. I was enough of a good sport to give you a drink. Come on, Dunc." Still in slow motion, with blurred, angry faces, with uncertain feet, they retired along the corridor.

"Good night," Charlie said.

"Good night!" responded Lorraine emphatically.

---

24 ***bonne à tout faire:*** French for "maid"

Left alone, Charlie sat tense in his chair. In the next room he could hear the children eating, talking in monosyllables, already oblivious to the scene between their elders.

When he went back into the salon Marion had not moved, only now her son was standing in the circle of her other arm. Lincoln was still swinging Honoria back and forth like a pendulum from side to side.

"What an outrage!" Charlie broke out. "What an absolute outrage!"

Neither of them answered. Charlie dropped into an armchair, picked up his drink, set it down again and said:

"People I haven't seen for two years having the colossal nerve—" He broke off. Marion had made the sound "Oh!" in one swift, furious breath, turned her body from him with a jerk and left the room.

Lincoln set down Honoria carefully.

"You children go in and start your soup," he said, and when they obeyed, he said to Charlie:

"Marion's not well and she can't stand shocks. That kind of people make her really physically sick."

"I didn't tell them to come here. They wormed your name out of somebody. They deliberately—"

"Well, it's too bad. It doesn't help matters. Excuse me a minute."

Left alone, Charlie sat tense in his chair. In the next room he could hear the children eating, talking in **monosyllables,** already oblivious to the scene between their elders. He heard a murmur of conversation from a farther room and then the ticking bell of a telephone receiver picked up, and in a panic he moved to the other side of the room and out of earshot.

In a minute Lincoln came back. "Look here, Charlie. I think we'd better call off dinner for tonight. Marion's in bad shape."

"Is she angry with me?"

"Sort of," he said, almost roughly. "She's not strong and—"

"You mean she's changed her mind about Honoria."

"She's pretty bitter right now. I don't know. You phone me at the bank tomorrow."

"I wish you'd explain to her I never dreamed these people would come here. I'm just as sore as you are."

"I couldn't explain anything to her now."

monosyllables: one-syllable words

Charlie got up. He took his coat and hat and started down the corridor. Then he opened the door of the dining room and said in a strange voice, "Good night, children."

Honoria rose and ran around the table to hug him.

"Good night, sweetheart," he said vaguely, and then trying to make his voice more tender, trying to **conciliate** something, "Good night, dear children."

conciliate: soothe; appease

V

Charlie went directly to the Ritz bar with the furious idea of finding Lorraine and Duncan, but they were not there, and he realized that in any case there was nothing he could do. He had not touched his drink at the Peters', and now he ordered a whisky-and-soda. Paul came over to say hello.

"It's a great change," he said sadly. "We do about half the business we did. So many fellows I hear about back in the States lost everything, maybe not in the first crash, but then in the second. Your friend George Hardt lost every cent, I hear. Are you back in the States?"

"No. I'm in business in Prague."

"I heard that you lost a lot in the crash."

"I did," and he added grimly, "but I lost everything I wanted in the boom."

"Selling short?"

"Something like that."

Again the memory of those days swept over him like a nightmare—the people they had met travelling; the people who couldn't add a row of figures or speak a coherent sentence. The little man Helen had consented to dance with at the ship's party, who had insulted her ten feet from the table, the women and girls carried screaming with drink or drugs out of public places . . . the men who locked their wives out in the snow because the snow of '29 wasn't real snow. If you didn't want it to be snow, you just paid some money.

He went to the phone and called the Peters apartment; Lincoln answered.

"I called up because this thing is on my mind. Has Marion said anything definite?"

"Marion's sick," Lincoln answered shortly. "I know this thing isn't altogether your fault, but I can't have her go to pieces about it. I'm afraid we'll have to let it slide for six months; I can't take the chance of working her up to this state again."

"I see."

"I'm sorry, Charlie."

He went back to his table. His whisky glass was empty, but he shook his head when Alix looked at it questioningly. There wasn't much he could do now except send Honoria some things; he would send her a lot of things tomorrow. He thought rather angrily that this was just money—he had given so many people money. . . .

"No, no more," he said to another waiter. "What do I owe you?"

He would come back some day; they couldn't make him pay forever. But he wanted his child, and nothing was much good now, beside that fact. He wasn't young any more, with a lot of nice thoughts and dreams to have by himself. He was absolutely sure Helen wouldn't have wanted him to be so alone.

Responding to the Story

I. LITERARY LENS How did you respond to being plunged down into the middle of the story without much setup?

2. Babylon was one of the greatest cities in the ancient world; now only ruins remain. How would you interpret the title "Babylon Revisited"?

3. One of the themes of this story is that everything we say or do has consequences. Using a chart like the one below, identify some actions (words and deeds) and their consequences in this story. Explain whether you think there is any one comment or deed that led inevitably to the story's conclusion.

Words and Deeds	Consequences

4. THE AUTHOR'S STYLE Fitzgerald was often singled out as the spokesman for "The Lost Generation" of the twenties. This was the group of artists and writers who seemed to lose their purpose as the excesses of the era led up to the stock market crash and its aftermath. His work is infused with a sense of time passing and of opportunities lost. Select a passage that you think demonstrates this sense of loss. Be prepared to explain your choice.

★★

Thomas Wolfe
1900–1938

About the Author

Growing up in Asheville, North Carolina, as the youngest of eight children, Thomas Wolfe became an observer of human nature early in life. The characters he encountered in the boardinghouse his mother ran turned up in his autobiographical novel, *Look Homeward, Angel.* Acclaimed by critics, the novel was nonetheless banned in the Asheville library because some of the characters so closely resembled people in the town.

A precocious student, Wolfe entered the University of North Carolina at Chapel Hill at 16 and later graduated from Harvard with a masters degree, intending to become a playwright. Eventually he became a writer of prose instead. His work was greatly influenced by Aline Bernstein, a married set and costume designer from New York with whom he had a long and turbulent relationship, and upon whom he based characters in his novels.

In 1938, Wolfe died of a brain tumor caused by an undetected case of tuberculosis. He left behind large manuscripts of unpublished work from which editors gleaned two novels and a collection of short stories. One of these novels is *You Can't Go Home Again.* People familiar with Wolfe's work believe that when the first President Bush made an often-quoted reference to "a thousand points of light" in a speech, the phrase was borrowed from Wolfe's description of "ten thousand points of light" in that novel.

★★★★★★★★★★★

The Author's Style

Thomas Wolfe was an intensely emotional person who poured his heart and soul onto the page. Thousands of his rapidly typed and handwritten pages were eventually shaped into stories and novels, many of them recognizable as having been drawn from his own life. Wolfe's writing is full of energy, turbulence, and extremes of feeling; he has been referred to as a writer of romance and doom. The sensitive presentation of childhood and adolescence in his novel *Look Homeward,* *Angel* has been widely recognized and praised.

Wolfe was more interested in expressing his longing and passion for experience than in taking the time to carefully shape his prose—just the opposite of Hemingway's approach to fiction writing. Because the short story requires a writer to complete a coherent narrative in a limited number of pages, some readers prefer Wolfe's more carefully shaped stories to his intense but sprawling novels.

LITERARY LENS A *fable* is a story meant to give the reader a single useful truth, often through marvelous elements such as talking animals. Look for the elements of a fable in this story.

THE
FAR AND
THE NEAR

THOMAS WOLFE

On the outskirts of a little town upon a rise of land that swept back from the railway there was a tidy little cottage of white boards, trimmed vividly with green blinds. To one side of the house there was a garden neatly patterned with plots of growing vegetables, and an arbor for the grapes which ripened late in August. Before the house there were three mighty oaks which sheltered it in their clean and massive shade in summer, and to the other side there was a border of gay flowers. The whole place had an air of tidiness, thrift, and modest comfort.

Every day, a few minutes after two o'clock in the afternoon, the limited express between two cities passed this spot. At that moment the great train, having halted for a breathing-space at the town near by, was beginning to lengthen evenly into its stroke, but it had not yet reached the full drive of its terrific speed. It swung into view deliberately, swept past with a powerful swaying motion of the engine, a low smooth rumble of its heavy cars upon pressed steel, and then it vanished in the cut. For a moment the progress of the engine could be marked by heavy bellowing puffs of smoke that burst at spaced intervals above the edges of the meadow grass, and finally nothing could be heard but the solid clacking tempo of the wheels receding into the drowsy stillness of the afternoon.

Every day for more than twenty years, as the train had approached this house, the engineer had blown on the whistle, and every day, as soon as she heard this signal, a woman had appeared on the back porch of the little house and waved to him. At first she had a small child clinging to her skirts, and now this child had grown to full womanhood, and every day she, too, came with her mother to the porch and waved.

The engineer had grown old and gray in service. He had driven his great train, loaded with its weight of lives, across the land ten thousand times. His own children had grown up and married, and four times he had seen before him on the tracks the ghastly dot of tragedy converging like a cannon ball to its eclipse of horror at the boiler head[1]—a light spring wagon filled with children, with its clustered row of small stunned faces; a cheap automobile stalled upon the tracks, set with the wooden figures of people paralyzed with fear; a battered hobo walking by the rail, too deaf and old to hear the whistle's warning; and a form flung past his window with a scream—all this the man had seen and known. He had known all the grief, the joy, the peril and the labor such a man could know; he had grown seamed and weathered in his loyal service, and now, schooled by the qualities of faith and courage and humbleness that attended his labor, he had grown old, and had the grandeur and the wisdom these men have.

But no matter what peril or tragedy he had known, the vision of the little house and the women waving to him with a brave free motion of the arm had become fixed in the mind of the engineer as something beautiful and enduring, something beyond all change and ruin, and something that would always be the same, no matter what mishap, grief or error might break the iron schedule of his days.

The sight of the little house and of these two women gave him the most extraordinary happiness he had ever known. He had seen them in a thousand lights, a hundred weathers. He had seen them through the harsh bare

---

1 **boiler head:** front of an engine, where water is converted into steam

light of wintry gray across the brown and frosted stubble of the earth, and he had seen them again in the green luring **sorcery** of April.

sorcery:
magic

He felt for them and for the little house in which they lived such tenderness as a man might feel for his own children, and at length the picture of their lives was carved so sharply in his heart that he felt that he knew their lives completely, to every hour and moment of the day, and he resolved that one day, when his years of service should be ended, he would go and find these people and speak at last with them whose lives had been so wrought into his own.

That day came. At last the engineer stepped from a train onto the station platform of the town where these two women lived. His years upon the rail had ended. He was a pensioned[2] servant of his company, with no more work to do. The engineer walked slowly through the station and out into the streets of the town. Everything was as strange to him as if he had never seen this town before. As he walked on, his sense of bewilderment and confusion grew. Could this be the town

TRAIN ON THE DESERT, Thomas Hart Benton, ca. 1926–28

he had passed ten thousand times? Were these the same houses he had seen so often from the high windows of his cab? It was all as unfamiliar, as disquieting as a city in a dream, and the perplexity of his spirit increased as he went on.

Presently the houses thinned into the straggling outposts of the town, and the street faded into a country road—the one on which the women lived. And the man plodded on slowly in the heat and dust. At length he stood before the house he sought. He knew at once that he had found the proper place. He saw the lordly oaks before the house, the flower beds, the garden and the arbor, and farther off, the glint of rails.

---

2 **pensioned:** having a pension, or retirement, fund

Yes, this was the house he sought, the place he had passed so many times, the destination he had longed for with such happiness. But now that he had found it, now that he was here, why did his hand falter on the gate; why had the town, the road, the earth, the very entrance to this place he loved turned unfamiliar as the landscape of some ugly dream? Why did he now feel this sense of confusion, doubt and hopelessness?

At length he entered by the gate, walked slowly up the path and in a moment more had mounted three short steps that led up to the porch, and was knocking at the door. Presently he heard steps in the hall, the door was opened, and a woman stood facing him.

And instantly, with a sense of bitter loss and grief, he was sorry he had come. He knew at once that the woman who stood there looking at him with a mistrustful eye was the same woman who had waved to him so many thousand times. But her face was harsh and pinched and meager, the flesh sagged wearily in sallow folds, and the small eyes peered at him with timid suspicion and uneasy doubt. All the brave freedom, the warmth and the affection that he had read into her gesture, vanished in the moment that he saw her and heard her unfriendly tongue.

And now his own voice sounded unreal and ghastly to him as he tried to explain his presence, to tell her who he was and the reason he had come. But he faltered on, fighting stubbornly against the horror of regret, confusion, disbelief that surged up in his spirit, drowning all his former joy and making his act of hope and tenderness seem shameful to him.

At length the woman invited him almost unwillingly into the house, and called her daughter in a harsh shrill voice. Then, for a brief agony of time, the man sat in an ugly little parlor, and he tried to talk while the two women stared at him with a dull, bewildered hostility, a sullen, **timorous** restraint.

timorous:
fearful

And finally, stammering a crude farewell, he departed. He walked away down the path and then along the road toward town, and suddenly he knew that he was an old man. His heart, which had been brave and confident when it looked along the familiar **vista** of the rails, was now sick with doubt and horror as it saw the strange and unsuspected visage of an earth which had always been within a stone's throw of him, and which he had never seen or known. And he knew that all the magic of that bright lost way, the vista of that shining line, the imagined corner of that small good universe of hope's desire, was gone forever, could never be got back again.

vista:
view

Thomas Wolfe

Responding to the Story

1. **LITERARY LENS** In what ways is this story both like and unlike a fable?

2. William Faulkner, whom you will read later in this book, once said that Wolfe's stories "put all the experience of the human heart on the head of a pin." In what way does this story demonstrate Wolfe's ability to summarize the human experience?

3. "The Far and the Near" begins with a faraway view, and then, like a movie camera, draws nearer. How does the mood of the story change as the focus narrows and sharpens?

4. A common theme of realistic literature is the exposure of a dark, even evil, "reality" hiding behind the mask of a pleasant appearance. Using a chart like the one below, identify and explore the contrasts between appearance and reality in this story.

Appearance	Reality

5. **THE AUTHOR'S STYLE** As in poetry, word choice is often crucial to the success of a short story. Compare and contrast Wolfe's choice of descriptive words in the opening three paragraphs to the descriptive words in the closing three paragraphs.

Carson McCullers
1917–1967

About the Author

Although her first dream was to study music at Julliard School of Music in New York City, Carson McCullers set her sights on writing instead because her parents could not afford to send her to the expensive private music school. Despite her ill health—the author contracted rheumatic fever as an adolescent and was consequently an invalid most of her life—she nonetheless focused her energies on her writing and published her first fiction, a short story, at 19. Although she lived for a time in New York and Paris after leaving home, McCullers set most of her work in the South of her youth—she was reared in Georgia.

As an adult, McCullers led a turbulent life. She was married twice to the same man. An alcoholic, she also battled severe depression. She attempted suicide but ultimately died of natural causes at the age of 50.

McCullers' work leant itself well to the stage and screen. Her novella *The Ballad of the Sad Café* and her novel *The Member of the Wedding* became stage plays. Her novels *The Heart Is a Lonely Hunter* and *Reflections in a Golden Eye* were both adapted to the screen.

****

The Author's Style

Carson McCullers began writing fiction as an adolescent, the age of many of her main characters. A key to her work is the sensitive presentation of the inner reality of these young protagonists—their needs, fears, and jealousies. The effect is particularly poignant when these characters do not fit easily into the expectations of their communities. Frankie Addams, the central character of *The Member of the Wedding*, is a young girl who "belonged to no club and was a member of nothing in the world." Such characters are rebellious, contradictory, vulnerable, and lonely; they struggle to find love and their place in life.

The narration and the dialogue in McCullers' stories develop out of common speech, precisely phrased to fit her characters. Their dialogue enables the reader to see how these characters see themselves and the world around them. McCullers uses both third person and first person narration, but always conveys effectively the inner moods of her "outsider" characters. Conflicts are not always acted out, but shown only to the reader through naïve observations, simple descriptions, and plain, direct judgments of people and events. These are often expressed in terms of everyday comparisons and figures of speech.

LITERARY LENS The author's choice of narrator, or point of view, determines how we learn about the characters in a short story. In "Sucker," the narrator is the main character who shares his thoughts, feelings, and story through an interior monologue. Be aware of these thoughts and feelings as you read.

SUCKER

CARSON McCULLERS

It was always like I had a room to myself. Sucker slept in my bed with me but that didn't interfere with anything. The room was mine and I used it as I wanted to. Once I remember sawing a trap door in the floor. Last year when I was a sophomore in high school I tacked on my wall some pictures of girls from magazines and one of them was just in her underwear. My mother never bothered me because she had the younger kids to look after. And Sucker thought anything I did was always swell.

Whenever I would bring any of my friends back to my room all I had to do was just glance once at Sucker and he would get up from whatever he was busy with and maybe half smile at me, and leave without saying a word. He never brought kids back there. He's

Now that Sucker has changed so much it is a little hard to remember him as he used to be. I never imagined anything would suddenly happen that would make us both very different.

twelve, four years younger than I am, and he always knew without me even telling him that I didn't want kids that age meddling with my things.

Half the time I used to forget that Sucker isn't my brother. He's my first cousin but practically ever since I remember he's been in our family. You see his folks were killed in a wreck when he was a baby. To me and my kid sisters he was like our brother.

Sucker used to always remember and believe every word I said. That's how he got his nick-name. Once a couple of years ago I told him that if he'd jump off our garage with an umbrella it would act as a parachute and he wouldn't fall hard. He did it and busted his knee. That's just one instance. And the funny thing was that no matter how many times he got fooled he would still believe me. Not that he was dumb in other ways—it was just the way he acted with me. He would look at everything I did and quietly take it in.

There is one thing I have learned, but it makes me feel guilty and is hard to figure out. If a person admires you a lot you despise him and don't care—and it is the person who doesn't notice you that you are apt to admire. This is not easy to realize. Maybelle Watts, this senior at school, acted like she was the Queen of Sheba and even humiliated me. Yet at this same time I would have done anything in the world to get her attentions. All I could think about day and night was Maybelle until I was nearly crazy. When Sucker was a little kid and on up until the time he was twelve I guess I treated him as bad as Maybelle did me.

Now that Sucker has changed so much it is a little hard to remember him as he used to be. I never imagined anything would suddenly happen that would make us both very different. I never knew that in order to get what has happened straight in my mind I would want to think back on him as he used to be and compare and try to get things settled. If I could have seen ahead maybe I would have acted different.

I never noticed him much or thought about him and when you consider how long we have had the same room together it is funny the few things I remember. He used to talk to himself a lot when he'd think he was alone—

all about him fighting gangsters and being on ranches and that sort of kids' stuff. He'd get in the bathroom and stay as long as an hour and sometimes his voice would go up high and excited and you could hear him all over the house. Usually, though, he was very quiet. He didn't have many boys in the neighborhood to buddy with and his face had the look of a kid who is watching a game and waiting to be asked to play. He didn't mind wearing the sweaters and coats that I outgrew, even if the sleeves did flop down too big and make his wrists look as thin and white as a little girl's. That is how I remember him—getting a little bigger every year but still being the same. That was Sucker up until a few months ago when all this trouble began.

Maybelle was somehow mixed up in what happened so I guess I ought to start with her. Until I knew her I hadn't given much time to girls. Last fall she sat next to me in General Science class and that was when I first began to notice her. Her hair is the brightest yellow I ever saw and occasionally she will wear it set into curls with some sort of gluey stuff. Her fingernails are pointed and manicured and painted a shiny red. All during class I used to watch Maybelle, nearly all the time except when I thought she was going to look my way or when the teacher called on me. I couldn't keep my eyes off her hands, for one thing. They are very little and white except for that red stuff, and when she would turn the pages of her book she always licked her thumb and held out her little finger and turned very slowly. It is impossible to describe Maybelle. All the boys are crazy about her but she didn't even notice me. For one thing she's almost two years older than I am. Between periods I used to try and pass very close to her in the halls but she would hardly ever smile at me. All I could do was sit and look at her in class—and sometimes it was like the whole room could hear my heart beating and I wanted to holler or light out and run for Hell.

At night, in bed, I would imagine about Maybelle. Often this would keep me from sleeping until as late as one or two o'clock. Sometimes Sucker would wake up and ask me why I couldn't get settled and I'd tell him to hush his mouth. I suppose I was mean to him lots of times. I guess I wanted to ignore somebody like Maybelle did me. You could always tell by Sucker's face when his feelings were hurt. I don't remember all the ugly remarks I must have made because even when I was saying them my mind was on Maybelle.

That went on for nearly three months and then somehow she began to change. In the halls she would speak to me and every morning she copied my homework. At lunch time once I danced with her in the gym. One afternoon

I got up nerve and went around to her house with a carton of cigarettes. I knew she smoked in the girls' basement and sometimes outside of school—and I didn't want to take her candy because I think that's been run into the ground. She was very nice and it seemed to me everything was going to change.

It was that night when this trouble really started. I had come into my room late and Sucker was already asleep. I felt too happy and keyed up to get in a comfortable position and I was awake thinking about Maybelle a long time. Then I dreamed about her and it seemed I kissed her. It was a surprise to wake up and see the dark. I lay still and a little while passed before I could come to and understand where I was. The house was quiet and it was a very dark night.

Sucker's voice was a shock to me. "Pete? . . ."

I didn't answer anything or even move.

"You do like me as much as if I was your own brother, don't you, Pete?"

I couldn't get over the surprise of everything and it was like this was the real dream instead of the other.

"You have liked me all the time like I was your own brother, haven't you?"

"Sure," I said.

Then I got up for a few minutes. It was cold and I was glad to come back to bed. Sucker hung on to my back. He felt little and warm and I could feel his warm breathing on my shoulder.

"No matter what you did I always knew you liked me."

I was wide awake and my mind seemed mixed up in a strange way. There was this happiness about Maybelle and all that—but at the same time something about Sucker and his voice when he said these things made me take notice. Anyway I guess you understand people better when you are happy than when something is worrying you. It was like I had never really thought about Sucker until then. I felt I had always been mean to him. One night a few weeks before I had heard him crying in the dark. He said he had lost a boy's beebee gun and was scared to let anybody know. He wanted me to tell him what to do. I was sleepy and tried to make him hush and when he wouldn't I kicked at him. That was just one of the things I remembered. It seemed to me he had always been a lonesome kid. I felt bad.

There is something about a dark cold night that makes you feel close to someone you're sleeping with. When you talk together it is like you are the only people awake in the town.

Carson McCullers

"You're a swell kid, Sucker," I said.

It seemed to me suddenly that I did like him more than anybody else I knew—more than any other boy, more than my sisters, more in a certain way even than Maybelle. I felt good all over and it was like when they play sad music in the movies. I wanted to show Sucker how much I really thought of him and make up for the way I had always treated him.

We talked for a good while that night. His voice was fast and it was like he had been saving up these things to tell me for a long time. He mentioned that he was going to try to build a canoe and that the kids down the block wouldn't let him in on their football team and I don't know what all. I talked some too and it was a good feeling to think of him taking in everything I said so seriously. I even spoke of Maybelle a little, only I made out like it was her who had been running after me all this time. He asked questions about high school and so forth. His voice was excited and he kept on talking fast like he could never get the words out in time. When I went to sleep he was still talking and I could still feel his breathing on my shoulder, warm and close.

During the next couple of weeks I saw a lot of Maybelle. She acted as though she really cared for me a little. Half the time I felt so good I hardly knew what to do with myself.

But I didn't forget about Sucker. There were a lot of old things in my bureau drawer I'd been saving—boxing gloves and Tom Swift books and second rate fishing tackle. All this I turned over to him. We had some more talks together and it was really like I was knowing him for the first time. When there was a long cut on his cheek I knew he had been monkeying around with this new first razor set of mine, but I didn't say anything. His face seemed different now. He used to look timid and sort of like he was afraid of a whack over the head. That expression was gone. His face, with those wide-open eyes and his ears sticking out and his mouth never quite shut, had the look of a person who is surprised and expecting something swell.

Once I started to point him out to Maybelle and tell her he was my kid brother. It was an afternoon when a murder mystery was on at the movie. I had earned a dollar working for my Dad and I gave Sucker a quarter to go and get candy and so forth. With the rest I took Maybelle. We were sitting near the back and I saw Sucker come in. He began to stare at the screen the minute he stepped past the ticket man and he stumbled down the aisle without noticing where he was going. I started to punch Maybelle but couldn't quite make up my mind. Sucker looked a little silly—walking like a drunk with his eyes glued to the movie. He was wiping his reading glasses on his shirt tail and his knickers flopped down. He went on until he got to the first few rows where the kids usually sit. I never did punch Maybelle. But I got to thinking it was good to have both of them at the movie with the money I earned.

I guess things went on like this for about a month or six weeks. I felt so good I couldn't settle down to study or put my mind on anything. I wanted to be friendly with everybody. There were times when I just had to talk to some person. And usually that would be Sucker. He felt as good as I did. Once he said: "Pete, I am gladder that you are like my brother than anything else in the world."

Then something happened between Maybelle and me. I never have figured out just what it was. Girls like her are hard to understand. She began to act different toward me. At first I wouldn't let myself believe this and tried to think it was just my imagination. She didn't act glad to see me anymore. Often she went out riding with this fellow on the football team who owns this yellow roadster. The car was the color of her hair and after school she would ride off with him, laughing and looking into his face. I couldn't think of anything to do about it and she was on my mind all day and night. When I did get a chance to go out with her she was snippy and didn't seem to notice me. This made me feel like something was the matter—I would worry about my shoes clopping too loud on the floor or the fly of my pants, or the bumps on my chin. Sometimes when Maybelle was around, a devil would get into me and I'd hold my face stiff and call grown men by their last names without the Mister and say rough things. In the night I would wonder what made me do all this until I was too tired for sleep.

At first I was so worried I just forgot about Sucker. Then later he began to get on my nerves. He was always hanging around until I would get back from high school, always looking like he had something to say to me or wanted me to tell him. He made me a magazine rack in his Manual Training class and one week he saved his lunch money and bought me three packs of cigarettes. He couldn't seem to take it in that I had things on my mind and didn't want to fool with him. Every afternoon it would be the same—him in my room with this waiting expression on his face. Then I wouldn't say anything or I'd maybe answer him rough-like and he would finally go on out.

I can't divide that time up and say this happened one day and that the next. For one thing I was so mixed up the weeks just slid along into each other and I felt like Hell and didn't care. Nothing definite was said or done. Maybelle still rode around with this fellow in his yellow roadster and sometimes she would smile at me and sometimes not. Every afternoon I went from one place to another where I thought she would be. Either she would act almost nice and I would begin thinking how things would finally clear up and she would care for me—or else she'd behave so that if she hadn't been a girl I'd have wanted to grab her by that white little neck and choke her. The more ashamed I felt for making a fool of myself the more I ran after her.

Sucker kept getting on my nerves more and more. He would look at me as though he sort of blamed me for something, but at the same time knew that it wouldn't last long. He was growing fast and for some reason began to stutter when he talked. Sometimes he had nightmares or would throw up his breakfast. Mom got him a bottle of cod liver oil.

Then the finish came between Maybelle and me. I met her going to the drug store and asked for a date. When she said no I remarked something sarcastic. She told me she was sick and tired of my being around and that she had never cared a rap about me. She said all that. I just stood there and didn't answer anything. I walked home very slowly.

For several afternoons I stayed in my room by myself. I didn't want to go anywhere or talk to anyone. When Sucker would come in and look at me sort of funny I'd yell at him to get out. I didn't want to think of Maybelle and I sat at my desk reading *Popular Mechanics* or whittling at a toothbrush rack I was making. It seemed to me I was putting that girl out of my mind pretty well.

But you can't help what happens to you at night. That is what made things how they are now.

You see a few nights after Maybelle said those words to me I dreamed about her again. It was like that first time and I was squeezing Sucker's arm so tight I woke him up. He reached for my hand.

"Pete, what's the matter with you?"

All of a sudden I felt so mad my throat choked—at myself and the dream and Maybelle and Sucker and every single person I knew. I remembered all the times Maybelle had humiliated me and everything bad that had ever happened. It seemed to me for a second that nobody would ever like me but a sap like Sucker.

"Why is it we aren't buddies like we were before? Why—?"

"Shut your damn trap!" I threw off the cover and got up and turned on the light. He sat in the middle of the bed, his eyes blinking and scared.

Afterward I could remember the change in Sucker's face. Slowly that blank look went away and he closed his mouth. His eyes got narrow and his fists shut.

There was something in me and I couldn't help myself. I don't think anybody ever gets that mad but once. Words came without me knowing what they would be. It was only afterward that I could remember each thing I said and see it all in a clear way.

"Why aren't we buddies? Because you're the dumbest slob I ever saw! Nobody cares anything about you! And just because I felt sorry for you sometimes and tried to act decent don't think I give a damn about a dumb-bunny like you!"

If I'd talked loud or hit him it wouldn't have been so bad. But my voice was slow and like I was very calm. Sucker's mouth was part way open and he looked as though he'd knocked his funny bone. His face was white and sweat came out on his forehead. He wiped it away with the back of his hand and for a minute his arm stayed raised that way as though he was holding something away from him.

"Don't you know a single thing? Haven't you ever been around at all? Why don't you get a girl friend instead of me? What kind of a sissy do you want to grow up to be anyway?"

I didn't know what was coming next. I couldn't help myself or think.

Sucker didn't move. He had on one of my pajama jackets and his neck stuck out skinny and small. His hair was damp on his forehead.

"Why do you always hang around me? Don't you know when you're not wanted?"

Afterward I could remember the change in Sucker's face. Slowly that blank look went away and he closed his mouth. His eyes got narrow and his fists shut. There had never been such a look on him before. It was like every second he was getting older. There was a hard look to his eyes you don't see usually in a kid. A drop of sweat rolled down his chin and he didn't notice. He just sat there with those eyes on me and he didn't speak and his face was hard and didn't move.

"No you don't know when you're not wanted. You're too dumb. Just like your name—a dumb Sucker."

It was like something had busted inside me. I turned off the light and sat down in the chair by the window. My legs were shaking and I was so tired I

WINTER, Andrew Wyeth, 1946, The North Carolina Museum of Art, Raleigh

could have bawled. The room was cold and dark. I sat there for a long time and smoked a squashed cigarette I had saved. Outside the yard was black and quiet. After a while I heard Sucker lie down.

I wasn't mad any more, only tired. It seemed awful to me that I had talked like that to a kid only twelve. I couldn't take it all in. I told myself I would go over to him and try to make it up. But I just sat there in the cold until a long time had passed. I planned how I could straighten it out in the morning. Then, trying not to squeak the springs, I got back in bed.

Sucker was gone when I woke up the next day. And later when I wanted to apologize as I had planned he looked at me in this new hard way so that I couldn't say a word.

All of that was two or three months ago. Since then Sucker has grown faster than any boy I ever saw. He's almost as tall as I am and his bones have gotten heavier and bigger. He won't wear any of my old clothes any more and has bought his first pair of long pants—with some leather suspenders to hold them up. Those are just the changes that are easy to see and put into words.

Our room isn't mine at all any more. He's gotten up this gang of kids and they have a club. When they aren't digging trenches in some vacant lot and fighting they are always in my room. On the door there is some foolishness written in Mercurochrome[1] saying "Woe to the Outsider who Enters" and signed with crossed bones and their secret initials. They have rigged up a radio and every afternoon it blares out music. Once as I was coming in I heard a boy telling something in a loud voice about what he saw in the back of his big brother's automobile. I could guess what I didn't hear. *That's what her and my brother do. It's the truth—parked in the car.* For a minute Sucker looked surprised and his face was almost like it used to be. Then he got hard and tough again. "Sure, dumbbell. We know all that." They didn't notice me. Sucker began telling them how in two years he was planning to be a trapper in Alaska.

But most of the time Sucker stays by himself. It is worse when we are alone together in the room. He sprawls across the bed in those long corduroy pants with the suspenders and just stares at me with that hard, half-sneering look. I fiddle around my desk and can't get settled because of those eyes of his. And the thing is I just have to study because I've gotten three bad cards this term already. If I flunk English I can't graduate next year. I don't want to be a bum and I just have to get my mind on it. I don't care a flip for Maybelle or any particular girl any more and it's only this thing between Sucker and me that is the trouble now. We never speak except when we have to before the family. I don't even want to call him Sucker any more and unless I forget I call him by his real name, Richard. At night I can't study with him in the room and I have to hang around the drug store, smoking and doing nothing, with the fellows who loaf there.

More than anything I want to be easy in my mind again. And I miss the way Sucker and I were for a while in a funny, sad way that before this I never would have believed. But everything is so different that there seems to be nothing I can do to get it right. I've sometimes thought if we could have it out in a big fight that would help. But I can't fight him because he's four years younger. And another thing—sometimes this look in his eyes makes me almost believe that if Sucker could he would kill me.

| **Mercurochrome:** trademark name for a red antiseptic that is meant to be brushed on skin

Responding to the Story

1. **LITERARY LENS**   Occasionally, the narrator stops telling his story and expresses his feelings directly. For example, near the end of the story he says, "More than anything, I want to be easy in my mind again." Find another example of the narrator's sharing of his feelings. What do these statements tell you about the narrator?

2. The plot of a story is usually built around a problem or issue facing the main character. What is the problem that drives the plot in "Sucker"?

3. "There was something in me and I couldn't help myself," Pete says of the incident with this cousin. Do you think it is true that people sometimes can't help themselves from doing or saying things they later deeply regret? Why or why not?

4. Why does Pete, the narrator, start addressing his cousin by his given name, Richard, instead of the nickname Sucker near the end of the story?

5. **THE AUTHOR'S STYLE**   Critics consider McCullers a master of showing the inner lives of lonely people. What are some of the elements of "Sucker" that help create an atmosphere of isolation and loneliness?

★★

John Steinbeck
1902–1968

About the Author

"The ancient commission of the writer has not changed," John Steinbeck said when he received the Nobel Prize for Literature in 1962. "He is charged with exposing our many grievous faults and failures, with dredging up to the light our dark and dangerous dreams for the purpose of improvement."

Reared in a middle class family in California, the setting for much of his fiction, Steinbeck learned about hard work and the potential for failure firsthand. He attended Stanford University, but dropped out and worked as a caretaker, fruit picker, and fisherman before achieving success as a novelist. He was a passion-ate writer of the Proletarian Literature of the thirties, litera-ture in which the most impor-tant characters are working class.

Steinbeck's *The Grapes of Wrath*, considered a landmark of 20th century literature, won the Pulitzer Prize despite the controversy it caused. The book follows a poor family traveling from Oklahoma to California in search of work during the Depression. It displeased officials in both states with its depiction of labor conditions. Other well-known works include *Of Mice and Men*, *East of Eden*, and *The Red Pony*.

★★★★★★★★★★★

The Author's Style

Factual, unemotional descriptions of setting are typical of Steinbeck's style. In his work, the natu-ral world often defines the terms under which his characters live. The author's flat, matter-of-fact tone is created by relatively short, declara-tive sentences. It is clear from the outset that the lives of Steinbeck's people are determined by external forces as much as human will. In part for this reason, and in part because they usually lack extensive education, these characters speak briefly and simply. Their eloquence comes from simple language and everyday dialect used with-out apology. Some Steinbeck characters express themselves through gestures as much as through speech itself.

Occasionally, Steinbeck develops an object from nature into a controlling symbol in a story or novel—a pearl, rabbits, a turtle, and—in the story you are about to read, through chrysan-themums.

LITERARY LENS Pay attention to the symbolism in this story.

THE
CHRYSANTHEMUMS

JOHN STEINBECK

The high grey-flannel fog of winter closed off the Salinas Valley[1] from the sky and from all the rest of the world. On every side it sat like a lid on the mountains and made of the great valley a closed pot. On the broad, level land floor the gang ploughs bit deep and left the black earth shining like metal where the shares had cut. On the foot-hill ranches across the Salinas River, the yellow stubble fields seemed to be bathed in pale cold sunshine, but there was no sunshine in the valley now in December. The thick willow scrub along the river flamed with sharp and positive yellow leaves.

It was a time of quiet and of waiting. The air was cold and tender. A light wind blew up from the southwest so that the farmers

---

1 **Salinas Valley:** a region in western California

were mildly hopeful of a good rain before long; but fog and rain do not go together.

Across the river, on Henry Allen's foot-hill ranch there was little work to be done, for the hay was cut and stored and the orchards were ploughed up to receive the rain deeply when it should come. The cattle on the higher slopes were becoming shaggy and rough-coated.

Elisa Allen, working in her flower garden, looked down across the yard and saw Henry, her husband, talking to two men in business suits. The three of them stood by the tractor-shed, each man with one foot on the side of the little Fordson. They smoked cigarettes and studied the machine as they talked.

Elisa watched them for a moment and then went back to her work. She was thirty-five. Her face was lean and strong and her eyes were as clear as water. Her figure looked blocked and heavy in her gardening costume, a man's black hat pulled low down over her eyes, clod-hopper shoes, a figured print dress almost completely covered by a big corduroy apron with four big pockets to hold the snips, the trowel and scratcher, the seeds and the knife she worked with. She wore heavy leather gloves to protect her hands while she worked.

She was cutting down the old year's chrysanthemum stalks with a pair of short and powerful scissors. She looked down toward the men by the tractor-shed now and then. Her face was eager and mature and handsome; even her work with the scissors was overeager, over-powerful. The chrysanthemum stems seemed too small and easy for her energy.

She brushed a cloud of hair out of her eyes with the back of her glove, and left a smudge of earth on her cheek in doing it. Behind her stood the neat white farmhouse with red geraniums close-banked around it as high as the windows. It was a hard-swept-looking little house, with hard-polished windows, and a clean mud-mat on the front steps.

Elisa cast another glance toward the tractor-shed. The strangers were getting into their Ford coupé. She took off a glove and put her strong fingers down into the forest of new green chrysanthemum sprouts that were growing around the old roots. She spread the leaves and looked down among the close-growing stems. No aphids were there, no sow bugs or snails or cutworms. Her terrier fingers destroyed such pests before they could get started.

Elisa started at the sound of her husband's voice. He had come near quietly, and he leaned over the wire fence that protected her flower garden from cattle and dogs and chickens.

"At it again," he said. "You've got a strong new crop coming."

Elisa straightened her back and pulled on the gardening glove again. "Yes. They'll be strong this coming year." In her tone and on her face there was a little smugness.

"You've got a gift with things," Henry observed. "Some of those yellow chrysanthemums you had this year were ten inches across. I wish you'd work out in the orchard and raise some apples that big."

Her eyes sharpened. "Maybe I could do it, too. I've a gift with things, all right. My mother had it. She could stick anything in the ground and make it grow. She said it was having planters' hands that knew how to do it."

"Well, it sure works with flowers," he said.

"Henry, who were those men you were talking to?"

"Why, sure, that's what I came to tell you. They were from the Western Meat Company. I sold those thirty head of three-year-old steers. Got nearly my own price, too."

"Good," she said. "Good for you."

"And I thought," he continued, "I thought how it's Saturday afternoon, and we might go into Salinas for dinner at a restaurant, and then to a picture show—to celebrate, you see."

"Good," she repeated. "Oh, yes. That will be good."

Henry put on his joking tone. "There's fights tonight. How'd you like to go to the fights?"

"Oh, no," she said breathlessly. "No, I wouldn't like fights."

"Just fooling, Elisa. We'll go to a movie. Let's see. It's two now. I'm going to take Scotty and bring down those steers from the hill. It'll take us maybe two hours. We'll go in town about five and have dinner at the Cominos Hotel. Like that?"

"Of course I'll like it. It's good to eat away from home."

"All right, then. I'll go get up a couple of horses."

She said: "I'll have plenty of time to transplant some of these sets, I guess."

She heard her husband calling Scotty down by the barn. And a little later she saw the two men ride up the pale yellow hillside in search of the steers.

There was a little square sandy bed kept for rooting the chrysanthemums. With her trowel she turned the soil over and over, and smoothed it and patted it firm. Then she dug ten parallel trenches to receive the sets. Back at the chrysanthemum bed she pulled out the little crisp shoots, trimmed off the leaves of each one with her scissors and laid it on a small orderly pile.

A squeak of wheels and plod of hoofs came from the road. Elisa looked up. The country road ran along the dense bank of willows and cottonwoods that bordered the river, and up this road came a curious vehicle, curiously drawn. It was an old spring-wagon, with a round canvas top on it like the cover of a prairie schooner. It was drawn by an old bay horse and a little grey-and-white burro. A big stubble-bearded man sat between the cover flaps and drove the crawling team. Underneath the wagon, between the hind wheels, a lean and rangy mongrel dog walked sedately. Words were painted on the canvas, in clumsy, crooked letters. "Pots, pans, knives, sisors, lawn mores, Fixed." Two rows of articles, and the triumphantly definitive "Fixed" below. The black paint had run down in little sharp points beneath each letter.

Elisa, squatting on the ground, watched to see the crazy, loose-jointed wagon pass by. But it didn't pass. It turned into the farm road in front of her house, crooked old wheels **skirling** and squeaking. The rangy dog darted from between the wheels and ran ahead. Instantly the two ranch shepherds flew out at him. Then all three stopped, and with stiff and quivering tails, with taut straight legs, with **ambassadorial** dignity, they slowly circled, sniffing daintily. The caravan pulled up to Elisa's wire fence and stopped. Now the newcomer dog, feeling outnumbered, lowered his tail and retired under the wagon with raised hackles and bared teeth.

skirling: making a shrill sound

ambassadorial: formal; diplomatic

The man on the wagon seat called out: "That's a bad dog in a fight when he gets started."

Elisa laughed. "I see he is. How soon does he generally get started?"

The man caught up her laughter and echoed it heartily. "Sometimes not for weeks and weeks," he said. He climbed stiffly down, over the wheel. The horse and the donkey drooped like unwatered flowers.

Elisa saw that he was a very big man. Although his hair and beard were greying, he did not look old. His worn black suit was wrinkled and spotted with grease. The laughter had disappeared from his face and eyes the moment his laughing voice ceased. His eyes were dark, and they were full of the brooding that gets in the eyes of teamsters and of sailors. The calloused

> The laughter had disappeared from his face and eyes the moment his laughing voice ceased. His eyes were dark, and they were full of the brooding that gets in the eyes of teamsters and of sailors.

hands he rested on the wire fence were cracked, and every crack was a black line. He took off his battered hat.

"I'm off my general road, ma'am," he said. "Does this dirt road cut over across the river to the Los Angeles highway?"

Elisa stood up and shoved the thick scissors in her apron pocket. "Well, yes, it does, but it winds around and then fords the river. I don't think your team could pull through the sand."

He replied with some **asperity**: "It might surprise you what them beasts can pull through."

"When they get started?" she asked.

He smiled for a second. "Yes. When they get started."

"Well," said Elisa, "I think you'll save time if you go back to the Salinas road and pick up the highway there."

He drew a big finger down the chicken wire and made it sing. "I ain't in any hurry, ma'am. I go from Seattle to San Diego and back every year. Takes all my time. About six months each way. I aim to follow nice weather."

Elisa took off her gloves and stuffed them in the apron pocket with the scissors. She touched the under edge of her man's hat, searching for fugitive hairs. "That sounds like a nice kind of way to live," she said.

He leaned confidentially over the fence. "Maybe you noticed the writing on my wagon. I mend pots and sharpen knives and scissors. You got any of them things to do?"

"Oh, no," she said quickly. "Nothing like that." Her eyes hardened with resistance.

"Scissors is the worst thing," he explained. "Most people just ruin scissors trying to sharpen 'em, but I know how. I got a special tool. It's a little bobbit kind of thing, and patented. But it sure does the trick."

"No. My scissors are all sharp."

"All right, then. Take a pot," he continued earnestly, "a bent pot, or a pot with a hole. I can make it like new so you don't have to buy no new ones. That's a saving for you."

"No," she said shortly. "I tell you I have nothing like that for you to do."

His face fell to an exaggerated sadness. His voice took on a whining undertone. "I ain't had a thing to do today. Maybe I won't have no supper tonight. You see I'm off my regular road. I know folks on the highway clear from Seattle to San Diego. They save their things for me to sharpen up because they know I do it so good and save them money."

"I'm sorry," Elisa said irritably. "I haven't anything for you to do."

His eyes left her face and fell to searching the ground. They roamed about until they came to the chrysanthemum bed where she had been working. "What's them plants, ma'am?"

The irritation and resistance melted from Elisa's face. "Oh, those are chrysanthemums, giant whites and yellows. I raise them every year, bigger than anybody around here."

"Kind of a long-stemmed flower? Looks like a quick puff of colored smoke?" he asked.

"That's it. What a nice way to describe them."

"They smell kind of nasty till you get used to them," he said.

"It's a good bitter smell," she retorted, "not nasty at all."

He changed his tone quickly. "I like the smell myself."

"I had ten-inch blooms this year," she said.

The man leaned farther over the fence. "Look. I know a lady down the road a piece, has got the nicest garden you ever seen. Got nearly every kind of flower but not chrysanthemums. Last time I was mending a copper-bottom washtub for her (that's a hard job but I do it good), she said to me: 'If you ever run acrost some nice chrysanthemums I wish you'd try to get me a few seeds.' That's what she told me."

Elisa's eyes grew alert and eager. "She couldn't have known much about chrysanthemums. You *can* raise them from seed, but it's much easier to root the little sprouts you see here."

"Oh," he said. "I s'pose I can't take none to her, then."

"Why yes you can," Elisa cried. "I can put some in damp sand, and you can carry them right along with you. They'll take root in the pot if you keep them damp. And then she can transplant them."

"She'd sure like to have some, ma'am. You say they're nice ones?"

"Beautiful," she said. "Oh, beautiful." Her eyes shone. She tore off the battered hat and shook out her dark pretty hair. "I'll put them in a flower-pot, and you can take them right with you. Come into the yard."

While the man came through the picket gate Elisa ran excitedly along the geranium-bordered path to the back of the house. And she returned carrying a big red flower-pot. The gloves were forgotten now. She kneeled on the ground by the starting bed and dug up the sandy soil with her fingers and scooped it into the bright new flower-pot. Then she picked up the little pile of shoots she had prepared. With her strong fingers she pressed them into the

sand and **tamped** around them with her knuckles. The man stood over her. **tamped:** packed tightly
"I'll tell you what to do," she said. "You remember so you can tell the lady."

"Yes, I'll try to remember."

"Well, look. These will take root in about a month. Then she must set them out, about a foot apart in good rich earth like this, see?" She lifted a handful of dark soil for him to look at. "They'll grow fast and tall. Now remember this: In July tell her to cut them down, about eight inches from the ground."

"Before they bloom?" he asked.

"Yes, before they bloom." Her face was tight with eagerness. "They'll grow right up again. About the last of September the buds will start."

She stopped and seemed perplexed. "It's the budding that takes the most care," she said hesitantly. "I don't know how to tell you." She looked deep into his eyes, searchingly. Her mouth opened a little, and she seemed to be listening. "I'll try to tell you," she said. "Did you ever hear of planting hands?"

"Can't say I have, ma'am."

"Well, I can only tell you what it feels like. It's when you're picking off the buds you don't want. Everything goes right down into your fingertips. You watch your fingers work. They do it themselves. You can feel how it is. They pick and pick the buds. They never make a mistake. They're with the plant. Do you see? Your fingers and the plant. You can feel that, right up your arm. They know. They never make a mistake. You can feel it. When you're like that you can't do anything wrong. Do you see that? Can you understand that?"

> The man leaned farther over the fence. "Look. I know a lady down the road a piece, has got the nicest garden you ever seen. Got nearly every kind of flower but not chrysanthemums."

She was kneeling on the ground looking up at him. Her breast swelled passionately.

The man's eyes narrowed. He looked away self-consciously.

"Maybe I know," he said. "Sometimes in the night in the wagon there—"

Elisa's voice grew husky. She broke in on him: "I've never lived as you do, but I know what you mean. When the night is dark—why, the stars are sharp-pointed, and there's quiet. Why, you rise up and up! Every pointed star gets driven into your body. It's like that. Hot and sharp and—lovely."

****

fawning: cringing

Kneeling there, her hand went out toward his legs in the greasy black trousers. Her hesitant fingers almost touched the cloth. Then her hand dropped to the ground. She crouched low like a **fawning** dog.

He said: "It's nice, just like you say. Only when you don't have no dinner, it ain't."

She stood up then, very straight, and her face was ashamed. She held the flower-pot out to him and placed it gently in his arms. "Here. Put it in your wagon, on the seat, where you can watch it. Maybe I can find something for you to do."

At the back of the house she dug in the can pile and found two old and battered aluminum saucepans. She carried them back and gave them to him. "Here, maybe you can fix these."

His manner changed. He became professional. "Good as new I can fix them." At the back of his wagon he set a little anvil, and out of an oily tool-box dug a small machine hammer. Elisa came through the gate to watch him while he pounded out the dents in the kettles. His mouth grew sure and knowing. At a difficult part of the work he sucked his underlip.

"You sleep right in the wagon?" Elisa asked.

"Right in the wagon, ma'am. Rain or shine I'm dry as a cow in there."

"It must be nice," she said. "It must be very nice. I wish women could do such things."

"It ain't the right kind of a life for a woman."

Her upper lip raised a little, showing her teeth. "How do you know? How can you tell?" she said.

"I don't know, ma'am," he protested. "Of course I don't know. Now here's your kettles, done. You don't have to buy no new ones."

"How much?"

"Oh, fifty cents'll do. I keep my prices down and my work good. That's why I have all them satisfied customers up and down the highway."

Elisa brought him a fifty-cent piece from the house and dropped it in his hand. "You might be surprised to have a rival some time. I can sharpen scissors, too. And I can beat the dents out of little pots. I could show you what a woman might do."

He put his hammer back in the oily box and shoved the little anvil out of sight. "It would be a lonely life for a woman, ma'am, and a scarey life, too, with animals creeping under the wagon all night." He climbed over the single-tree, steadying himself in the seat, picked up the lines. "Thank you kindly ma'am," he said. "I'll do like you told me; I'll go back and catch the Salinas road."

"Mind," she called, "if you're long in getting there, keep the sand damp."

"Sand, ma'am? . . . Sand? Oh, sure. You mean around the chrysanthemums. Sure I will." He clucked his tongue. The beasts leaned luxuriously into their collars. The mongrel dog took his place between the back wheels. The wagon turned and crawled out the entrance road and back the way it had come, along the river.

Elisa stood in front of her wire fence watching the slow progress of the caravan. Her shoulders were straight, her head thrown back, her eyes half-closed, so that the scene came vaguely into them. Her lips moved silently, forming the words "Good-bye—good-bye." Then she whispered: "That's a bright direction. There's a glowing there." The sound of her whisper startled her. She shook herself free and looked about to see whether anyone had been listening. Only the dogs had heard. They lifted their heads toward her from their sleeping in the dust, and then stretched out their chins and settled asleep again. Elisa turned and ran hurriedly into the house.

In the kitchen she reached behind the stove and felt the water tank. It was full of hot water from the noonday cooking. In the bathroom she tore off her soiled clothes and flung them into the corner. And then she scrubbed herself with a little block of pumice,[2] legs and thighs, loins and chest and arms, until her skin was scratched and red. When she had dried herself she stood in front of a mirror in her bedroom and looked at her body. She tightened her stomach and threw out her chest. She turned and looked over her shoulders at her back.

Elisa stood in front of her wire fence watching the slow progress of the caravan. Her shoulders were straight, her head thrown back, her eyes half-closed, so that the scene came vaguely into them.

After a while she began to dress, slowly. She put on her newest underclothing and her nicest stockings and the dress which was the symbol of her prettiness. She worked carefully on her hair, penciled her eyebrows and rouged her lips.

Before she was finished she heard the little thunder of hoofs and the shouts of Henry and his helper as they drove the red steers into the corral. She heard the gate bang shut and set herself for Henry's arrival.

---

2 **pumice:** finely powdered volcanic glass used to smooth and polish

His step sounded on the porch. He entered the house calling: "Elisa, where are you?"

"In my room, dressing. I'm not ready. There's hot water for your bath. Hurry up. It's getting late."

When she heard him splashing in the tub, Elisa laid his dark suit on the bed, and shirt and socks and tie beside it. She stood his polished shoes on

EARTH PATTERNS, Rinaldo Cuneo, 1932, The Oakland Museum of California

the floor beside the bed. Then she went to the porch and sat primly and stiffly down. She looked toward the river road where the willow-line was still yellow with frosted leaves so that under the high grey fog they seemed a thin band of sunshine. This was the only color in the grey afternoon. She sat unmoving for a long time. Her eyes blinked rarely.

Henry came banging out of the door, shoving his tie inside his vest as he came. Elisa stiffened and her face grew tight. Henry stopped short and looked at her. "Why—why, Elisa. You look so nice!"

"Nice? You think I look nice? What do you mean by 'nice'?"

Henry blundered on. "I don't know. I mean you look different, strong and happy."

"I am strong? Yes, strong. What do you mean 'strong'?"

He looked bewildered. "You're playing some kind of a game," he said helplessly. "It's a kind of a play. You look strong enough to break a calf over your knee, happy enough to eat it like a watermelon."

For a second she lost her rigidity. "Henry! Don't talk like that. You didn't know what you said." She grew complete again. "I'm strong," she boasted. "I never knew before how strong."

"I'm strong," she boasted. "I never knew before how strong."

Henry looked down toward the tractor-shed, and when he brought his eyes back to her, they were his own again. "I'll get out the car. You can put on your coat while I'm starting."

Elisa went into the house. She heard him drive to the gate and idle down his motor, and then she took a long time to put on her hat. She pulled it here and pressed it there. When Henry turned the motor off she slipped into her coat and went out.

The little roadster bounced along on the dirt road by the river, raising the birds and driving the rabbits into the brush. Two cranes flapped heavily over the willow-line and dropped into the river-bed.

Far ahead on the road Elisa saw a dark speck. She knew.

She tried not to look as they passed it, but her eyes would not obey. She whispered to herself sadly: "He might have thrown them off the road. That wouldn't have been much trouble, not very much. But he kept the pot," she explained. "He had to keep the pot. That's why he couldn't get them off the road."

The roadster turned a bend and she saw the caravan ahead. She swung full around toward her husband so she could not see the little covered wagon and the mis-matched team as the car passed them.

In a moment it was over. The thing was done. She did not look back.

She said loudly, to be heard above the motor: "It will be good, tonight, a good dinner."

"Now you've changed again," Henry complained. He took one hand from the wheel and patted her knee. "I ought to take you in to dinner oftener. It would be good for both of us. We get so heavy out on the ranch."

"Henry," she asked, "could we have wine at dinner?"

"Sure we could. Say! That will be fine."

She was silent for a while; then she said: "Henry, at those prizefights, do the men hurt each other very much?"

"Sometimes a little, not often. Why?"

"Well, I've read how they break noses, and blood runs down their chests. I've read how the fighting gloves get heavy and soggy with blood."

He looked around at her. "What's the matter, Elisa? I didn't know you read things like that." He brought the car to a stop, then turned to the right over the Salinas River bridge.

"Do any women ever go to the fights?" she asked.

"Oh, sure, some. What's the matter, Elisa? Do you want to go? I don't think you'd like it, but I'll take you if you really want to go."

She relaxed limply in the seat. "Oh, no. No. I don't want to go. I'm sure I don't." Her face was turned away from him. "It will be enough if we can have wine. It will be plenty." She turned up her coat collar so he could not see that she was crying weakly—like an old woman.

Responding to the Story

1. LITERARY LENS What do you think are some of the ideas or feelings the chrysanthemums might symbolize?

2. Why do you think Elisa is so anxious to share her chrysanthemums with the woman up the road?

3. Steinbeck begins creating an ominous atmosphere as soon as the pot fixer approaches. Use a chart like the one below to trace clues such as dialogue and gestures. In the second column, chart what the readers' resulting expectations are. An example has been done for you.

Clue	Expectation
The fixer's manner is jovial but his eyes are brooding.	*He is a dangerous person who will harm Elisa.*

4. What does Elisa gain and then lose in this story?

5. THE AUTHOR'S STYLE People's lives in Steinbeck's fiction are often ruled by outside forces. Thus, setting is very important. How do the land and the ranch govern the characters' lives in this story? Find two specific examples.

Eudora Welty
1909–2001

About the Author

An illness at the age of seven had an influence on Eudora Welty's decision to become a writer. In her autobiography, *One Writer's Beginnings,* the beloved Southern writer recalls the months she was confined to bed: "As I read away, I was Rapunzel, or the Goose Girl, or the Princess Labam in one of the *Thousand and One Nights* who mounted the roof of her palace every night and of her own radiance faithfully lighted the whole city . . . ."

Born in Jackson, Mississippi, where she lived most of her life, Welty set much of her work in the small town South. She worked early in her career as a newspaper reporter and photographer.

Welty was known as an unassuming writer who had an instinctive style, a profound empathy for others, and a down-to-earth sense of humor. In the introduction to her collection of stories *A Curtain of Green,* the author is quoted as having once commented: "I haven't a literary life at all. . . I do feel that the people and things I love are of a true and human world, and there is no clutter about them. . . I would not understand a literary life." Today's email software program Eudora is named in tribute to the author and to the story you are about to read.

★★★★★★★★★★★

The Author's Style

Eudora Welty's fiction always conveys a distinct sense of personality and place. Her characters—often quirky, obsessive, introspective, and disconcerting—typically live in small-town, rural Mississippi. This "local color" aspect of her work is created in part through her skillful use of dialect and everyday language. Her creation of a narrative tone that we associate with gossip and innuendo helps intensify the local color.

In reading Welty's stories it is always helpful to pay close attention to what family and community conversation reveal in the way of hostility and affection. Welty's families are peculiar and universal at the same time—in their dreams, funny habits, jealousies, and expressions of human nature. The humor and comic ironies of her stories have much to do with her characters understanding considerably less about what their own words reveal than do Welty's readers.

Sometimes Welty's characters behave so oddly that we are inclined to write them off as crackpots. But when we find their comments and conversations compelling enough to eavesdrop on, we find ourselves asking what Welty might be saying about the rest of us through this particular family.

LITERARY LENS
Welty is well-known for her skillful characterization. Take a close look at the personal qualities of this story's narrator.

WHY I LIVE AT THE P.O.

EUDORA WELTY

I was getting along fine with Mama, Papa-Daddy, and Uncle Rondo until my sister Stella-Rondo just separated from her husband and came back home again. Mr. Whitaker! Of course I went with Mr. Whitaker first, when he first appeared here in China Grove, taking "Pose Yourself" photos, and Stella-Rondo broke us up. Told him I was one-sided. Bigger on one side than the other, which is a deliberate, calculated falsehood: I'm the same. Stella-Rondo is exactly twelve months to the day younger than I am and for that reason she's spoiled.

She's always had anything in the world she wanted and then she'd throw it away. Papa-Daddy give her this gorgeous Add-a-Pearl necklace when she was eight years old and she threw it away playing baseball when she was nine, with only two pearls.

So as soon as she got married and moved away from home the first thing she did was separate! From Mr. Whitaker! This photographer with the popeyes she said she trusted. Came home from one of those towns up in Illinois and to our complete surprise brought this child of two.

Mama said she like to made her drop dead for a second. "Here you had this marvelous blonde child and never so much as wrote your mother a word about it," says Mama. "I'm thoroughly ashamed of you." But of course she wasn't.

So Papa-Daddy l-a-y-s down his knife and fork! He's real rich. Mama says he is, he says he isn't. So he says, "Have I heard correctly? You don't understand why I don't cut off my beard?"

Stella-Rondo just calmly takes off this *hat*, I wish you could see it. She says, "Why, Mama, Shirley-T.'s adopted, I can prove it."

"How?" says Mama, but all I says was, "H'm!" There I was over the hot stove, trying to stretch two chickens over five people and a completely unexpected child into the bargain, without one moment's notice.

"What do you mean—'H'm'?" says Stella-Rondo, and Mama says, "I heard that, Sister."

I said that oh, I didn't mean a thing, only that whoever Shirley-T. was, she was the spit-image of Papa-Daddy if he'd cut off his beard, which of course he'd never do in the world. Papa-Daddy's Mama's papa and sulks.

Stella-Rondo got furious! She said, "Sister, I don't need to tell you you got a lot of nerve and always did have and I'll thank you to make no future reference to my adopted child whatsoever."

"Very well," I said. "Very well, very well. Of course I noticed at once she looks like Mr. Whitaker's side too. That frown. She looks like a cross between Mr. Whitaker and Papa-Daddy."

"Well, all I can say is she isn't."

"She looks exactly like Shirley Temple to me," says Mama, but Shirley-T. just ran away from her.

So the first thing Stella-Rondo did at the table was turn Papa-Daddy against me.

"Papa-Daddy," she says. He was trying to cut up his meat. "Papa-Daddy!" I was taken completely by surprise. Papa-Daddy is about a million years old and's got this long-long beard. "Papa-Daddy, Sister says she fails to understand why you don't cut off your beard."

So Papa-Daddy l-a-y-s down his knife and fork! He's real rich. Mama says he is, he says he isn't. So he says, "Have I heard correctly? You don't understand why I don't cut off my beard?"

"Why," I says, "Papa-Daddy, of course I understand, I did not say any such a thing, the idea!"

He says, "Hussy!"

I says, "Papa-Daddy, you know I wouldn't any more want you to cut off your beard than the man in the moon. It was the farthest thing from my mind! Stella-Rondo sat there and made that up while she was eating breast of chicken."

But he says, "So the postmistress fails to understand why I don't cut off my beard. Which job I got you through my influence with the government. 'Bird's nest'—is that what you call it?"

Not that it isn't the next to smallest P.O. in the entire state of Mississippi.

I says, "Oh, Papa-Daddy," I says, "I didn't say any such a thing, I never dreamed it was a bird's nest, I have always been grateful though this is the next to smallest P.O. in the state of Mississippi, and I do not enjoy being referred to as a hussy by my own grandfather."

But Stella-Rondo says, "Yes, you did say it too. Anybody in the world could of heard you, that had ears."

"Stop right there," says Mama, looking at *me.*

So I pulled my napkin straight back through the napkin ring and left the table.

As soon as I was out of the room Mama says, "Call her back, or she'll starve to death," but Papa-Daddy says, "This is the beard I started growing on the Coast when I was fifteen years old." He would of gone on till nightfall if Shirley-T. hadn't lost the Milky Way she ate in Cairo.[1]

So Papa-Daddy says, "I am going out and lie in the hammock, and you can all sit here and remember my words: I'll never cut off my beard as long as I live, even one inch, and I don't appreciate it in you at all." Passed right by me in the hall and went straight out and got in the hammock.

It would be a holiday. It wasn't five minutes before Uncle Rondo suddenly appeared in the hall in one of Stella-Rondo's flesh-colored kimonos,[2]

---

1 **Cairo:** Cairo, Illinois

2 **kimono:** a loose robe worn as a dressing gown, imitated from robes originally worn by the Japanese

all cut on the bias, like something Mr. Whitaker probably thought was gorgeous.

"Uncle Rondo!" I says. "I didn't know who that was! Where are you going?"

"Sister," he says, "get out of my way, I'm poisoned."

"If you're poisoned stay away from Papa-Daddy," I says. "Keep out of the hammock. Papa-Daddy will certainly beat you on the head if you come within forty miles of him. He thinks I deliberately said he ought to cut off his beard after he got me the P.O., and I've told him and told him and told him, and he acts like he just don't hear me. Papa-Daddy must of gone stone deaf."

"He picked a fine day to do it then," says Uncle Rondo, and before you could say "Jack Robinson"[3] flew out in the yard.

What he'd really done, he'd drunk another bottle of that prescription. He does it every single Fourth of July as sure as shooting, and it's horribly expensive. Then he falls over in the hammock and snores. So he insisted on zigzagging right on out to the hammock, looking like a half-wit.

Papa-Daddy woke up with this horrible yell and right there without moving an inch he tried to turn Uncle Rondo against me. I heard every word he said. Oh, he told Uncle Rondo I didn't learn to read till I was eight years old and he didn't see how in the world I ever got the mail put up at the P.O., much less read it all, and he said if Uncle Rondo could only fathom the lengths he had gone to get me that job! And he said on the other hand he thought Stella-Rondo had a brilliant mind and deserved credit for getting out of town. All the time he was just lying there swinging as pretty as you please and looping out his beard, and poor Uncle Rondo was *pleading* with him to slow down the hammock, it was making him as dizzy as a witch to watch it. But that's what Papa-Daddy likes about a hammock. So Uncle Rondo was too dizzy to get turned against me for the time being. He's Mama's only brother and is a good case of a one-track mind. Ask anybody. A certified pharmacist.

Just then I heard Stella-Rondo raising the upstairs window. While she was married she got this peculiar idea that it's cooler with the windows shut and locked. So she has to raise the window before she can make a soul hear her outdoors.

So she raises the window and says, "*Oh!*" You would have thought she was mortally wounded.

---

3 **before you could say "Jack Robinson":** an idiom that indicates immediacy. Jack Robinson was disputably a man who changed his mind frequently, dropping in on neighbors and leaving almost before they realized he was there.

★★

Uncle Rondo and Papa-Daddy didn't even look up, but kept right on with what they were doing. I had to laugh.

I flew up the stairs and threw the door open! I says, "What in the wide world's the matter, Stella-Rondo? You mortally wounded?"

"No," she says, "I am not mortally wounded but I wish you would do me the favor of looking out that window there and telling me what you see."

So I shade my eyes and look out the window.

"I see the front yard," I says.

"Don't you see any human beings?" she says.

"I see Uncle Rondo trying to run Papa-Daddy out of the hammock," I says. "Nothing more. Naturally, it's so suffocating-hot in the house, with all the windows shut and locked, everybody who cares to stay in their right mind will have to go out and get in the hammock before the Fourth of July is over."

All the time he was just lying there swinging as pretty as you please and looping out his beard, and poor Uncle Rondo was *pleading* with him to slow down the hammock, it was making him as dizzy as a witch to watch it.

"Don't you notice anything different about Uncle Rondo?" asks Stella-Rondo.

"Why, no, except he's got on some terrible-looking flesh-colored contraption I wouldn't be found dead in, is all I can see," I says.

"Never mind, you won't be found dead in it, because it happens to be part of my trousseau,[4] and Mr. Whitaker took several dozen photographs of me in it," says Stella-Rondo. "What on earth could Uncle Rondo *mean* by wearing part of my trousseau out in the broad open daylight without saying so much as 'Kiss my foot,' *knowing* I only got home this morning after my separation and hung my negligee[5] up on the bathroom door, just as nervous as I could be?"

"I'm sure I don't know, and what do you expect me to do about it?" I says. "Jump out the window?"

"No, I expect nothing of the kind. I simply declare that Uncle Rondo looks like a fool in it, that's all," she says. "It makes me sick to my stomach."

---

4 **trousseau:** the clothing and linens provided by her family and assembled by a bride before her marriage

5 **negligee:** a loose dressing gown made of soft fabric and worn by women

"Well, he looks as good as he can," I says. "As good as anybody in reason could." I stood up for Uncle Rondo, please remember. And I said to Stella-Rondo, "I think I would do well not to criticize so freely if I were you and came home with a two-year-old child I had never said a word about, and no explanation whatever about my separation."

"I asked you the instant I entered this house not to refer one more time to my adopted child, and you gave me your word of honor you would not," was all Stella-Rondo would say, and started pulling out every one of her eyebrows with some cheap Kress[6] tweezers.

So I merely slammed the door behind me and went down and made some green-tomato pickle. Somebody had to do it. Of course Mama had turned both the Negroes loose; she always said no earthly power could hold one anyway on the Fourth of July, so she wouldn't even try. It turned out that Jaypan fell in the lake and came within a very narrow limit of drowning.

So Mama trots in. Lifts up the lid and says, "H'm! Not very good for your Uncle Rondo in his precarious condition, I must say. Or poor little adopted Shirley-T. Shame on you!"

That made me tired. I says, "Well, Stella-Rondo had better thank her lucky stars it was her instead of me came trotting in with that very peculiar-looking child. Now if it had been me that trotted in from Illinois and brought a peculiar-looking child of two, I shudder to think of the reception I'd of got, much less controlled the diet of an entire family."

"But you must remember, Sister, that you were never married to Mr. Whitaker in the first place and didn't go up to Illinois to live," says Mama, shaking a spoon in my face. "If you had I would of been just as overjoyed to see you and your little adopted girl as I was to see Stella-Rondo, when you wound up with your separation and came on back home."

"You would not," I says.

"Don't contradict me, I would," says Mama.

But I said she couldn't convince me though she talked till she was blue in the face. Then I said, "Besides, you know as well as I do that that child is not adopted."

"She most certainly is adopted," says Mama, stiff as a poker.

I says, "Why, Mama, Stella-Rondo had her just as sure as anything in this world, and just too stuck up to admit it."

"Why, Sister," said Mama. "Here I thought we were going to have a pleas-

---

6 **Kress:** a chain of dime stores

ant Fourth of July, and you start right out not believing a word your own baby sister tells you!"

"Just like Cousin Annie Flo. Went to her grave denying the facts of life," I reminded Mama.

"I told you if you ever mentioned Annie Flo's name I'd slap your face," says Mama, and slaps my face.

"All right, you wait and see," I says.

"I," says Mama, "I prefer to take my children's word for anything when it's humanly possible." You ought to see Mama, she weighs two hundred pounds and has real tiny feet.

Just then something perfectly horrible occurred to me.

"Mama," I says, "can that child talk?" I simply had to whisper! "Mama, I wonder if that child can be—you know—in any way? Do you realize?" I says, "that she hasn't spoken one single, solitary word to a human being up to this minute? This is the way she looks," I says, and I looked like this.

Well, Mama and I just stood there and stared at each other. It was horrible!

"I remember well that Joe Whitaker frequently drank like a fish," says Mama. "I believed to my soul he drank *chemicals*." And without another word she marches to the foot of the stairs and calls Stella-Rondo.

"Stella-Rondo? O-o-o-o-o! Stella-Rondo!"

"What?" says Stella-Rondo from upstairs. Not even the grace to get up off the bed.

"Can that child of yours talk?" asks Mama. Stella-Rondo says, "Can she what?"

"Talk! Talk!" says Mama. "Burdyburdyburdyburdy!"

So Stella-Rondo yells back, "Who says she can't talk?"

"Sister says so," says Mama.

"You didn't have to tell me, I know whose word of honor don't mean a thing in this house," says Stella-Rondo.

And in a minute the loudest Yankee voice I ever heard in my life yells out, "OE'm Pop-OE the Sailor-r-r-r Ma-a-an!" and then somebody jumps up and down in the upstairs hall. In another second the house would of fallen down.

> I remember well that Joe Whitaker frequently drank like a fish," says Mama. "I believed to my soul he drank *chemicals*." And without another word she marches to the foot of the stairs and calls Stella-Rondo.

"Not only talks, she can tap-dance!" calls Stella-Rondo. "Which is more than some people I won't name can do."

"Why, the little precious darling thing!" Mama says, so surprised. "Just as smart as she can be!" Starts talking baby talk right there. Then she turns on me. "Sister, you ought to be thoroughly ashamed! Run upstairs this instant and apologize to Stella-Rondo and Shirley-T."

"Apologize for what?" I says. "I merely wondered if the child was normal, that's all. Now that she's proved she is, why, I have nothing further to say."

But Mama just turned on her heel and flew out, furious. She ran right upstairs and hugged the baby. She believed it was adopted. Stella-Rondo hadn't done a thing but turn her against me from upstairs while I stood there helpless over the hot stove. So that made Mama, Papa-Daddy and the baby all on Stella-Rondo's side.

Next, Uncle Rondo.

I must say that Uncle Rondo has been marvelous to me at various times in the past and I was completely unprepared to be made to jump out of my skin, the way it turned out. Once Stella-Rondo did something perfectly horrible to him—broke a chain letter from Flanders Field[7]—and he took the radio back he had given her and gave it to me. Stella-Rondo was furious! For six months we all had to call her Stella instead of Stella-Rondo, or she wouldn't answer. I always thought Uncle Rondo had all the brains of the entire family. Another time he sent me to Mammoth Cave,[8] with all expenses paid.

But this would be the day he was drinking that prescription, the Fourth of July.

So at supper Stella-Rondo speaks up and says she thinks Uncle Rondo ought to try to eat a little something. So finally Uncle Rondo said he would try a little cold biscuits and ketchup, but that was all. So *she* brought it to him.

disport: frolic; play around

"Do you think it wise to **disport** with ketchup in Stella-Rondo's flesh-colored kimono?" I says. Trying to be considerate! If Stella-Rondo couldn't watch out for her trousseau, somebody had to.

"Any objections?" asks Uncle Rondo, just about to pour out all the ketchup.

"Don't mind what she says, Uncle Rondo," says Stella-Rondo. "Sister has

---

7 **Flanders Field:** WWI battlefield in Belgium where American soldiers are buried. In 1927, nine days after making his trans-Atlantic flight, Charles Lindbergh flew over the cemetery during Memorial Day ceremonies, dropping poppies.

8 **Mammoth Cave:** Located in Mammoth Cave National Park in south central Kentucky, the Mammoth Cave system is the largest known cave system in the world.

been devoting this solid afternoon to sneering out my bedroom window at the way you look."

"What's that?" says Uncle Rondo. Uncle Rondo has got the most terrible temper in the world. Anything is liable to make him tear the house down if it comes at the wrong time.

So Stella-Rondo says, "Sister says, 'Uncle Rondo certainly does look like a fool in that pink kimono!'"

Do you remember who it was really said that?

Uncle Rondo spills out all the ketchup and jumps out of his chair and tears off the kimono and throws it down on the dirty floor and puts his foot on it. It had to be sent all the way to Jackson to the cleaners and repleated.

"So that's your opinion of your Uncle Rondo, is it?" he says. "I look like a fool, do I? Well, that's the last straw. A whole day in this house with nothing to do, and then to hear you come out with a remark like that behind my back!"

"I didn't say any such of a thing, Uncle Rondo," I says, "and I'm not saying who did, either. Why, I think you look all right. Just try to take care of yourself and not talk and eat at the same time," I says. "I think you better go lie down."

"Lie down my foot," says Uncle Rondo. I ought to of known by that he was fixing to do something perfectly horrible.

So he didn't do anything that night in the **precarious** state he was in—just played Casino with Mama and Stella-Rondo and Shirley-T. and gave Shirley-T. a nickel with a head on both sides. It tickled her nearly to death, and she called him "Papa." But at 6:30 A.M. the next morning, he threw a whole five cent package of some unsold one-inch firecrackers from the store as hard as he could into my bedroom and then every one went off. Not one bad one in the string. Anybody else, there'd be one that wouldn't go off.

Well, I'm just terribly susceptible to noise of any kind, the doctor has always told me I was the most sensitive person he had ever seen in his whole life, and I was simply **prostrated**. I couldn't eat! People tell me they heard it as far as the cemetery, and old Aunt Jep Patterson, that had been holding her own so good, thought it was Judgment Day and she was going to meet her whole family. It's usually so quiet here.

And I'll tell you it didn't take me any longer than a minute to make up my mind what to do. There I was with the whole entire house on Stella-Rondo's side and turned against me. If I have anything at all I have pride.

So I just decided I'd go straight down to the P.O. There's plenty of room there in the back, I says to myself.

precarious: uncertain; dangerous

prostrated: exhausted; flattened

Well! I made no bones about letting the family catch on to what I was up to. I didn't try to conceal it.

The first thing they knew, I marched in where they were all playing Old Maid and pulled the electric oscillating fan out by the plug, and everything got real hot. Next I snatched the pillow I'd done the needlepoint on right off the davenport from behind Papa-Daddy. He went "Ugh!" I beat Stella-Rondo up the stairs and finally found my charm bracelet in her bureau drawer under a picture of Nelson Eddy[9].

"So that's the way the land lies," says Uncle Rondo. There he was, **piecing** on the ham. "Well, Sister, I'll be glad to donate my army cot if you got any place to set it up, providing you'll leave right this minute and let me get some peace." Uncle Rondo was in France.

"Thank you kindly for the cot and 'peace' is hardly the word I would select if I had to resort to firecrackers at 6:30 A.M. in a young girl's bedroom," I says to him. "And as to where I intend to go, you seem to forget my position as postmistress of China Grove, Mississippi," I says. "I've always got the P.O."

Well, that made them all sit up and take notice.

I went out front and started digging up some four-o'clocks to plant around the P.O.

"Ah-ah-ah!" says Mama, raising the window. "Those happen to be my four-o'clocks. Everything planted in that star is mine. I've never known you to make anything grow in your life."

"Very well," I says. "But I take the fern. Even you, Mama, can't stand there and deny that I'm the one watered that fern. And I happen to know where I can send in a box top and get a packet of one thousand mixed seeds, no two the same kind, free."

"Oh, where?" Mama wants to know.

But I says, "Too late. You 'tend to your house, and I'll 'tend to mine. You hear things like that all the time if you know how to listen to the radio. Perfectly marvelous offers. Get anything you want free."

So I hope to tell you I marched in and got that radio, and they could of all bit a nail in two, especially Stella-Rondo, that it used to belong to, and she well knew she couldn't get it back, I'd sue for it like a shot. And I very politely took the sewing-machine motor I helped pay the most on to give Mama for Christmas back in 1929, and a good big calendar, with the first-aid remedies

---

9 **Nelson Eddy:** (1901–1967) an opera and Hollywood musical star of the 1920s and '30s who went on to perform as part of a famous traveling nightclub trio

on it. The thermometer and the Hawaiian ukulele certainly were rightfully mine, and I stood on the step-ladder and got all my watermelon-rind preserves and every fruit and vegetable I'd put up, every jar. Then I began to pull the tacks out of the bluebird wall vases on the archway to the dining room.

"Who told you you could have those, Miss Priss?" says Mama, fanning as hard as she could.

INTERIOR, Walker Evans, 1934, The Metropolitan Museum of Art

"I bought 'em and I'll keep track of 'em," I says. "I'll tack 'em up one on each side the post-office window, and you can see 'em when you come to ask me for your mail, if you're so dead to see 'em."

"Not I! I'll never darken the door to that post office again if I live to be a hundred," Mama says. "Ungrateful child! After all the money we spent on you at the Normal."

"Me either," says Stella-Rondo. "You can just let my mail lie there and *rot*, for all I care. I'll never come and relieve you of a single, solitary piece."

"I should worry," I says. "And who you think's going to sit down and write you all those big fat letters and postcards, by the way? Mr. Whitaker? Just because he was the only man ever dropped down in China Grove and you got him—unfairly—is he going to sit down and write you a lengthy correspondence after you come home giving no rhyme nor reason whatsoever for your separation and no explanation for the presence of that child? I may not have your brilliant mind, but I fail to see it."

So Mama says, "Sister, I've told you a thousand times that Stella-Rondo simply got homesick, and this child is far too big to be hers," and she says, "Now, why don't you all just sit down and play Casino?"

Then Shirley-T. sticks out her tongue at me in this perfectly horrible way. She has no more manners than the man in the moon. I told her she was going to cross her eyes like that some day and they'd stick.

"It's too late to stop me now," I says. "You should have tried that yesterday. I'm going to the P.O. and the only way you can possibly see me is to visit me there."

So Papa-Daddy says, "You'll never catch me setting foot in that post office, even if I should take a notion into my head to write a letter some place." He says, "I won't have you reachin' out of that little old window with a pair of shears and cuttin' off any beard of mine. I'm too smart for you!"

"We all are," says Stella-Rondo.

But I said, "If you're so smart, where's Mr. Whitaker?"

So then Uncle Rondo says, "I'll thank you from now on to stop reading all the orders I get on postcards and telling everybody in China Grove what you think is the matter with them," but I says, "I draw my own conclusions and will continue in the future to draw them." I says, "If people want to write their inmost secrets on penny postcards, there's nothing in the wide world you can do about it, Uncle Rondo."

"And if you think we'll ever *write* another postcard you're sadly mistaken," says Mama.

"Cutting off your nose to spite your face then," I says. "But if you're all determined to have no more to do with the U.S. mail, think of this: What will Stella-Rondo do now, if she wants to tell Mr. Whitaker to come after her?"

"Wah!" says Stella-Rondo. I knew she'd cry. She had a conniption fit right there in the kitchen.

"It will be interesting to see how long she holds out," I says. "And now— I am leaving."

"Good-bye," says Uncle Rondo.

"Oh, I declare," says Mama, "to think that a family of mine should quarrel on the Fourth of July, or the day after, over Stella-Rondo leaving old Mr. Whitaker and having the sweetest little adopted child! It looks like we'd all be glad!"

"Wah!" says Stella-Rondo, and has a fresh conniption fit.

"He left *her*—you mark my words," I says. "That's Mr. Whitaker. I know

FRAME HOUSES
1936
Walker Evans
The Metropolitan
Museum of Art

Mr. Whitaker. After all, I knew him first. I said from the beginning he'd up and leave her. I foretold every single thing that's happened."

"Where did he go?" asks Mama.

"Probably to the North Pole, if he knows what's good for him," I says.

But Stella-Rondo just bawled and wouldn't say another word. She flew to her room and slammed the door.

"Now look what you've gone and done, Sister," says Mama. "You go apologize."

"I haven't got time, I'm leaving," I says.

"Well, what are you waiting around for?" asks Uncle Rondo.

So I just picked up the kitchen clock and marched off, without saying "Kiss my foot" or anything, and never did tell Stella-Rondo good-bye.

There was a nigger girl going along on a little wagon right in front.

"Nigger girl," I says, "come help me haul these things down the hill, I'm going to live in the post office."

Took her nine trips in her express wagon. Uncle Rondo came out on the porch and threw her a nickel.

And that's the last I've laid eyes on any of my family or my family laid eyes on me for five solid days and nights. Stella-Rondo may be telling the most horrible tales in the world about Mr. Whitaker, but I haven't heard them. As I tell everybody, I draw my own conclusions.

But oh, I like it here. It's ideal, as I've been saying. You see, I've got everything cater-cornered, the way I like it. Hear the radio? All the war news. Radio, sewing machine, book ends, ironing board and that great big piano lamp—peace, that's what I like. Butter-bean vines planted all along the front where the strings are.

Of course, there's not much mail. My family are naturally the main people in China Grove, and if they prefer to vanish from the face of the earth, for all the mail they get or the mail they write, why, I'm not going to open my mouth. Some of the folks here in town are taking up for me and some turned against me. I know which is which. There are always people who will quit buying stamps just to get on the right side of Papa-Daddy.

But here I am, and here I'll stay. I want the world to know I'm happy.

And if Stella-Rondo should come to me this minute, on bended knees, and *attempt* to explain the incidents of her life with Mr. Whitaker, I'd simply put my fingers in both my ears and refuse to listen.

Responding to the Story

1. **LITERARY LENS** Some readers have said that Sister, the teller of this story, is an "unreliable narrator"—one who twists the truth and comes to false conclusions. Do you agree? Support your answer with evidence from the story.

2. Readers of this story often wonder what, if anything, has caused Sister's hostility toward her family members, and why she chooses to dwell on her grievances. Use a chart like the one below to note how Sister relates to each member of her family. Why do you think she feels and acts as she does?

Family Member	Sister's attitude, descriptions, and actions
Papa-Daddy	*Sister wants to find favor with him but also seems to resent him.*
Stella-Rondo	
Shirley Temple	
Mama	
Uncle Rondo	

3. Besides her writing, Welty also worked as a photographer for the Works Progress Administration. A photographer's interest in focus and detail can be seen in her fiction. Find a scene in the story that you think would make a telling snapshot of this eccentric family. Be prepared to explain how your "snapshot" reveals the characters in it.

4. The members of the family in this story are memorably eccentric yet they share some of the problems and concerns of all families. What are some of those universal problems and concerns?

5. **THE AUTHOR'S STYLE** Welty is known as a local color writer. Local color writing had its origins in the 1880s with such writers as Mark Twain and Bret Harte. They attempted to accurately depict the speech, dress, and mannerisms of a certain place. Local color writers often emphasized eccentric characters and used humor and innuendo to distinguish the region they were depicting. Detail some of the aspects of "Why I Live at the P.O." that make it an example of local color writing.

Ralph Ellison
1914–1994

About the Author

Ralph Ellison's father had such high literary hopes for him that he named him after the poet Ralph Waldo Emerson. Unfortunately, Ellison's father died when the author was a boy, and so couldn't witness his son's success. After his father died, Ellison's mother went to work as a house cleaner in Oklahoma City, where Ellison grew up. She brought home used books from her employers, which is how Ellison learned to love reading.

As a young man, Ellison studied music and became a fine trumpet player but was denied entrance into the navy band. Such early experiences with racism helped shape his fiction. After a move to New York, he studied sculpture and was mentored in his writing by Richard Wright, author of *Black Boy*, who helped him publish his early work. This led to a period in Rome as a fellow of the American Academy of Arts and Letters, followed by a return to the United States, where Ellison continued to write while teaching at colleges.

Known primarily as a short story writer and essayist, Ellison's only novel, *Invisible Man*, won the National Book Award for fiction in 1953.

* * * * * * * * * * *

The Author's Style

Ralph Ellison was a path-breaking writer with a talent for addressing the issue of race in America in imaginative ways. His stories often develop complex metaphors to explore racial conflict, especially in the stories "King of the Bingo Game" and "The Black Ball," as well as in his novel *Invisible Man*.

A key feature of Ellison's style is a tone of pathos, a sense of the helplessness and frustration his African American characters experience because of bigotry. Often discrimination in Ellison's stories is based on arbitrary distinctions of "blackness," "brownness," and "whiteness." The author's frustration is expressed in the irony that pervades his stories. This is especially true when his first-person narrators are naively unaware of, or stubbornly resistant to, the messages they are being sent by those around them, both black and white. In the following story, "black ball" is used as both a noun and a verb.

In essays and in his novel *Invisible Man*, Ellison shows the sustaining power of music, particularly jazz and the blues, for forging identity and sustaining African American life.

LITERARY LENS Ellison wrote this short story before the Civil Rights movement addressed issues of race and class in American society. Watch for the subtle ways Ellison describes the social standing of the narrator.

THE
BLACK
BALL

RALPH ELLISON

had rushed through the early part of the day mopping the lobby, placing fresh sand in the tall green jars, sweeping and dusting the halls, and emptying the trash to be burned later on in the day into the incinerator. And I had stopped only once to chase out after a can of milk for Mrs. Johnson, who had a new baby and who was always nice to my boy. I had started at six o'clock, and around eight I ran out to the quarters where we lived over the garage to dress the boy and give him his fruit and cereal. He was very thoughtful sitting there in his high chair and paused several times with his spoon midway to his mouth to watch me as I chewed my toast.

"What's the matter, son?"

"Daddy, am I black?"

"Of course not, you're brown. You know you're not black."

"Well yesterday Jackie said I was so black."

"He was just kidding. You mustn't let them kid you, son."

"Brown's much nicer than white, isn't it, Daddy?"

[He was four, a little brown boy in blue rompers,[1] and when he talked and laughed with imaginary playmates, his voice was soft and round in its accents like those of most Negro Americans.]

"Some people think so. But American is better than both, son."

"Is it, Daddy?"

"Sure it is. Now forget this talk about you being black, and Daddy will be back as soon as he finishes his work."

I left him to play with his toys and a book of pictures until I returned. He was a pretty nice fellow, as he used to say after particularly quiet afternoons while I tried to study, and for which quietness he expected a treat of candy or a "picture movie," and I often let him alone while I attended to my duties in the apartments.

I had gone back and started doing the brass on the front doors when a fellow came up and stood watching from the street. He was lean and red in the face with that redness that comes from a long diet of certain foods. You see much of it in the deep South, and here in the Southwest it is not uncommon. He stood there watching, and I could feel his eyes in my back as I polished the brass.

I gave special attention to that brass because for Berry, the manager, the luster of these brass panels and door handles was the measure of all my industry. It was near time for him to arrive.

"Good morning, John," he would say, looking not at me but at the brass.

"Good morning, sir," I would say, looking not at him but at the brass. Usually his face was reflected there. For him, I *was* there. Besides that brass, his money, and the half-dozen or so plants in his office, I don't believe he had any other real interests in life.

---

1 **rompers:** a one-piece outfit worn by children, mostly for play

There must be no flaws this morning. Two fellows who worked at the building across the street had already been dismissed because whites had demanded their jobs, and with the boy at that age needing special foods and me planning to enter school again next term, I couldn't afford to allow something like that out on the sidewalk to spoil my chances. Especially since Berry had told one of my friends in the building that he didn't like that "damned educated nigger."

I was so concerned with the brass that when the fellow spoke, I jumped with surprise.

"Howdy," he said. The expected drawl was there. But something was missing, something usually behind that kind of drawl.

"Good morning."

"Looks like you working purty hard over that brass."

"It gets pretty dirty overnight."

That part wasn't missing. When they did have something to say to us, they always became familiar.

"You been working here long?" he asked, leaning against the column with his elbow.

"Two months."

I turned my back to him as I worked.

"Any other colored folks working here?"

"I'm the only one," I lied. There were two others. It was none of his business anyway.

"Have much to do?"

"I have enough," I said. Why, I thought, doesn't he go on in and ask for the job? Why bother me? Why tempt me to choke him? Doesn't he know we aren't afraid to fight his kind out this way?

As I turned, picking up the bottle to pour more polish into my rag, he pulled a tobacco sack from the pocket of his old blue coat. I noticed his hands were scarred as though they had been burned.

"Ever smoke Durham?" he asked.

"No thank you," I said.

He laughed.

"Not used to anything like that, are you?"

"Not used to what?"

A little more from this guy and I would see red.

"Fellow like me offering a fellow like you something besides a rope."

I stopped to look at him. He stood there smiling with the sack in his outstretched hand. There were many wrinkles around his eyes, and I had to smile in return. In spite of myself I had to smile.

"Sure you won't smoke some Durham?"

"No thanks," I said.

He was fooled by the smile. A smile couldn't change things between my kind and his.

"I'll admit it ain't much," he said. "But it's a helluva lot different."

I stopped the polishing again to see what it was he was trying to get after.

"But," he said, "I've got something really worth a lot; that is, if you're interested."

"Let's hear it," I said.

Here, I thought, is where he tries to put one over on old "George."

"You see, I come out from the union and we intend to organize all the building-service help in this district. Maybe you been reading 'bout it in the papers?"

"I saw something about it, but what's it to do with me?"

"Well, first place we'll make 'em take some of this work off you. It'll mean shorter hours and higher wages, and better conditions in general."

"What you really mean is that you'll get in here and bounce me out. Unions don't want Negro members."

UNTITLED
Ruth Marten

Ralph Ellison

"You mean *some* unions don't. It used to be that way, but things have changed."

"Listen, fellow. You're wasting your time and mine. Your damn unions are like everything else in the country—for whites only. What ever caused *you* to give a damn about a Negro anyway? Why should *you* try to organize Negroes?"

His face had become a little white.

"See them hands?"

He stretched out his hands.

"Yes," I said, looking not at his hands but at the color draining from his face.

"Well, I got them scars in Macon County, Alabama, for saying a colored friend of mine was somewhere else on a day he was supposed to have raped a woman. He was, too, 'cause I was with him. Me and him was trying to borrow some seed fifty miles away when it happened—if it did happen. They made them scars with a gasoline torch and run me out of the county 'cause they said I tried to help a nigger make a white woman out a lie. That same night they lynched him and burned down his house. They did that to him and this to me, and both of us was fifty miles away."

He was looking down at his outstretched hands as he talked.

"God," was all I could say. I felt terrible when I looked closely at his hands for the first time. It must have been hell. The skin was drawn and puckered and looked as though it had been fried. Fried hands.

"Since that time I learned a lot," he said, "I been at this kinda thing. First it was the croppers, and when they got to know me and made it too hot, I quit the country and came to town. First it was in Arkansas and now it's here. And the more I move around, the more I see, and the more I see, the more I work."

He was looking into my face now, his eyes blue in his red skin. He was looking very earnestly. I said nothing. I didn't know what to say to that. Perhaps he was telling the truth; I didn't know. He was smiling again.

"Listen," he said. "Now, don't you go trying to figger it all out right now. There's going to be a series of meetings at this number starting tonight, and I'd like mighty much to see you there. Bring any friends along you want to."

> ...*I* quit the country and came to town. First it was in Arkansas and now it's here. And the more I move around, the more I see, and the more I see, the more I work."

He handed me a card with a number and 8 P.M. sharp written on it. He smiled as I took the card and made as if to shake my hand but turned and walked down the steps to the street. I noticed that he limped as he moved away.

Good morning, John," Mr. Berry said. I turned, and there he stood; derby, long black coat, stick, nose glasses, and all. He stood gazing into the brass like the wicked queen into her looking glass in the story which the boy liked so well.

"Good morning, sir," I said.

I should have finished long before.

"Did the man I saw leaving wish to see me, John?"

"Oh no, sir. He only wished to buy old clothes."

Satisfied with my work for the day, he passed inside, and I walked around to the quarters to look after the boy. It was near twelve o'clock.

I found the boy pushing a toy back and forth beneath a chair in the little room which I used for a study.

"Hi, Daddy," he called.

"Hi, son," I called. "What are you doing today?"

"Oh, I'm trucking."

"I thought you had to stand up to truck."

"Not that kind, Daddy, this kind."

He held up the toy.

"Ooh," I said. "*That* kind."

"Aw, Daddy, you're kidding. You always kid, don't you, Daddy?"

"No. When you're bad I don't kid, do I?"

"I guess not."

In fact, he wasn't—only enough to make it unnecessary for me to worry because he wasn't.

The business of trucking soon absorbed him, and I went back to the kitchen to fix his lunch and to warm up the coffee for myself.

The boy had a good appetite, so I didn't have to make him eat. I gave him his food and settled into a chair to study, but my mind wandered away, so I got up and filled a pipe hoping that would help, but it didn't, so I threw the book aside and picked up Malraux's *Man's Fate*, which Mrs. Johnson had given me, and tried to read it as I drank a cup of coffee. I had to give that up also. Those hands were on my brain, and I couldn't forget that fellow.

"Daddy," the boy called softly; it's always softly when I'm busy.

"Yes, son."

"When I grow up I think I'll drive a truck."

"You do?"

"Yes, and then I can wear a lot of buttons on my cap like the men that bring the meat to the grocery. I saw a colored man with some today, Daddy. I looked out the window, and a colored man drove the truck today, and, Daddy, he had two buttons on his cap. I could see 'em plain."

He had stopped his play and was still on his knees, beside the chair in his blue overalls. I closed the book and looked at the boy a long time. I must have looked queer.

"What's the matter, Daddy?" he asked. I explained that I was thinking, and got up and walked over to stand looking out the front window. He was quiet for a while; then he started rolling his truck again.

The only nice feature about the quarters was that they were high up and offered a view in all directions. It was afternoon and the sun was brilliant. Off to the side, a boy and girl were playing tennis in a driveway. Across the street a group of little fellows in bright sunsuits were playing on a long stretch of lawn before a white stone building. Their nurse, dressed completely in white except for her dark glasses, which I saw when she raised her head, sat still as a picture, bent over a book on her knees. As the children played, the wind blew their cries over to where I stood, and as I watched, a flock of pigeons swooped down into the driveway near the stretch of green, only to take flight again wheeling in a mass as another child came skipping up the drive pulling some sort of toy. The children saw him and were running toward him in a group when the nurse looked up and called them back. She called something to the child and pointed back in the direction of the garages where he had just come from. I could see him turn slowly around and drag his toy, some kind of bird that flapped its wings like an eagle, slowly after him. He stopped and pulled a flower from one of the bushes that lined the drive, turning to look hurriedly at the nurse, and then ran back down the drive. The child had been Jackie, the little son of the white gardener who worked across the street.

As I turned away I noticed that my boy had come to stand beside me.

"What you looking at, Daddy?" he said.

"I guess Daddy was just looking out on the world."

I picked up the book to read again, and must have fallen asleep immediately, for when I came to it was almost time to go water the lawn. When I got down-stairs the boy was not there.

Then he asked if he could go out and play with his ball, and since I would soon have to go down myself to water the lawn, I told him it would be all right. But he couldn't find the ball; I would have to find it for him.

"All right now," I told him. "You stay in the back out of everybody's way, and you mustn't ask anyone a lot of questions."

I always warned about the questions, even though it did little good. He ran down the stairs, and soon I could hear the *bump bump bump* of his ball bouncing against the garage doors underneath. But since it didn't make a loud noise, I didn't ask him to stop.

I picked up the book to read again, and must have fallen asleep immediately, for when I came to it was almost time to go water the lawn. When I got downstairs the boy was not there. I called, but no answer. Then I went out into the alley in back of the garages to see if he was playing there. There were three older white boys sitting talking on a pile of old packing cases. They looked uneasy when I came up. I asked if they had seen a little Negro boy, but they said they hadn't. Then I went farther down the alley behind the grocery store where the trucks drove up, and asked one of the fellows working there if he had seen my boy. He said he had been working on the platform all after-noon and that he was sure the boy had not been there. As I started away, the four o'clock whistle blew and I had to go water the lawn. I wondered where the boy could have gone. As I came back up the alley I was becoming alarmed. Then it occurred to me that he might have gone out in front in spite of my warning not to. Of course, that was where he would go, out in front to sit on the grass. I laughed at myself for becoming alarmed and decided not to punish him, even though Berry had given instructions that he was not to be seen out in the front without me. A boy that size will make you do that.

As I came around the building past the tall new evergreens, I could hear the boy crying in just that note no other child has, and when I came com-pletely around I found him standing looking up into a window with tears on his face.

"What is it, son?" I asked. "What happened?"

"My ball, my ball, Daddy. My ball," he cried, looking up at the window.

"Yes, son. But what about the ball?"

"He threw it up in the window."

"Who did? Who threw it, son? Stop crying and tell Daddy about it."

He made an effort to stop, wiping the tears away with the back of his hand.

"A big white boy asked me to throw him my ball an', an' he took it and threw it up in that window and ran," he said, pointing.

I looked up just as Berry appeared at the window. The ball had gone into his private office.

"John, is that your boy?" he snapped.

He was red in the face.

"Yessir, but—"

"Well, he's taken his damned ball and ruined one of my plants."

"Yessir."

"You know he's got no business around here in front, don't you?"

"Yes!"

"Well, if I ever see him around here again, you're going to find yourself behind the black ball. Now get him on round to the back and then come up here and clean up this mess he's made."

I gave him one long hard look and then felt for the boy's hand to take him back to the quarters. I had a hard time seeing as we walked back, and scratched myself by stumbling into the evergreens as we went around the building.

The boy was not crying now, and when I looked down at him, the pain in my hand caused me to notice that it was bleeding. When we got upstairs, I sat the boy in a chair and went looking for iodine to doctor my hand.

"If anyone should ask me, young man, I'd say your face needed a good washing."

He didn't answer then, but when I came out of the bathroom, he seemed more inclined to talk.

"Daddy, what did that man mean?"

"Mean how, son?"

"About a black ball. You know, Daddy."

"Oh—that."

"You know, Daddy. What'd he mean?"

"He meant, son, that if your ball landed in his office again, Daddy would go after it behind the old black ball."

"Oh," he said, very thoughtful again. Then, after a while he told me: "Daddy, that white man can't see very good, can he, Daddy?"

"Why do you say that, son?"

"Daddy," he said impatiently. "Anybody can see my ball is white."

For the second time that day I looked at him a long time.

"Yes, son," I said. "Your ball *is* white." Mostly white, anyway, I thought.

"Will I play with the black ball, Daddy?"

"In time, son," I said. "In time."

He had already played with the ball; that he would discover later. He was learning the rules of the game already, but he didn't know it. Yes, he would play with the ball. Indeed, poor little rascal, he would play until he grew sick of playing. My, yes, the old ball game. But I'd begin telling him the rules later.

My hand was still burning from the scratch as I dragged the hose out to water the lawn, and looking down at the iodine stain, I thought of the fellow's fried hands, and felt in my pocket to make sure I still had the card he had given me. Maybe there was a color other than white on the old ball.

Responding to the Story

1. **LITERARY LENS** Locate two or three words or phrases in the first paragraph from which you can infer that the narrator is of a low social standing.

2. The color words in this short story do more than describe objects; they are also used as code words for race, social status, and political views. Using a chart such as the one below, outline the meanings of the color words and phrases. Some words may have more than one meaning.

Code Word or Phrase	Meanings
Black	
White	
Red	
Black ball	
Seeing red	

3. Several times, the narrator of this story stretches the truth, or else lies outright. Find an example and explain the narrator's motivation for being less than truthful.

4. What are some of the "black balls" that exist in today's society?

5. List three of the narrator's reactions to, and concerns for, his son. Then decide which are universal among fathers, and which are attributable mainly to race.

6. **THE AUTHOR'S STYLE** Ellison is often noted for his use of pathos in his short stories and novels. *Pathos* is the quality in art or literature that stimulates pity, compassion, or sorrow. List at least two instances where Ellison evokes pathos in this story.

★★★

James Thurber
1894–1961

About the Author

Writer, reporter, cartoonist, and humorist James Thurber developed his famous sense of humor under the influence of his practical joker mother. An accident had an influence on his choice of career, too. After a stray arrow struck his eye when he was a child, Thurber had lifelong vision problems that eventually led to total blindness. Poor vision kept him from participating in sports when he was growing up, and instead he turned to reading and writing. After leaving his hometown of Columbus, Ohio, he held several jobs as a newspaper reporter both at home and abroad. In 1927, his career was launched when he went to work at a newly established magazine, *The New Yorker.*

The weekly magazine became influential, and Thurber helped set the tone with his polished writing and whimsical cartoons. Often his subjects were nagging wives, timid husbands, and placid, observant animals. A typical caption is "Well if I called the wrong number, then why did you answer the phone?" With E. B. White he wrote and illustrated a spoof of pop psychology called *Is Sex Necessary?* He also wrote autobiographical sketches, a memoir of his time at *The New Yorker,* a play, and fantasies for children.

In *The Secret Life of Walter Mitty,* Thurber created the widely recognized character of a henpecked man so befuddled by modern urban life that he escapes into a world of fantasy. In fact, the Walter Mitty Syndrome was described in a British medical journal as a diagnosable condition.

★★★★★★★★★★★

The Author's Style

James Thurber's stories often read as contemporary fables that make use of simple, familiar story lines. Though his endings are often comical or farcical, his final purpose was to create a balance between whimsicality and sober reality. He often explored the tension between the human inclination toward confusion on one hand and the need for order on the other. He once wrote, "Humor is emotional chaos remembered in tranquility." In other words, some experiences aren't funny until afterward.

Though the tone in Thurber's work is often sardonic and sophisticated, his stories generally end by affirming the power of love in a troubled world. His work manages to have a gentle tone yet still take a clear-eyed look at human foibles. In typical self-deprecating style, he once wrote, "I myself have accomplished nothing of excellence except a remarkable and, to some of my friends, unaccountable expertness in hitting empty ginger ale bottles with small rocks at a distance of thirty paces."

Lᴉᴛᴇʀᴀʀʏ Lᴇɴs
An *antihero* is a progatonist who is lacking in the qualities usually associated with a hero, such as daring, honesty, and a willingness to sacrifice. Look for the antihero in this story.

THE
SECRET LIFE
OF
WALTER MITTY

JAMES THURBER

"We're going through!" The Commander's voice was like thin ice breaking. He wore his full-dress uniform, with the heavily braided white cap pulled down rakishly over one cold gray eye. "We can't make it, sir. It's spoiling for a hurricane, if you ask me." "I'm not asking you, Lieutenant Berg," said the Commander. "Throw on the power lights! Rev her up to 8,500! We're going through!" The pounding of the cylinders increased: ta-pocketa-pocketa-pocketa-*pocketa-pocketa*. The Commander stared at the ice forming on the pilot window. He walked over and twisted a row of complicated dials. "Switch on No. 8 auxiliary!" he shouted. "Switch on No. 8 auxiliary!" repeated Lieutenant Berg. "Full strength in No. 3 turret!" shouted the commander. "Full strength in No. 3 turret!"

The crew, bending to their various tasks in the huge, hurtling eight-engined Navy hydroplane, looked at each other and grinned. "The Old Man'll get us through," they said to one another. "The Old Man ain't afraid of Hell!" . . .

BLAM, Roy Lichtenstein, 1962, Yale University Art Gallery

"Not so fast! You're driving too fast!" said Mrs. Mitty. "What are you driving so fast for?"

"Hmm?" said Walter Mitty. He looked at his wife, in the seat beside him, with shocked astonishment. She seemed grossly unfamiliar, like a strange woman who had yelled at him in a crowd. "You were up to fifty-five," she said. "You know I don't like to go more than forty. You were up to fifty-five." Walter Mitty drove on toward Waterbury in silence, the roaring of the SN202 through the worst storm in twenty years of Navy flying fading in the remote, intimate airways of his mind. "You're tensed up again," said Mrs. Mitty. "It's one of your days. I wish you'd let Dr. Renshaw look you over."

Walter Mitty stopped the car in front of the building where his wife went to have her hair done. "Remember to get those overshoes while I'm having my hair done," she said. "I don't need overshoes," said Mitty. She put her mirror back into her bag. "We've been all through that," she said, getting out of the car. "You're not a young man any longer." He raced the engine a little. "Why don't you wear your gloves? Have you lost your gloves?" Walter Mitty reached in a pocket and brought out the gloves. He put them on, but after she had turned and gone into the building and he had driven on to a red light, he took them off again. "Pick it up, brother!" snapped a cop as the light changed, and Mitty hastily pulled on his gloves and lurched ahead. He drove

128   James Thurber

around the streets aimlessly for a time, and then he drove past the hospital on his way to the parking lot.

. . . "It's the millionaire banker, Wellington McMillan," said the pretty nurse. "Yes?" said Walter Mitty, removing his gloves slowly. "Who has the case?" "Dr. Renshaw and Dr. Benbow, but there are two specialists here, Dr. Remington from New York and Mr. Pritchard-Mitford from London. He flew over." A door opened down a long, cool corridor and Dr. Renshaw came out. He looked distraught and haggard. "Hello, Mitty," he said. "We're having the devil's own time with McMillan, the millionaire banker and close personal friend of Roosevelt. Obstreosis of the ductal tract. Tertiary. Wish you'd take a look at him." "Glad to," said Mitty.

In the operating room there were whispered introductions: "Dr. Remington, Dr. Mitty. Mr. Pritchard-Mitford, Dr. Mitty." "I've read your book on streptothricosis," said Pritchard-Mitford, shaking hands.

In the operating room there were whispered introductions: "Dr. Remington, Dr. Mitty. Mr. Pritchard-Mitford, Dr. Mitty." "I've read your book on streptothricosis," said Pritchard-Mitford, shaking hands. "A brilliant performance, sir." "Thank you," said Walter Mitty. "Didn't know you were in the States, Mitty," grumbled Remington. "Coals to Newcastle,[1] bringing Mitford and me up here for a tertiary." "You are very kind," said Mitty. A huge, complicated machine, connected to the operating table, with many tubes and wires, began at this moment to go pocketa-pocketa-pocketa. "The new anesthetizer is giving way!" shouted an interne. "There is no one in the East who knows how to fix it!" "Quiet, man!" said Mitty, in a low, cool voice. He sprang to the machine, which was now going pocketa-pocketa-queep-pocketa-queep. He began fingering delicately a row of glistening dials: "Give me a fountain pen!" he snapped. Someone handed him a fountain pen. He pulled a faulty piston out of the machine and inserted the pen in its place. "That will hold for ten minutes," he said. "Get on with the operation." A nurse hurried over and whispered to Renshaw, and Mitty saw the man turn pale. "Coreopsis has set in," said Renshaw nervously. "If you would take over, Mitty?" Mitty looked at him and at the **craven** figure of Benbow, who drank, and at the

craven: cowardly; contemptible

---

1 **Coals to Newcastle:** an expression meaning an unecessary act. (Because Newcastle is a coal mining city, there is no reason to take coals to it.)

grave uncertain faces of the two great specialists. "If you wish," he said. They slipped a white gown on him, he adjusted a mask and drew on thin gloves; nurses handed him shining . . .

"Back it up, Mac! Look out for that Buick!" Walter Mitty jammed on the brakes. "Wrong lane, Mac," said the parking-lot attendant, looking at Mitty closely. "Gee. Yeh," muttered Mitty. He began cautiously to back out of the lane marked "Exit Only." "Leave her sit there," said the attendant: "I'll put her away." Mitty got out of the car. "Hey, better leave the key." "Oh," said Mitty, handing the man the ignition key. The attendant vaulted into the car, backed it up with insolent skill, and put it where it belonged.

They're so damn cocky, thought Walter Mitty, walking along Main Street; they think they know everything. Once he had tried to take his chains off, outside New Milford, and he had got them wound around the axles. A man had had to come out in a wrecking car and unwind them, a young, grinning garageman. Since then Mrs. Mitty always made him drive to a garage to have the chains taken off. The next time, he thought, I'll wear my right arm in a sling; they won't grin at me then. I'll have my right arm in a sling and they'll see I couldn't possibly take the chains off myself. He kicked at the slush on the sidewalk. "Overshoes," he said to himself, and he began looking for a shoe store.

When he came out into the street again, with the overshoes in a box under his arm, Walter Mitty began to wonder what the other thing was his wife had told him to get. She had told him, twice, before they set out from their house for Waterbury. In a way he hated these weekly trips to town—he was always getting something wrong. Kleenex, he thought, Squibb's, razor blades? No. Toothpaste, toothbrush, bicarbonate, carborundum, initiative and referendum? He gave it up. But she would remember it. "Where's the what's-its-name?" she would ask. "Don't tell me you forgot the what's-its-name." A newsboy went by shouting something about the Waterbury trial.

. . . "Perhaps this will refresh your memory." The District Attorney suddenly thrust a heavy automatic at the quiet figure on the witness stand. "Have you ever seen this before?" Walter Mitty took the gun and examined it expertly. "This is my Webley-Vickers 50.80," he said calmly. An excited buzz ran around the courtroom. The Judge rapped for order. "You are a crack shot with any sort of firearms, I believe?" said the District Attorney, insinuatingly. "Objection!" shouted Mitty's attorney. "We have shown that the defendant could not have fired the shot. We have shown that he wore his right arm in a sling on the night of the fourteenth of July." Walter Mitty raised his hand briefly and the bickering attorneys were stilled. "With any known make of gun," he said evenly, "I could have killed Gregory Fitzhurst at three hundred feet *with my left hand.*" Pandemonium broke loose in the courtroom. A woman's scream rose above the bedlam and suddenly a lovely, dark-haired girl was in Walter Mitty's arms. The District Attorney struck at her savagely. Without rising from his chair, Mitty let the man have it on the point of the chin. "You miserable cur!" . . .

"Puppy biscuit," said Walter Mitty. He stopped walking and the buildings of Waterbury rose up out of the misty courtroom and surrounded him again. A woman who was passing laughed. "He said 'Puppy biscuit,'" she said to her companion. "That man said 'Puppy biscuit' to himself." Walter Mitty hurried on. He went into an A & P, not the first one he came to but a smaller one farther up the street. "I want some buscuit for small, young dogs," he said to the clerk. "Any special brand, sir?" The greatest pistol shot in the world thought a moment. "It says 'Puppies Bark for It' on the box," said Walter Mitty.

He said 'Puppy biscuit,'" she said to her companion. "That man said 'Puppy biscuit' to himself." Walter Mitty hurried on. He went into an A & P, not the first one he came to but a smaller one farther up the street.

His wife would be through at the hairdresser's in fifteen minutes, Mitty saw in looking at his watch, unless they had trouble drying it; sometimes they had trouble drying it. She didn't like to get to the hotel first; she would want him to be there waiting for her as usual. He found a big leather chair in the lobby, facing a window, and he put the overshoes and the puppy biscuit on the floor beside it. He picked up an old copy of *Liberty* and sank down into the chair. "Can Germany Conquer the World Through the Air?" Walter Mitty looked at the pictures of bombing planes and of ruined streets.

. . . "The cannonading[2] has got the wind up in young Raleigh, sir," said the sergeant. Captain Mitty looked up at him through tousled hair. "Get him to bed," he said wearily. "With the others. I'll fly alone." "But you can't sir," said the sergeant anxiously. "It takes two men to handle that bomber and the Archies are pounding hell out of the air. Von Richtman's circus is between

---

2 **cannonading:** heavily firing with artilery

here and Saulier." "Somebody's got to get that ammunition dump," said Mitty. "I'm going over. Spot of brandy?" He poured a drink for the sergeant and one for himself. War thundered and whined around the dugout and battered at the door. There was a rending of wood and splinters flew through the room. "A bit of a near thing," said Captain Mitty carelessly. "The box barrage is closing in," said the sergeant. "We only live once, Sergeant," said Mitty, with his faint, fleeting smile. "Or do we?" He poured another brandy and tossed it off. "I never see a man could hold his brandy like you, sir," said the sergeant. "Begging your pardon, sir." Captain Mitty stood up and strapped on his huge Webley-Vickers automatic. "It's forty kilometers through hell, sir," said the sergeant. Mitty finished one last brandy. "After all," he said softly, "what isn't?" The pounding of the cannon increased; there was the rat-tat-tatting of machine guns, and from somewhere came the menacing pocketa-pocketa-pocketa of the new flame-throwers. Walter Mitty walked to the door of the dugout humming "Auprès de Ma Blonde." He turned and waved to the sergeant. "Cheerio!" he said. . . .

Something struck his shoulder. "I've been looking all over this hotel for you," said Mrs. Mitty. "Why do you have to hide in this old chair? How did you expect me to find you?" "Things close in," said Walter Mitty vaguely. "What?" Mrs. Mitty said. "Did you get the what's-its-name? The puppy biscuit? What's in that box?" "Overshoes," said Mitty. "Couldn't you have put them on in the store?" "I was thinking," said Walter Mitty. "Does it ever occur to you that I am sometimes thinking?" She looked at him. "I'm going to take your temperature when I get you home," she said.

They went out through the revolving doors that made a faintly derisive whistling sound when you pushed them. It was two blocks to the parking lot. At the drugstore on the corner she said, "Wait here for me. I forgot something. I won't be a minute." She was more than a minute. Walter Mitty lighted a cigarette. It began to rain, rain with sleet in it. He stood up against the wall of the drugstore, smoking. . . . He put his shoulders back and his heels together. "To hell with the handkerchief," said Walter Mitty scornfully. He took one last drag on his cigarette and snapped it away. Then, with a faint, fleeting smile playing about his lips, he faced the firing squad; erect and motionless, proud and disdainful, Walter Mitty the Undefeated, inscrutable to the last.

Responding to the Story

1. **LITERARY LENS** What qualities make Walter Mitty a humorous antihero?

2. James Thurber was a renowned cartoonist as well as a writer. What qualities of the writing make this story seem cartoonish?

3. The author of this story once said, "All men should strive to learn before they die, what they are running from, and to, and why." What do you think Walter Mitty is running from, and why?

4. Do you laugh with Walter Mitty, at him, or both? Explain your response.

5. Walter Mitty lives in two worlds: a fantasy world and the real world. Each world is represented by its own language or *register*. For example, in his fantasy sequences, the language is often "hyped up," consisting of jargon and a liberal use of exclamation points. In the reality scenes, on the other hand, the language is down-to-earth and mundane. Select one fantasy passage and one mundane passage. Then rewrite each one using the other style or register. An example has been done for you.

Dialogue	Rewrite in Opposite Register
"Switch on No. 8 auxiliary!" he shouted.	*"Please turn on the engine," said Walter Mitty.*

6. **THE AUTHOR'S STYLE** "Nowadays most men lead lives of noisy desperation," James Thurber once quipped. This was a paraphrase of Henry David Thoreau's famous observation that "The mass of men lead lives of quiet desperation. An unconscious despair is concealed even under what are the games and amusements of mankind." The quip is typical of James Thurber's style: whimsicality contrasted with sober reality. In what ways do you think "The Secret Life of Walter Mitty" is both funny and serious?

Shirley Jackson
1916–1965

About the Author

Shirley Jackson knew she wanted to be a writer at an early age. Her mother said she started composing verse nearly as soon as she could form letters. In 1935 she enrolled at Syracuse University, where she first edited the campus humor magazine and then launched a literary magazine with Stanley Edgar Hyman, a fellow student who would become both her husband and a well-known literary critic.

A versatile writer, Jackson is best remembered for horror stories and novels with a tone of dark pessimism. Yet she also enjoyed writing humor, publishing two volumes of memoirs that took a comic look at the couple's family life rearing four children in a small Vermont town.

The Lottery, which provoked public outrage along with critical praise, remains Jackson's best-known work. This chilling tale was published originally as a short story in *The New Yorker* in 1948 and was later adapted for both the stage and television. For many years it was one of the most frequently performed plays in the country, particularly in productions put on by small theatre groups and high schools. It is still so popular that probably somewhere a high school theatre group is in rehearsal for it even as you read.

★★★★★★★★★★★

The Author's Style

Some critics consider Shirley Jackson a master of horror and psychological suspense. The deceptively casual tone of her writing is one of its most important stylistic features. This casualness helps to disguise the dark motives in her characters and the even darker truths behind her plots.

Jackson's novels and stories sometimes read as moral allegories, parables, or fable-like commentaries on collective social behavior. Her writing often takes the form of a cautionary tale—that is, a story that carries with it a warning, such as blind obedience to tradition can be dangerous, or people are not what they seem.

The author is often more interested in showing how people behave in groups than in examining the lives of individuals. Thus her characters might strike readers less as fully drawn characters than as types. Sometimes their names reflect this fact. In the story you are about to read, for example, Old Man Warner sounds more like a type representing all old men than a unique individual.

LITERARY LENS A *parable* is a story in which the events point to a deeper moral lesson. Look for the deeper meaning or lesson in this parable.

THE
LOTTERY

S HIRLEY J ACKSON

The morning of June 27th was clear and sunny, with the fresh warmth of a full-summer day; the flowers were blossoming profusely and the grass was richly green. The people of the village began to gather in the square, between the post office and the bank, around ten o'clock; in some towns there were so many people that the lottery took two days and had to be started on June 26th, but in this village, where there were only about three hundred people, the whole lottery took less than two hours, so it could begin at ten o'clock in the morning and still be through in time to allow the villagers to get home for noon dinner.

The children assembled first, of course. School was recently over for the summer, and the feeling of liberty sat uneasily on most of them; they tended to gather together quietly for a while before they

Soon the men began to gather, surveying their own children, speaking of planting and rain, tractors and taxes. They stood together, away from the pile of stones in the corner, and their jokes were quiet and they smiled rather than laughed.

broke into boisterous play, and their talk was still of the classroom and the teacher, of books and reprimands. Bobby Martin had already stuffed his pockets full of stones, and the other boys soon followed his example, selecting the smoothest and roundest stones; Bobby and Harry Jones and Dickie Delacroix—the villagers pronounced this name "Dellacroy"—eventually made a great pile of stones in one corner of the square and guarded it against the raids of the other boys. The girls stood aside, talking among themselves, looking over their shoulders at the boys, and the very small children rolled in the dust or clung to the hands of their older brothers or sisters.

Soon the men began to gather, surveying their own children, speaking of planting and rain, tractors and taxes. They stood together, away from the pile of stones in the corner, and their jokes were quiet and they smiled rather than laughed. The women, wearing faded house dresses and sweaters, came shortly after their menfolk. They greeted one another and exchanged bits of gossip as they went to join their husbands. Soon the women, standing by their husbands, began to call to their children, and the children came reluctantly, having to be called four or five times. Bobby Martin ducked under his mother's grasping hand and ran, laughing, back to the pile of stones. His father spoke up sharply, and Bobby came quickly and took his place between his father and his oldest brother.

The lottery was conducted—as were the square dances, the teenage club, the Halloween program—by Mr. Summers, who had time and energy to devote to civic activities. He was a round-faced, jovial man and he ran the coal business, and people were sorry for him, because he had no children and his wife was a scold. When he arrived in the square, carrying the black wooden box, there was a murmur of conversation among the villagers, and he waved and called, "Little late today, folks." The postmaster, Mr. Graves, followed him, carrying a three-legged stool, and the stool was put in the center of the square and Mr. Summers set the black box down on it. The villagers kept their distance, leaving a space between themselves and the stool, and when Mr. Summers said, "Some of you fellows want to give me a hand?" there was a hesitation before two men, Mr. Martin and his oldest son, Baxter, came forward to hold the box steady on the stool while Mr. Summers stirred up the papers inside it.

The original paraphernalia for the lottery had been lost long ago, and the black box now resting on the stool had been put into use even before Old Man Warner, the oldest man in town, was born. Mr. Summers spoke frequently to the villagers about making a new box, but no one liked to upset even as much tradition as was represented by the black box. There was a story that the present box had been made with some pieces of the box that had preceded it, the one that had been constructed when the first people settled down to make a village here. Every year, after the lottery, Mr. Summers began talking again about a new box, but every year the subject was allowed to fade

STONE CITY IOWA, Grant Wood, 1930, Joslyn Art Museum

off without anything's being done. The black box grew shabbier each year; by now it was no longer completely black but splintered badly along one side to show the original wood color, and in some places faded or stained.

Mr. Martin and his oldest son, Baxter, held the black box securely on the stool until Mr. Summers had stirred the papers thoroughly with his hand. Because so much of the ritual had been forgotten or discarded, Mr. Summers had been successful in having slips of paper substituted for the chips of wood that had been used for generations. Chips of wood, Mr. Summers had argued, had been all very well when the village was tiny, but now that the population was more than three hundred and likely to keep on growing, it was necessary to use something that would fit more easily into the black box. The night before the lottery, Mr. Summers and Mr. Graves made up the slips of paper and put them in the box, and it was then taken to the safe of Mr. Summers's coal company and locked up until Mr. Summers was ready to take it to the square next morning. The rest of the year, the box was put away, sometimes one place, sometimes another; it had spent one year in Mr. Graves's barn and another year underfoot in the post office, and sometimes it was set on a shelf in the Martin grocery and left there. There was a great deal of fussing to be done before Mr. Summers declared the lottery open.

There were the lists to make up—of heads of families, heads of households in each family, members of each household in each family. There was the proper swearing-in of Mr. Summers by the postmaster, as the official of the lottery; at one time, some people remembered, there had been a recital of some sort, performed by the official of the lottery, a perfunctory, tuneless chant that had been rattled off duly each year; some people believed that the official of the lottery used to stand just so when he said or sang it, others believed that he was supposed to walk among the people, but years and years ago this part of the ritual had been allowed to lapse. There had been, also, a ritual salute, which the official of the lottery had had to use in addressing each person who came up to draw from the box, but this also had changed with time, until now it was felt necessary only for the official to speak to each person approaching. Mr. Summers was very good at all this; in his clean white shirt and blue jeans, with one hand resting carelessly on the black box, he seemed very proper and important as he talked **interminably** to Mr. Graves and the Martins.

interminably: endlessly

Just as Mr. Summers finally left off talking and turned to the assembled villagers, Mrs. Hutchinson came hurriedly along the path to the square, her sweater thrown over her shoulders, and slid into place in the back of the crowd. "Clean forgot what day it was," she said to Mrs. Delacroix, who stood next to her, and they both laughed softly. "Thought my old man was out back stacking wood," Mrs. Hutchinson went on, "and then I looked out the window and the kids was gone, and then I remembered it was the twenty-seventh and came a-running." She dried her hands on her apron, and Mrs. Delacroix said, "You're in time, though. They're still talking away up there."

Mrs. Hutchinson craned her neck to see through the crowd and found her husband and children standing near the front. She tapped Mrs. Delacroix on the arm as a farewell and began to make her way through the crowd. The people separated good-humoredly to let her through; two or three people said, in voices just loud enough to be heard across the crowd, "Here comes your Missus, Hutchinson," and "Bill, she made it after all." Mrs. Hutchinson reached her husband, and Mr. Summers, who had been waiting, said cheerfully, "Thought we were going to have to get on without you, Tessie." Mrs. Hutchinson said, grinning, "Wouldn't have me leave m'dishes in the sink, now, would you, Joe?" and soft laughter ran through the crowd as the people stirred back into position after Mrs. Hutchinson's arrival.

"Well, now," Mr. Summers said soberly, "guess we better get started, get this over with, so's we can go back to work. Anybody ain't here?"

"Dunbar," several people said. "Dunbar, Dunbar."

Mr. Summers consulted his list. "Clyde Dunbar," he said. "That's right. He's broke his leg, hasn't he? Who's drawing for him?"

"Me, I guess," a woman said, and Mr. Summers turned to look at her. "Wife draws for her husband," Mr. Summers said. "Don't you have a grown boy to do it for you, Janey?" Although Mr. Summers and everyone else in the village knew the answer perfectly well, it was the business of the official of the lottery to ask such questions formally. Mr. Summers waited with an expression of polite interest while Mrs. Dunbar answered.

> "Wife draws for her husband," Mr. Summers said. "Don't you have a grown boy to do it for you, Janey?" Although Mr. Summers and everyone else in the village knew the answer perfectly well, it was the business of the official of the lottery to ask such questions formally.

"Horace's not but sixteen yet," Mrs. Dunbar said regretfully. "Guess I gotta fill in for the old man this year."

"Right," Mr. Summers said. He made a note on the list he was holding. Then he asked, "Watson boy drawing this year?"

A tall boy in the crowd raised his hand. "Here," he said. "I'm drawing for m' mother and me." He blinked his eyes nervously and ducked his head as several voices in the crowd said things like "Good fellow, Jack," and "Glad to see your mother's got a man to do it."

By now, all through the crowd there were men holding the small folded papers in their large hands, turning them over and over nervously.

"Well," Mr. Summers said, "guess that's everyone. Old Man Warner make it?"

"Here," a voice said, and Mr. Summers nodded.

A sudden hush fell on the crowd as Mr. Summers cleared his throat and looked at the list. "All ready?" he called. "Now, I'll read the names—heads of families first—and the men come up and take a paper out of the box. Keep the paper folded in your hand without looking at it until everyone has had a turn. Everything clear?"

The people had done it so many times that they only half listened to the directions; most of them were quiet, wetting their lips, not looking around. Then Mr. Summers raised one hand high and said, "Adams." A man disengaged himself from the crowd and came forward. "Hi, Steve," Mr. Summers said, and Mr. Adams said, "Hi, Joe." They grinned at one another humorlessly and nervously. Then Mr. Adams reached into the black box and took out a folded paper. He held it firmly by one corner as he turned and went hastily back to his place in the crowd, where he stood a little apart from his family, not looking down at his hand.

"Allen," Mr. Summers said. "Anderson. . . . Bentham."

"Seems like there's no time at all between lotteries any more." Mrs. Delacroix said to Mrs. Graves in the back row. "Seems like we got through with the last one only last week."

"Time sure goes fast," Mrs. Graves said.

"Clark. . . . Delacroix."

"There goes my old man," Mrs. Delacroix said. She held her breath while her husband went forward.

"Dunbar," Mr. Summers said, and Mrs. Dunbar went steadily to the box while one of the women said, "Go on, Janey," and another said, "There she goes."

"We're next," Mrs. Graves said. She watched while Mr. Graves came around from the side of the box, greeted Mr. Summers gravely, and selected a slip of paper from the box. By now, all through the crowd there were men holding the small folded papers in their large hands, turning them over and over nervously. Mrs. Dunbar and her two sons stood together, Mrs. Dunbar holding the slip of paper.

"Harburt. . . . Hutchinson."

"Get up there, Bill," Mrs. Hutchinson said, and the people near her laughed.

"Jones."

"They do say," Mr. Adams said to Old Man Warner, who stood next to him, "that over in the north village they're talking of giving up the lottery."

Old Man Warner snorted. "Pack of crazy fools," he said. "Listening to the young folks, nothing's good enough for *them*. Next thing you know, they'll be wanting to go back to living in caves, nobody work any more, live *that* way for a while. Used to be a saying about 'Lottery in June, corn be heavy soon.' First thing you know, we'd all be eating stewed chickweed and acorns. There's *always* been a lottery," he added petulantly. "Bad enough to see young Joe Summers up there joking with everybody."

"Some places have already quit lotteries," Mrs. Adams said.

"Nothing but trouble in *that*," Old Man Warner said stoutly. "Pack of young fools."

"Martin." And Bobby Martin watched his father go forward. "Overdyke. . . . Percy."

"I wish they'd hurry," Mrs. Dunbar said to her older son. "I wish they'd hurry."

"They're almost through," her son said.

"You get ready to run tell Dad," Mrs. Dunbar said.

Mr. Summers called his own name and then stepped forward precisely and selected a slip from the box. Then he called, "Warner."

"Seventy-seventh year I been in the lottery," Old Man Warner said as he went through the crowd. "Seventy-seventh time."

"Watson." The tall boy came awkwardly through the crowd. Someone said, "Don't be nervous, Jack," and Mr. Summers said, "Take your time, son."

"Zanini."

After that, there was a long pause, a breathless pause, until Mr. Summers,

People began to look around to see the Hutchinsons. Bill Hutchinson was standing quiet, staring down at the paper in his hand.

holding his slip of paper in the air, said, "All right, fellows." For a minute, no one moved, and then all the slips of paper were opened. Suddenly, all the women began to speak at once, saying, "Who is it?," "Who's got it?," "Is it the Dunbars?," "Is it the Watsons?" Then the voices began to say, "It's Hutchinson. It's Bill," "Bill Hutchinson's got it."

"Go tell your father," Mrs. Dunbar said to her older son.

People began to look around to see the Hutchinsons. Bill Hutchinson was standing quiet, staring down at the paper in his hand. Suddenly, Tessie Hutchinson shouted to Mr. Summers, "You didn't give him time enough to take any paper he wanted. I saw you. It wasn't fair!"

"Be a good sport, Tessie," Mrs. Delacroix called, and Mrs. Graves said, "All of us took the same chance."

"Shut up, Tessie," Bill Hutchinson said.

"Well, everyone," Mr. Summers said, "that was done pretty fast, and now we've got to be hurrying a little more to get done in time." He consulted his next list. "Bill," he said, "you draw for the Hutchinson family. You got any other households in the Hutchinsons?"

"There's Don and Eva," Mrs. Hutchinson yelled. "Make *them* take their chance!"

"Daughters draw with their husbands' families, Tessie," Mr. Summers said gently. "You know that as well as anyone else."

"It wasn't *fair*," Tessie said.

"I guess not, Joe," Bill Hutchinson said regretfully. "My daughter draws with her husband's family, that's only fair. And I've got no other family except the kids."

"Then, as far as drawing for families is concerned, it's you," Mr. Summers said in explanation, "and as far as drawing for households is concerned, that's you, too. Right?"

"Right," Bill Hutchinson said.

"How many kids, Bill?" Mr. Summers asked formally.

"Three," Bill Hutchinson said. "There's Bill, Jr., and Nancy, and little Dave. And Tessie and me."

"All right, then," Mr. Summers said. "Harry, you got their tickets back?"

Mr. Graves nodded and held up the slips of paper. "Put them in the box, then," Mr. Summers directed. "Take Bill's and put it in."

"I think we ought to start over," Mrs. Hutchinson said, as quietly as she could. "I tell you it wasn't *fair*. You didn't give him time enough to choose. *Every*body saw that."

Mr. Graves had selected the five slips and put them in the box, and he dropped all the papers but those onto the ground, where the breeze caught them and lifted them off.

"Listen, everybody," Mrs. Hutchinson was saying to the people around her.

"Ready, Bill?" Mr. Summers asked, and Bill Hutchinson, with one quick glance around at his wife and children, nodded.

"Remember," Mr. Summers said, "take the slips and keep them folded until each person has taken one. Harry, you help little Dave." Mr. Graves took the hand of the little boy, who came willingly with him up to the box. "Take a paper out of the box, Davy," Mr. Summers said. Davy put his hand into the box and laughed. "Take just *one* paper," Mr. Summers said. "Harry, you hold it for him." Mr. Graves took the child's hand and removed the folded paper from the tight fist and held it while little Dave stood next to him and looked up at him wonderingly.

"Nancy next," Mr. Summers said. Nancy was twelve, and her school friends breathed heavily as she went forward, switching her skirt, and took a slip daintily from the box. "Bill, Jr.," Mr. Summers said, and Billy, his face red and his feet overlarge, nearly knocked the box over as he got a paper out. "Tessie," Mr. Summers said. She hesitated for a minute, looking around defiantly, and then set her lips and went up to the box. She snatched a paper out and held it behind her.

*S*he hesitated for a minute, looking around defiantly, and then set her lips and went up to the box. She snatched a paper out and held it behind her.

"Bill," Mr. Summers said, and Bill Hutchinson reached into the box and felt around, bringing his hand out at last with the slip of paper in it.

The crowd was quiet. A girl whispered, "I hope it's not Nancy," and the sound of the whisper reached the edges of the crowd.

"It's not the way it used to be," Old Man Warner said clearly. "People ain't the way they used to be."

"All right," Mr. Summers said. "Open the papers. Harry, you open little Dave's."

Mr. Graves opened the slip of paper and there was a general sigh through the crowd as he held it up and everyone could see that it was blank. Nancy and Bill, Jr., opened theirs at the same time, and both beamed and laughed, turning around to the crowd and holding their slips of paper above their heads.

"Tessie," Mr. Summers said. There was a pause, and then Mr. Summers looked at Bill Hutchinson, and Bill unfolded his paper and showed it. It was blank.

"It's Tessie," Mr. Summers said, and his voice was hushed. "Show us her paper, Bill."

Bill Hutchinson went over to his wife and forced the slip of paper out of her hand. It had a black spot on it, the black spot Mr. Summers had made the night before with the heavy pencil in the coal-company office. Bill Hutchinson held it up, and there was a stir in the crowd.

"All right, folks," Mr. Summers said. "Let's finish quickly."

Although the villagers had forgotten the ritual and lost the original black box, they still remembered to use stones. The pile of stones the boys had made earlier was ready; there were stones on the ground with the blowing scraps of paper that had come out of the box. Mrs. Delacroix selected a stone so large she had to pick it up with both hands and turned to Mrs. Dunbar. "Come on," she said. "Hurry up."

Mrs. Dunbar had small stones in both hands, and she said, gasping for breath, "I can't run at all. You'll have to go ahead and I'll catch up with you."

The children had stones already. And someone gave little Davy Hutchinson a few pebbles.

Tessie Hutchinson was in the center of a cleared space by now, and she held her hands out desperately as the villagers moved in on her. "It isn't fair," she said. A stone hit her on the side of the head.

Old Man Warner was saying, "Come on, come on, everyone." Steve Adams was in the front of the crowd of villagers, with Mrs. Graves beside him.

"It isn't fair, it isn't right," Mrs. Hutchinson screamed, and then they were upon her.

Responding to the Story

1. LITERARY LENS What do you think is the main lesson of this story?

2. Explain what this story implies about the author's attitude toward the concepts of tradition, conformity, and obedience.

3. This story provoked outrage from many when it first appeared in *The New Yorker* in 1948. What do you think were some reasons for this response?

4. Explain how the tone of this story is deceiving.

5. THE AUTHOR'S STYLE Critics often refer to Jackson as a master of horror and psychological suspense. Would you agree? Explain.

Truman Capote
1924–1984

About the Author

Flamboyant. Gifted. Social. Unique. These qualities helped catapult Truman Capote into literary fame early and kept him there until his death of a drug overdose at 60. Born in New Orleans to a 16-year-old beauty queen, Capote stayed in the South with relatives when his mother moved to New York after her divorce from his father. As a child, Capote was a neighbor of Harper Lee, who would also become a writer; in *To Kill a Mockingbird*, Lee modeled the precocious character "Dill" after Capote.

Capote published his first novel, *Other Voices, Other Rooms,* the story of a boy's search for his father, at 24. Living in New York for most of his adult life, Capote published screenplays and a musical as well as prose. His best-known book is *In Cold Blood*, based on an actual multiple murder committed by two sociopaths. The book blended the techniques of fiction and journalism; Capote called it a "nonfiction novel."

Capote himself was perhaps the most famous character he ever created. He often turned up on talk shows wearing outrageous hats and criticizing other writers in his distinctive high-pitched voice. After he published an excerpt from a novel he was working on that thinly disguised his rich friends, he was shunned by them and succumbed to drug addiction and alcoholism.

★★★★★★★★★★★

The Author's Style

"What I am trying to achieve is a voice sitting by a fireplace telling you a story on a winter's evening," Truman Capote is quoted as saying in the 1990 collection *Writers on Writing*. Capote is more interested in personality and mood—that is, character—than in logic and plot. Often he puts his eccentric, "outsider" characters into odd situations that have a poetic and dream-like aura. For this reason his short pieces are sometimes referred to as tales.

Capote's fiction often involves either children or adults who have a child-like way of looking at and interacting with the "real" world. Generally they are in search of security and a sense of identity.

His style is brilliantly descriptive, using precise phrases to reveal character and mood. A careful writer, Capote once said that because what is taken out is as important as what is put in, he believed in using scissors more than pencils.

Capote is interested in human psychology, and the fantasies of his characters often concern love, understanding, and acceptance. In this and other respects his work has been compared to that of fellow southern writers Carson McCullers and Eudora Welty.

LITERARY LENS Take note of the changes in weather in this story.

MIRIAM

TRUMAN CAPOTE

For several years, Mrs. H. T. Miller had lived alone in a pleasant apartment (two rooms with kitchenette) in a remodeled brownstone near the East River. She was a widow: Mr. H. T. Miller had left a reasonable amount of insurance. Her interests were narrow, she had no friends to speak of, and she rarely journeyed farther than the corner grocery. The other people in the house never seemed to notice her: her clothes were matter-of-fact, her hair iron-gray, clipped and casually waved; she did not use cosmetics, her features were plain and inconspicuous, and on her last birthday she was sixty-one. Her activities were seldom spontaneous: she kept the two rooms immaculate, smoked an occasional cigarette, prepared her own meals, and tended a canary.

Then she met Miriam. It was snowing that night. Mrs. Miller had finished drying the supper dishes and was thumbing through an afternoon paper when she saw an advertisement of a picture playing at a neighborhood theater. The title sounded good, so she struggled into her beaver coat, laced her galoshes, and left the apartment, leaving one light burning in the foyer: she found nothing more disturbing than a sensation of darkness.

The snow was fine, falling gently, not yet making an impression on the pavement. The wind from the river cut only at street crossings. Mrs. Miller hurried, her head bowed, oblivious as a mole burrowing a blind path. She stopped at a drugstore and bought a package of peppermints.

Her hair was the longest and strangest Mrs. Miller had ever seen: absolutely silver-white, like an albino's.

A long line stretched in front of the box office; she took her place at the end. There would be (a tired voice groaned) a short wait for all seats. Mrs. Miller rummaged in her leather handbag till she collected exactly the correct change for admission. The line seemed to be taking its own time and, looking around for some distraction, she suddenly became conscious of a little girl standing under the edge of the marquee.

Her hair was the longest and strangest Mrs. Miller had ever seen: absolutely silver-white, like an albino's. It flowed waistlength in smooth, loose lines. She was thin and fragilely constructed. There was a simple, special elegance in the way she stood with her thumbs in the pockets of a tailored plum-velvet coat.

Mrs. Miller felt oddly excited, and when the little girl glanced toward her, she smiled warmly. The little girl walked over and said, "Would you care to do me a favor?"

"I'd be glad to, if I can," said Mrs. Miller.

"Oh, it's quite easy. I merely want you to buy a ticket for me; they won't let me in otherwise. Here, I have the money." And gracefully she handed Mrs. Miller two dimes and a nickel.

They went into the theater together. An usherette directed them to a lounge; in twenty minutes the picture would be over.

"I feel just like a genuine criminal," said Mrs. Miller gaily, as she sat down. "I mean that sort of thing's against the law, isn't it? I do hope I haven't done the wrong thing. Your mother knows where you are, dear? I mean she does, doesn't she?"

The little girl said nothing. She unbuttoned her coat and folded it across her lap. Her dress underneath was prim and dark blue. A gold chain dangled about her neck, and her fingers, sensitive and musical-looking, toyed with it. Examining her more attentively, Mrs. Miller decided the truly distinctive feature was not her hair, but her eyes; they were hazel, steady, lacking any childlike quality whatsoever and, because of their size, seemed to consume her small face.

Mrs. Miller offered a peppermint. "What's your name, dear?"

"Miriam," she said, as though, in some curious way, it were information already familiar.

"Why, isn't that funny—my name's Miriam, too. And it's not a terribly common name either. Now, don't tell me your last name's Miller!"

"Just Miriam."

"But isn't that funny?"

"Moderately," said Miriam, and rolled the peppermint on her tongue.

Mrs. Miller flushed and shifted uncomfortably. "You have such a large vocabulary for such a little girl."

"Do I?"

"Well, yes," said Mrs. Miller, hastily changing the topic to: "Do you like the movies?"

"I really wouldn't know," said Miriam. "I've never been before."

Women began filling the lounge; the rumble of the newsreel bombs[1] exploded in the distance. Mrs. Miller rose, tucking her purse under her arm. "I guess I'd better be running now if I want to get a seat," she said. "It was nice to have met you."

Miriam nodded ever so slightly.

It snowed all week. Wheels and footsteps moved soundlessly on the street, as if the business of living continued secretly behind a pale but impenetrable curtain. In the falling quiet there was no sky or earth, only snow lifting in the wind, frosting the window glass, chilling the rooms, deadening and hushing the city. At all hours it was necessary to keep a lamp lighted, and Mrs. Miller lost track of the days: Friday was no different from Saturday and on Sunday she went to the grocery: closed, of course.

That evening she scrambled eggs and fixed a bowl of tomato soup. Then, after putting on a flannel robe and cold-creaming her face, she propped her-

---

1 **newsreel bombs:** Newsreels were brief news stories on film, shown before a movie; in this instance, the newsreel covered war news.

self up in bed with a hot-water bottle under her feet. She was reading the *Times* when the doorbell rang. At first she thought it must be a mistake and whoever it was would go away. But it rang and rang and settled to a persistent buzz. She looked at the clock: a little after eleven; it did not seem possible, she was always asleep by ten.

Climbing out of bed, she trotted barefoot across the living room. "I'm coming, please be patient." The latch was caught; she turned it this way and that way and the bell never paused an instant. "Stop it," she cried. The bolt gave way and she opened the door an inch. "What in heaven's name?"

"Hello," said Miriam.

"Oh . . . why, hello," said Mrs. Miller, stepping hesitantly into the hall. "You're that little girl."

"I thought you'd never answer, but I kept my finger on the button; I knew you were home. Aren't you glad to see me?"

Mrs. Miller did not know what to say. Miriam, she saw, wore the same plum-velvet coat and now she had also a beret to match; her white hair was braided in two shining plaits and looped at the ends with enormous white ribbons.

"Since I've waited so long, you could at least let me in," she said.

"It's awfully late. . . ."

Miriam regarded her blankly. "What difference does that make? Let me in. It's cold out here and I have on a silk dress." Then, with a gentle gesture, she urged Mrs. Miller aside and passed into the apartment.

She dropped her coat and beret on a chair. She was indeed wearing a silk dress. White silk. White silk in February. The skirt was beautifully pleated and the sleeves long; it made a faint rustle as she strolled about the room. "I like your place," she said. "I like the rug, blue's my favorite color." She touched a paper rose in a vase on the coffee table. "Imitation," she commented wanly. "How sad. Aren't imitations sad?" She seated herself on the sofa, daintily spreading her skirt.

"What do you want?" asked Mrs. Miller.

"Sit down," said Miriam. "It makes me nervous to see people stand."

White silk. White silk in February. The skirt was beautifully pleated and the sleeves long; it made a faint rustle as she strolled about the room.

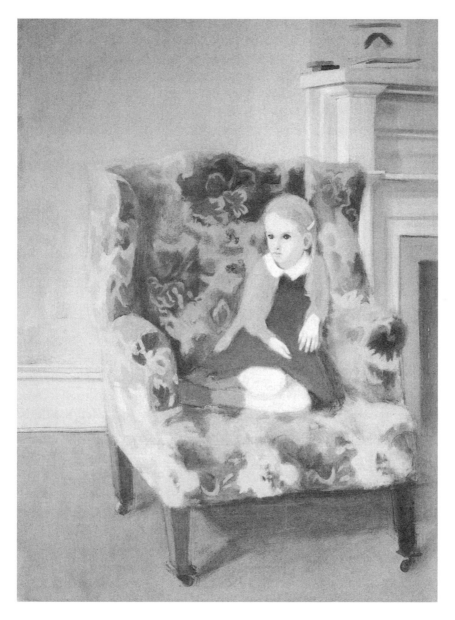

KATIE IN AN
ARMCHAIR
1954
Fairfield Porter

Mrs. Miller sank to a hassock.[2] "What do you want?" she repeated.
"You know, I don't think you're glad I came."
For a second time Mrs. Miller was without an answer; her hand motioned

---

2 **hassock:** a thickly padded cushion or low stool that serves as a small seat or footrest

vaguely. Miriam giggled and pressed back on a mound of chintz pillows. Mrs. Miller observed that the girl was less pale than she remembered; her cheeks were flushed.

"How did you know where I lived?"

Miriam frowned. "That's no question at all. What's your name? What's mine?"

"But I'm not listed in the phone book."

"Oh, let's talk about something else."

Mrs. Miller said, "Your mother must be insane to let a child like you wander around at all hours of the night—and in such ridiculous clothes. She must be out of her mind."

Miriam got up and moved to a corner where a covered bird cage hung from a ceiling chain. She peeked beneath the cover. "It's a canary," she said. "Would you mind if I woke him? I'd like to hear him sing."

"Leave Tommy alone," said Mrs. Miller, anxiously. "Don't you dare wake him."

"Certainly," said Miriam. "But I don't see why I can't hear him sing." And then, "Have you anything to eat? I'm starving! Even milk and a jam sandwich would be fine."

"Look," said Mrs. Miller, rising from the hassock, "look—if I make some nice sandwiches will you be a good child and run along home? It's past midnight, I'm sure."

"It's snowing," reproached Miriam. "And cold and dark."

"Well, you shouldn't have come here to begin with," said Mrs. Miller, struggling to control her voice. "I can't help the weather. If you want anything to eat you'll have to promise to leave."

Miriam brushed a braid against her cheek. Her eyes were thoughtful, as if weighing the proposition. She turned toward the bird cage. "Very well," she said, "I promise."

H*ow old is she? Ten? Eleven?* Mrs. Miller, in the kitchen, unsealed a jar of strawberry preserves and cut four slices of bread. She poured a glass of milk and paused to light a cigarette. *And why has she come?* Her hand shook as she held the match, fascinated, till it burned her finger. The canary was singing; singing as he did in the morning and at no other time. "Miriam," she called, "Miriam, I told you not to disturb Tommy." There was no answer. She called again; all she heard was the canary. She inhaled the cigarette and discovered she had lighted the cork-tip end and—oh, really, she mustn't lose her temper.

She carried the food in on a tray and set it on the coffee table. She saw first that the bird cage still wore its night cover. And Tommy was singing. It gave her a queer sensation. And no one was in the room. Mrs. Miller went through an alcove leading to her bedroom: at the door she caught her breath.

> *S*he saw first that the bird cage still wore its night cover. And Tommy was singing. It gave her a queer sensation.

"What are you doing?" she asked.

Miriam glanced up and in her eyes there was a look that was not ordinary. She was standing by the bureau, a jewel case opened before her. For a minute she studied Mrs. Miller, forcing their eyes to meet, and she smiled. "There's nothing good here," she said. "But I like this." Her hand held a cameo brooch. "It's charming."

"Suppose—perhaps you'd better put it back," said Mrs. Miller, feeling suddenly the need of some support. She leaned against the door frame; her head was unbearably heavy; a pressure weighted the rhythm of her heartbeat. The light seemed to flutter defectively. "Please, child—a gift from my husband . . ."

"But it's beautiful and I want it," said Miriam. *"Give it to me."*

As she stood, striving to shape a sentence which would somehow save the brooch, it came to Mrs. Miller there was no one to whom she might turn; she was alone; a fact that had not been among her thoughts for a long time. Its sheer emphasis was stunning. But here in her own room in the hushed snow-city were evidences she could not ignore or, she knew with startling clarity, resist.

Miriam ate ravenously, and when the sandwiches and milk were gone, her fingers made cobweb movements over the plate, gathering crumbs. The cameo gleamed on her blouse, the blonde profile like a trick reflection of its wearer. "That was very nice," she sighed, "though now an almond cake or a cherry would be ideal. Sweets are lovely, don't you think?"

Mrs. Miller was perched precariously on the hassock, smoking a cigarette. Her hair net had slipped lopsided and loose strands straggled down her face. Her eyes were stupidly concentrated on nothing and her cheeks were mottled in red patches, as though a fierce slap had left permanent marks.

"Is there a candy—a cake?"

Mrs. Miller tapped ash on the rug. Her head swayed slightly as she tried to focus her eyes. "You promised to leave if I made the sandwiches," she said.

"Dear me, did I?"

"It was a promise and I'm tired and I don't feel well at all."

"Mustn't fret," said Miriam, "I'm only teasing."

She picked up her coat, slung it over her arm, and arranged her beret in front of a mirror. Presently she bent close to Mrs. Miller and whispered, "Kiss me good night."

"Please—I'd rather not," said Mrs. Miller.

Miriam lifted a shoulder, arched an eyebrow. "As you like," she said, and went directly to the coffee table, seized the vase containing the paper roses, carried it to where the hard surface of the floor lay bare, and hurled it downward. Glass sprayed in all directions and she stamped her foot on the bouquet.

Then slowly she walked to the door, but before closing it she looked back at Mrs. Miller with a slyly innocent curiosity.

Mrs. Miller spent the next day in bed, rising once to feed the canary and drink a cup of tea; she took her temperature and had none, yet her dreams were feverishly agitated; their unbalanced mood lingered even as she lay staring wide-eyed at the ceiling. One dream threaded through the others like an elusively mysterious theme in a complicated

154   Truman Capote

symphony, and the scenes it depicted were sharply outlined, as though sketched by a hand of gifted intensity: a small girl, wearing a bridal gown and a wreath of leaves, led a gray procession down a mountain path, and among them there was unusual silence till a woman at the rear asked, "Where is she taking us?" "No one knows," said an old man marching in front. "But isn't she pretty?" volunteered a third voice, "Isn't she like a frost flower… so shining and white?"

Tuesday morning she woke up feeling better; harsh slats of sunlight, slanting through Venetian blinds, shed a disrupting light on her unwholesome fancies. She opened the window to discover a thawed, mild-as-spring day; a sweep of clean new clouds crumpled against a vastly blue, out-of-season sky; and across the low line of roof-tops she could see the river and smoke curving from tug-boat stacks in a warm wind. A great silver truck plowed the snow-banked street, its machine sound humming in the air.

After straightening the apartment, she went to the grocer's, cashed a check and continued to Schrafft's where she ate breakfast and chatted happily with the waitress. Oh, it was a wonderful day—more like a holiday—and it would be so foolish to go home.

She boarded a Lexington Avenue bus and rode up to Eighty-sixth Street; it was here that she had decided to do a little shopping.

She had no idea what she wanted or needed, but she idled along, intent only upon the passers-by, brisk and preoccupied, who gave her a disturbing sense of separateness.

It was while waiting at the corner of Third Avenue that she saw the man: an old man, bowlegged and stooped under an armload of bulging packages; he wore a shabby brown coat and a checkered cap. Suddenly she realized they were exchanging a smile: there was nothing friendly about this smile, it was merely two cold flickers of recognition. But she was certain she had never seen him before.

He was standing next to an El pillar,[3] and as she crossed the street he turned and followed. He kept quite close; from the corner of her eye she watched his reflection wavering on the shop windows.

Then in the middle of the block she stopped and faced him. He stopped also and cocked his head, grinning. But what could she say? Do? Here, in broad daylight, on Eighty-sixth Street? It was useless and, despising her own helplessness, she quickened her steps.

---

3 **El pillar:** The El is the elevated sections of the New York City subway system. Pillars hold up the platforms where riders get on and off the trains.

But a series of unaccountable purchases had begun, as if by pre-arranged plan: a plan of which she had not the least knowledge or control.

Now Second Avenue is a dismal street, made from scraps and ends; part cobblestone, part asphalt, part cement; and its atmosphere of desertion is permanent. Mrs. Miller walked five blocks without meeting anyone, and all the while the steady crunch of his footfalls in the snow stayed near. And when she came to a florist's shop, the sound was still with her. She hurried inside and watched through the glass door as the old man passed; he kept his eyes straight ahead and didn't slow his pace, but he did one strange, telling thing: he tipped his cap.

Six white ones, did you say?" asked the florist. "Yes," she told him, "white roses." From there she went to a glassware store and selected a vase, presumably a replacement for the one Miriam had broken, though the price was intolerable and the vase itself (she thought) grotesquely vulgar. But a series of unaccountable purchases had begun, as if by pre-arranged plan: a plan of which she had not the least knowledge or control.

She bought a bag of glazed cherries, and at a place called the Knickerbocker Bakery she paid forty cents for six almond cakes.

Within the last hour the weather had turned cold again; like blurred lenses, winter clouds cast a shade over the sun, and the skeleton of an early dusk colored the sky; a damp mist mixed with the wind and the voices of a few children who romped high on mountains of gutter snow seemed lonely and cheerless. Soon the first flake fell, and when Mrs. Miller reached the brownstone house, snow was falling in a swift screen and foot tracks vanished as they were printed.

The white roses were arranged decoratively in the vase. The glazed cherries shone on a ceramic plate. The almond cakes, dusted with sugar, awaited a hand. The canary fluttered on its swing and picked at a bar of seed.

At precisely five the doorbell rang. Mrs. Miller *knew* who it was. The hem of her housecoat trailed as she crossed the floor. "Is that you?" she called.

"Naturally," said Miriam, the word resounding shrilly from the hall. "Open this door."

"Go away," said Mrs. Miller.

"Please hurry… I have a heavy package."

"Go away," said Mrs. Miller. She returned to the living room, lighted a cigarette, sat down, and calmly listened to the buzzer; on and on and on. "You might as well leave. I have no intention of letting you in."

Shortly the bell stopped. For possibly ten minutes Mrs. Miller did not move. Then, hearing no sound, she concluded Miriam had gone. She tiptoed to the door and opened it a sliver; Miriam was half-reclining atop a cardboard box with a beautiful French doll cradled in her arms.

"Really, I thought you were never coming," she said peevishly. "Here, help me get this in, it's awfully heavy."

It was not spell-like compulsion that Mrs. Miller felt, but rather a curious passivity; she brought in the box, Miriam the doll. Miriam curled up on the sofa, not troubling to remove her coat or beret, and watched disinterestedly as Mrs. Miller dropped the box and stood trembling, trying to catch her breath.

"Thank you," she said. In the daylight she looked pinched and drawn, her hair less luminous. The French doll she was loving wore an exquisite powdered wig and its idiot glass eyes sought solace in Miriam's. "I have a surprise," she continued. "Look into my box."

Kneeling, Mrs. Miller parted the flaps and lifted out another doll; then a blue dress which she recalled as the one Miriam had worn that first night at the theater; and of the remainder she said, "It's all clothes. Why?"

"Because I've come to live with you," said Miriam, twisting a cherry stem. "Wasn't it nice of you to buy me the cherries. . . ?"

"But you can't! For God's sake go away—go away and leave me alone!"

". . . and the roses and the almond cakes? How really wonderfully generous. You know, these cherries are delicious. The last place I lived was with an old man; he was terribly poor and we never had good things to eat. But I think I'll be happy here." She paused to snuggle her doll closer. "Now, if you'll just show me where to put my things . . ."

Mrs. Miller's face dissolved into a mask of ugly red lines; she began to cry, and it was an unnatural, tearless sort of weeping, as though, not having wept for a long time, she had forgotten how. Carefully she edged backward till she touched the door.

She fumbled through the hall and own the stairs to a landing below. She pounded frantically on the door of the first apartment she came to; a short, red-headed man answered and she pushed past him. "Say, what the hell is this?" he said. "Anything wrong, lover?" asked a young woman who appeared from the kitchen, drying her hands. And it was to her that Mrs. Miller turned.

"Listen," she cried, "I'm ashamed behaving this way but—well, I'm Mrs. H. T. Miller and I live upstairs and . . ." She pressed her hands over her face. "It sounds so absurd. . . ."

The woman guided her to a chair, while the man excitedly rattled pocket change. "Yeah?"

"I live upstairs and there's a little girl visiting me, and I suppose that I'm afraid of her. She won't leave and I can't make her and—she's going to do something terrible. She's already stolen my cameo, but she's about to do something worse—something terrible!"

The man asked, "Is she a relative, huh?"

Mrs. Miller shook her head. "I don't know who she is. Her name's Miriam, but I don't know for certain who she is."

"You gotta calm down, honey," said the woman, stroking Mrs. Miller's arm. "Harry here'll tend to this kid. Go on, lover." And Mrs. Miller said, "The door's open—5A."

After the man left, the woman brought a towel and bathed Mrs. Miller's face. "You're very kind," Mrs. Miller said. "I'm sorry to act like such a fool, only this wicked child . . ."

"Sure, honey," consoled the woman. "Now, you better take it easy."

Mrs. Miller rested her head in the crook of her arm; she was quiet enough to be asleep. The woman turned a radio dial; a piano and a husky voice filled the silence and the woman, tapping her foot, kept excellent time. "Maybe we oughta go up too," she said.

"I don't want to see her again. I don't want to be anywhere near her."

"Uh huh, but what you shoulda done, you shoulda called a cop."

Presently they heard the man on the stairs. He strode into the room frowning and scratching the back of his neck. "Nobody there," he said, honestly embarrassed. "She musta beat it."

"Harry, you're a jerk," announced the woman. "We been sitting here the whole time and we woulda seen . . ." She stopped abruptly, for the man's glance was sharp.

"I looked all over," he said, "and there just ain't nobody there. Nobody, understand?"

"Tell me," said Mrs. Miller, rising, "tell me, did you see a large box? Or a doll?"

"No, ma'am, I didn't."

And the woman, as if delivering a verdict, said, "Well, for cryin out loud…"

The sofa loomed before her with a new strangeness: its vacancy had a meaning that would have been less penetrating and terrible had Miriam been curled on it.

Mrs. Miller entered her apartment softly; she walked to the center of the room and stood quite still. No, in a sense it had not changed: the roses, the cakes, and the cherries were in place. But this was an empty room, emptier than if the furnishings and familiars were not present, lifeless and petrified as a funeral parlor. The sofa loomed before her with a new strangeness: its vacancy had a meaning that would have been less penetrating and terrible had Miriam been curled on it. She gazed fixedly at the space where she remembered setting the box and, for a moment, the hassock spun desperately. And she looked through the window; surely the river was real, surely snow was falling—but then, one could not be certain witness to anything: Miriam, so vividly *there*—and yet, where was she? Where, where?

As though moving in a dream, she sank to a chair. The room was losing shape; it was dark and getting darker and there was nothing to be done about it; she could not lift her hand to light a lamp.

Suddenly, closing her eyes, she felt an upward surge, like a diver emerging from some deeper, greener depth. In times of terror or immense distress,

skein:
loose coil, as of
thread or yarn

there are moments when the mind waits, as though for a revelation, while a **skein** of calm is woven over thought; it is like a sleep, or a supernatural trance; and during this lull one is aware of a force of quiet reasoning: well, what if she had never really known a girl named Miriam? That she had been foolishly frightened on the street? In the end, like everything else, it was of no importance. For the only thing she had lost to Miriam was her identity, but now she knew she had found again the person who lived in this room, who cooked her own meals, who owned a canary, who was someone she could trust and believe in: Mrs. H. T. Miller.

Listening in contentment, she became aware of a double sound: a bureau drawer opening and closing: she seemed to hear it long after completion—opening and closing. Then gradually, the harshness of it was replaced by the murmur of a silk dress and this, delicately faint, was moving nearer and swelling in intensity till the walls trembled with the vibration and the room was caving under a wave of whispers. Mrs. Miller stiffened and opened her eyes to a dull, direct stare.

"Hello," said Miriam.

Responding to the Story

1. **LITERARY LENS** Trace the manner in which the mood changes with the changes in the weather.

2. Mrs. Miller dreams that a girl who resembles Miriam is leading a bridal procession when one of the party asks, "Where is she taking us?" Where do you think young Miriam is taking Mrs. Miller?

3. Do you think young Miriam really exists, or is she a figment of Mrs. Miller's imagination?

4. An enigma is something mysterious and difficult to explain. Miriam often delivers *enigmatic* statements such as her observation upon touching the paper roses on Mrs. Miller's coffee table: "How sad, aren't imitations sad?" Find one of these mysterious statements in the text, and explain what you think it could mean.

5. **THE AUTHOR'S STYLE** Capote's short works of fiction are often referred to as tales instead of stories. A *tale* is a highly imaginative telling of sometimes fanciful events. What stylistic techniques does Capote use to give "Miriam" the feel of a tale rather than a story?

RESPONDING TO UNIT ONE

Experiencing

1. For their grotesque and macabre incidents, both "The Lottery" and "Miriam" might appear in a collection of horror stories. Which do you find more satisfyingly creepy and why?

2. Reread the last paragraph of each story in this unit. Which do you think is the most memorable and why?

Interpreting

3. In three of the stories in this unit—"He," "The Far and the Near," and "The Chrysanthemums"—at least one important character is never given a name. Why do you think the authors made this choice in each instance?

4. The theme of the mysterious stranger is common in literature. In the traditional form of this theme, a mysterious stranger appears in the life of an individual or community. In a series of dramatic events, the stranger makes a sacrifice through which the life of the individual or community is improved. Choose one of the short stories in this chapter that features a stranger: "The Chrysanthemums," "Miriam," or "The Black Ball." Explain how the story fits, or deviates from, the theme of the mysterious stranger.

5. The ball is important in "The Black Ball" and the black box plays a central role in "The Lottery." What do these two objects have in common?

Evaluating

6. The first six stories in this unit have a theme of loss in common. In your opinion, which story evokes the most pathos?

7. Hemingway and Fitzgerald were both friends and competitors, moving in the same social circles and writing during the same era. What differences and similarities do you see between "In Another Country" and "Babylon Revisited"?

8. The opening sentence of *Anna Karenina* by the Russian author Leo Tolstoy reads: "All happy families resemble one another; every unhappy family is unhappy in its own way." In what unique ways are the families in "He" and "Why I Live at the P.O." unhappy?

WRITING ABOUT THE LITERATURE

Staying Power

The stories in this unit were all written more than 50 years ago. Write a persuasive essay about which story you think has best stood the test of time. You may want to use passages from the story as evidence. Consider what is timeless about the style, theme, or characters of the story you choose.

WRITING WITH STYLE

Choose one of these two assignments.

Sucker's Point of View

Using McCullers' style, rewrite the climax of "Sucker" as an interior monologue from the point of view of Sucker.

"The Secret Life of _____"

Fill in the blank with the name of a seemingly ordinary character of your own creation. Using Thurber's style, put this character into an everyday situation that the character converts into a grandiose fantasy starring him- or herself.

IN YOUR OWN STYLE

After reflecting on how important the theme of loss is in many of the stories in this unit, consider your own life. What have you or someone you know either already lost or would most hate to lose? Write about this in your own style. Choose between taking a nonfiction approach or using your own or others' experiences as a starting point for fiction.

UNIT TWO

Literature from the 1950s and 1960s

Literature from the 1950s and 1960s

American fiction flourished in the 1950s and 1960s, a time during which the United States benefited from the affluence created by a burgeoning post-World War II economy. Soldiers came home from the war, many women were able to quit work to stay home with children, and a war hero was elected president. The novels and short stories of John Updike and John Cheever are typical of the fiction of the period. Both writers focus on the relatively comfortable lives of people living in the cities and suburbs of a country that was rapidly becoming much more urban than rural. For many of these people, economic well-being was a fact of life. Updike and Cheever's characters—as well as many of their readers—were free to focus on leisure time. Thus writers began to explore the moral dilemmas that grew out of the social and personal lives of the middle and upper-middle classes.

Even though these authors and their characters did well economically, there was more to the era than the familiar notion that the fifties were a placid decade of peace and prosperity. Not everyone prospered, and trouble was brewing under the surface calm. For example, international relations and domestic politics in the fifties focused on the Cold War with the Communist Bloc. The country was shaken by a short and costly war in Korea. Nuclear war was such a looming possibility that children in school were drilled on what to do when the first bomb hit.

The fifties also marked the beginning of the Civil Rights movement. Many writers found their themes in pointing out the hidden limitations and shortcomings of an affluent society that prided itself on justice for all. The 1960s were not only the

top to bottom:
Marilyn Monroe, 1967
by Andy Warhol.
Marilyn won her first leading movie role in 1951 and quickly became a legend. Her brief career and tumultuous personal life ended in 1961 with an overdose of barbiturates. ★ 1969: On July 20, Neil Armstrong landed on the moon, meeting the challenge issued by President John F. Kennedy in 1961 and initiating further space exploration. ★ 1953: John and Jacqueline Kennedy at their wedding on September 12th. Kennedy, the country's youngest president, won the election of 1960 and was assassinated in 1963. His brief term in office was known as "Camelot."

years of civil rights, the Vietnam War, and political protest, but of social shifts and cultural change. Authors responded to the shocking and tragic assassinations of President John F. Kennedy and civil rights leader Martin Luther King Jr. They also used their fiction to weigh in on such issues as protests against the war, the generation gap between parents and children, and criticism of the government. From rock musicians to pop art practitioners to fiction writers, many artists objected to "business as usual." They used their work as a place to challenge conventional thinking and the status quo.

While the U.S. competed with Russia in what came to be known as the Space Race, Ray Bradbury and Kurt Vonnegut used their imaginations and the strategies of science fiction to sound an alarm. They warned that in the future (not to mention the present), technology and a constant stream of inventions might mean that Americans would be tyrannized by gadgets instead of liberated by them.

Other writers explored the issues of race and ethnicity. Ernest J. Gaines, William Faulkner, and Bernard Malamud created characters who were still able to make moral choices despite the burden of oppression. Publishing in magazines from *The Saturday Evening Post* to *The New Yorker*, such authors brought into their stories the workaday lives, hopes, and dreams of people from parts of American society who had seldom been heard from before. In this they followed the tradition of Mark Twain's *Huckleberry Finn*.

Once women, blue-collar workers, immigrants, the poor, and the unemployed were given a voice, the chorus was deafening. American literature would never be the same.

top to bottom: In response to the conflict in Vietnam, "flower children" of the 1960s infuriated their elders by adopting the slogan "Make love not war." ★ Nikita Khrushchev, powerful leader of the Soviet Union, came to symbolize the Cold War—an ideological battle between Democracy and Communism. ★ 1966: *South of the DMZ, South Vietnam* by Larry Burrows, renowned *LIFE* photographer who died while covering the war in Vietnam. ★ 1965: Civil Rights activists led by Dr. Martin Luther King Jr., marched 54 miles from Selma to Montgomery, Alabama, to protest segregation.

★★★

Ray Bradbury
1920

About the Author

Ray Bradbury is known for writing highly imaginative fantasies about science and technology. Yet oddly enough, he himself has never flown in an airplane nor learned to drive. The author grew up in the Midwest, attended high school in California, and never went to college. Two of the most striking things about Bradbury are his sheer literary output and his legendary energy. In an introduction to *The Stories of Ray Bradbury* in 1980, he explained that ideas simply come to him: "My [stories] run up and bite me on the leg—I respond by writing down everything that goes on during the bite. When I finish, the idea lets go and runs off."

Bradbury sold his first short story at age 19.

Since then, he has written hundreds more, many of which he adapted for television's *Ray Bradbury's Theater*. He has also worked in animated film, published more than 30 books, and served as a consultant for science-related projects, including an exhibit at Epcot Center in Florida and a space ride at Euro-Disney in France.

Among his most famous novels are *The Martian Chronicles*, *Fahrenheit 451*, and *Something Wicked This Way Comes*, all of which were made into movies. He is the recipient of many awards, including the World Fantasy Award for Lifetime Achievement.

★★★★★★★★★★★

The Author's Style

Bradbury's skill as a science fiction writer lies in his ability to convey a simultaneous sense of the familiar and the alien. His work reveals both the attractiveness and the dangers of science by creating contemporary settings that are fascinating but about to spin out of control. He has even "predicted" scientific innovations such as virtual reality or artificial environment technologies by imagining them in his fiction before they became realities.

Adept at making readers laugh, marvel, or shudder, Bradbury uses eerie details to foreshadow how his stories might end. A consistent theme in the author's work is that too much of anything isn't good for anyone. The author is known for his skillful use of descriptive language, particularly for striking and memorable metaphors and similes. A versatile author, he also writes poetry and children's stories.

Bradbury uses the technique of giving his made-up technologies general names that could be used anywhere. In the story you are about to read, for example, readers soon realize that what happens in the "Happylife Home" system may not be unique to this particular family. In fact, he implies it could happen anywhere.

LITERARY LENS Authors will sometimes juxtapose (or place in opposition) two concepts or ideas in order to compare them. Watch for juxtapositions in this story.

THE VELDT

RAY BRADBURY

eorge, I wish you'd look at the nursery."

"What's wrong with it?"

"I don't know."

"Well, then."

"I just want you to look at it, is all, or call a psychologist in to look at it."

"What would a psychologist want with a nursery?"

"You know very well what he'd want." His wife paused in the middle of the kitchen and watched the stove busy humming to itself, making supper for four.

"It's just that the nursery is different now than it was."

"All right, let's have a look."

They walked down the hall of their soundproofed, Happylife

Home, which had cost them thirty thousand dollars installed, this house which clothed and fed and rocked them to sleep and played and sang and was good to them. Their approach sensitized a switch somewhere and the nursery light flicked on when they came within ten feet of it. Similarly, behind them, in the halls, lights went on and off as they left them behind, with a soft automaticity.

"Well," said George Hadley.

They stood on the thatched floor of the nursery. It was forty feet across by forty feet long and thirty feet high; it had cost half again as much as the rest of the house. "But nothing's too good for our children," George had said.

The nursery was silent. It was empty as a jungle glade at hot high noon. The walls were blank and two dimensional. Now, as George and Lydia Hadley stood in the center of the room, the walls began to purr and recede into **crystalline** distance, it seemed, and presently an African veldt[1] appeared, in three dimensions; on all sides, in colors reproduced to the final pebble and bit of straw. The ceiling above them became a deep sky with a hot yellow sun.

crystalline: spakling; made of crystal

George Hadley felt the perspiration start on his brow.

"Let's get out of the sun," he said. "This is a little too real. But I don't see anything wrong."

"Wait a moment, you'll see," said his wife.

Now the hidden odorophonics were beginning to blow a wind of odor at the two people in the middle of the baked veldtland. The hot straw smell of lion grass, the cool green smell of the hidden water hole, the great rusty smell of animals, the smell of dust like a red paprika in the hot air. And now the sounds: the thump of distant antelope feet on grassy sod, the papery rustling of vultures. A shadow passed through the sky. The shadow flickered on George Hadley's upturned, sweating face.

"Filthy creatures," he heard his wife say.

"The vultures."

"You see, there are the lions, far over, that way. Now they're on their way to the water hole. They've just been eating," said Lydia. "I don't know what."

"Some animal." George Hadley put his hand up to shield off the burning light from his squinted eyes. "A zebra or a baby giraffe, maybe."

"Are you sure?" His wife sounded peculiarly tense.

"No, it's a little late to be sure," he said, amused. "Nothing over there I can see but cleaned bone, and the vultures dropping for what's left."

---

1 **veldt:** a grassland with scattered shrubs or trees

Ray Bradbury

"Did you hear that scream?" she asked.

"No."

"About a minute ago?"

"Sorry, no."

The lions were coming. And again George Hadley was filled with admiration for the mechanical genius who had conceived this room. A miracle of efficiency selling for an absurdly low price. Every home should have one. Oh, occasionally they frightened you with their clinical accuracy, they startled you, gave you a twinge, but most of the time what fun for everyone, not only your own son and daughter, but for yourself when you felt like a quick jaunt to a foreign land, a quick change of scenery. Well, here it was!

And here were the lions now, fifteen feet away, so real, so feverishly and startlingly real that you could feel the prickling fur on your hand...

And here were the lions now, fifteen feet away, so real, so feverishly and startlingly real that you could feel the prickling fur on your hand, and your mouth was stuffed with the dusty upholstery smell of their heated pelts, and the yellow of them was in your eyes like the yellow of an exquisite French tapestry, the yellows of lions and summer grass, and the sound of the matted lion lungs exhaling on the silent noontide, and the smell of meat from the panting, dripping mouths.

The lions stood looking at George and Lydia Hadley with terrible green-yellow eyes.

"Watch out!" screamed Lydia.

The lions came running at them.

Lydia bolted and ran. Instinctively, George sprang after her. Outside, in the hall, with the door slammed, he was laughing and she was crying, and they both stood appalled at the other's reaction.

"George!"

"Lydia! Oh, my dear poor sweet Lydia!"

"They almost got us!"

"Walls, Lydia, remember; crystal walls, that's all they are. Oh, they look real, I must admit—Africa in your parlor—but it's all dimensional superre-actionary, supersensitive color film and mental tape film behind glass screens. It's all odorophonics and sonics, Lydia. Here's my handkerchief."

"I'm afraid." She came to him and put her body against him and cried steadily. "Did you see? Did you *feel*? It's too real."

"Now, Lydia . . ."

"You've got to tell Wendy and Peter not to read any more on Africa."

"Of course—of course." He patted her.

"Promise?"

"Sure."

"And lock the nursery for a few days until I get my nerves settled."

"You know how difficult Peter is about that. When I punished him a month ago by locking the nursery for even a few hours—the tantrum he threw! And Wendy too. They *live* for the nursery."

"It's got to be locked, that's all there is to it."

"All right." Reluctantly he locked the huge door. "You've been working too hard. You need a rest."

"I don't know—I don't know," she said, blowing her nose, sitting down in a chair that immediately began to rock and comfort her. "Maybe I don't have enough to do. Maybe I have time to think too much. Why don't we shut the whole house off for a few days and take a vacation?"

"You mean you want to fry my eggs for me?"

"Yes." She nodded.

"And darn my socks?"

"Yes." A frantic, watery-eyed nodding.

"And sweep the house?"

"Yes, yes—oh yes!"

"But I thought that's why we bought this house, so we wouldn't have to do anything?"

"That's just it. I feel like I don't belong here. The house is wife and mother now and nursemaid. Can I compete with an African veldt? Can I give a bath and scrub the children as efficiently or quickly as the automatic scrub bath can? I can not. And it isn't just me. It's you. You've been awfully nervous lately."

"I suppose I have been smoking too much."

"You look as if you didn't know what to do with yourself in this house, either. You smoke a little more every morning and drink a little more every afternoon and need a little more sedative every night. You're beginning to feel unnecessary too."

"Am I?" He paused and tried to feel into himself to see what was really there.

"Oh, George!" She looked beyond him, at the nursery door. "Those lions can't get out of there, can they?"

He looked at the door and saw it tremble as if something had jumped against it from the other side.

"Of course not," he said.

At dinner they ate alone, for Wendy and Peter were at a special plastic carnival across town and had televised home to say they'd be late, to go ahead eating. So George Hadley, bemused, sat watching the dining-room table produce warm dishes of food from its mechanical interior.

"We forgot the ketchup," he said.

"Sorry," said a small voice within the table, and ketchup appeared.

As for the nursery, thought George Hadley, it won't hurt for the children to be locked out of it awhile. Too much of anything isn't good for anyone. And it was clearly indicated that the children had been spending a little too much time on Africa. That sun. He could feel it on his neck, still, like a hot paw. And the lions. And the smell of blood. Remarkable how the nursery caught the telepathic **emanations** of the children's minds and created life to fill their every desire. The children thought lions, and there were lions. The children thought zebras, and there were zebras. Sun—sun. Giraffes—giraffes. Death and death.

> **emanations:** transmissions; messages

That last. He chewed tastelessly on the meat that the table had cut for him. Death thoughts. They were awfully young, Wendy and Peter, for death thoughts. Or, no, you were never too young, really. Long before you knew what death was you were wishing it on someone else. When you were two years old you were shooting people with cap pistols.

But this—the long, hot African veldt—the awful death in the jaws of a lion. And repeated again and again.

"Where are you going?"

He didn't answer Lydia. Preoccupied, he let the lights glow softly on ahead of him, extinguished behind him as he padded to the nursery door. He listened against it. Far away, a lion roared.

He unlocked the door and opened it. Just before he stepped inside, he heard a faraway scream. And then another roar from the lions, which subsided quickly.

He stepped into Africa. How many times in the last year had he opened this door and found Wonderland, Alice, the Mock Turtle, or Aladdin and his

Magical Lamp, or Jack Pumpkinhead of Oz, or Dr. Doolittle, or the cow jumping over a very real-appearing moon—all the delightful contraptions of a make-believe word. How often had he seen Pegasus[2] flying in the sky ceiling, or seen fountains of red fireworks, or heard angel voices singing. But now, this yellow hot Africa, this bake oven with murder in the heat. Perhaps Lydia was right. Perhaps they needed a little vacation from the fantasy which was growing a bit too real for ten-year-old children. It was all right to exercise one's mind with gymnastic fantasies, but when the lively child mind settled on *one* pattern . . . ? It seemed that, at a distance, for the past month, he had heard lions roaring, and smelled their strong odor seeping as far away as his study door. But, being busy, he had paid it no attention.

George Hadley stood on the African grassland alone. The lions looked up from their feeding, watching him. The only flaw to the illusion was the open door through which he could see his wife, far down the dark hall, like a framed picture, eating her dinner **abstractedly**.

abstractedly:
absentmindedly

"Go away," he said to the lions.

They did not go.

He knew the principle of the room exactly. You sent out your thoughts. Whatever you thought would appear.

"Let's have Aladdin and his lamp," he snapped.

The veldtland remained; the lions remained.

"Come on, room! I demand Aladdin!" he said.

Nothing happened. The lions mumbled in their baked pelts.

"Aladdin!"

He went back to dinner. "The fool room's out of order," he said. "It won't respond."

"Or—"

"Or what?"

"Or it *can't* respond," said Lydia, "because the children have thought about Africa and lions and killing so many days that the room's in a rut."

"Could be."

"Or Peter's set it to remain that way."

"*Set* it?"

"He may have got into the machinery and fixed something."

"Peter doesn't know machinery."

"He's a wise one for ten. That I.Q. of his—"

---

2 **Pegasus:** a flying horse in Greek mythology

"Nevertheless—"

"Hello, Mom. Hello, Dad."

The Hadleys turned. Wendy and Peter were coming in the front door, cheeks like peppermint candy, eyes like bright blue agate[3] marbles, a smell of ozone on their jumpers from their trip in the helicopter.

"You're just in time for supper," said both parents.

"We're full of strawberry ice cream and hot dogs," said the children, holding hands. "But we'll sit and watch."

"Yes, come tell us about the nursery," said George Hadley.

The brother and sister blinked at him and then at each other. "Nursery?"

"All about Africa and everything," said the father with false **joviality**.

"I don't understand," said Peter.

joviality:
cheerfulness

"Your mother and I were just traveling through Africa with rod and reel; Tom Swift and his Electric Lion,"[4] said George Hadley.

"There's no Africa in the nursery," said Peter simply.

"Oh, come now, Peter. We know better."

"I don't remember any Africa," said Peter to Wendy. "Do you?"

"No."

"Run see and come tell."

She obeyed.

"Wendy, come back here!" said George Hadley, but she was gone. The house lights followed her like a flock of fireflies. Too late, he realized he had forgotten to lock the nursery door after his last inspection.

"Wendy'll look and come tell us," said Peter.

"She doesn't have to tell *me*. I've seen it."

"I'm sure you're mistaken, Father."

"I'm not, Peter. Come along now."

But Wendy was back. "It's not Africa," she said breathlessly.

"We'll see about this," said George Hadley, and they all walked down the hall together and opened the nursery door.

There was a green, lovely forest, a lovely river, a purple mountain, high voices singing, and Rima,[5] lovely and mysterious, lurking in the trees with colorful flights of butterflies, like animated bouquets, lingering on her long

---

3 **agate:** having colors blended like clouds

4 **Tom Swift . . . Lion:** title of a book in a series of adventure novels by Victor Appleton

5 **Rima:** a character in *Green Mansions*, an early-20th-century romance novel by British author William Henry Hudson. Raised in a rain forest of South America, Rima is able to speak the language of the forest, including the songs of birds.

don't know anything," he said, "except that I'm beginning to be sorry we bought that room for the children. If children are neurotic at all, a room like that—"

hair. The African veldtland was gone. The lions were gone. Only Rima was here now, singing a song so beautiful that it brought tears to your eyes.

George Hadley looked in at the changed scene. "Go to bed," he said to the children.

They opened their mouths.

"You heard me," he said.

They went off to the air closet, where a wind sucked them like brown leaves up the flue to their slumber rooms.

George Hadley walked through the singing glade and picked up something that lay in the corner near where the lions had been. He walked slowly back to his wife.

"What is that?" she asked.

"An old wallet of mine," he said.

He showed it to her. The smell of hot grass was on it and the smell of a lion. There were drops of saliva on it, it had been chewed and there were blood smears on both sides.

He closed the nursery door and locked it, tight.

In the middle of the night he was still awake and he knew his wife was awake. "Do you think Wendy changed it?" she said at last, in the dark room.

"Of course."

"Made it from a veldt into a forest and put Rima there instead of lions?"

"Yes."

"Why?"

"I don't know. But it's staying locked until I find out."

"How did your wallet get there?"

"I don't know anything," he said, "except that I'm beginning to be sorry we bought that room for the children. If children are **neurotic** at all, a room like that—"

"It's supposed to help them work off their neuroses in a healthful way."

"I'm starting to wonder." He stared at the ceiling.

"We've given the children everything they ever wanted. Is this our reward—secrecy, disobedience?"

"Who was it said, 'Children are carpets, they should be stepped on occasionally'? We've never lifted a hand. They're insufferable—let's admit it. They

neurotic: mentally or emotionally disturbed

come and go when they like; they treat us as if *we* were offspring. They're spoiled and we're spoiled."

"They've been acting funny ever since you forbade them to take the rocket to New York a few months ago."

"They're not old enough to do that alone, I explained."

"Nevertheless, I've noticed they've been decidedly cool toward us since."

"I think I'll have Dave McClean come tomorrow morning to have a look at Africa."

"But it's not Africa now, it's Green Mansions country and Rima."

"I have a feeling it'll be Africa again before then."

A moment later they heard the screams.

Two screams. Two people screaming from downstairs. And then a roar of lions.

"Wendy and Peter aren't in their rooms," said his wife.

He lay in his bed with his beating heart. "No," he said. "They've broken into the nursery."

"Those screams—they sound familiar."

"Do they?"

"Yes, awfully."

And although their beds tried very hard, the two adults couldn't be rocked to sleep for another hour. A smell of cats was in the night air.

F ather?" said Peter.

"Yes."

Peter looked at his shoes. He never looked at his father any more, nor at his mother. "You aren't going to lock up the nursery for good, are you?"

"That all depends."

"On what?" snapped Peter.

"On you and your sister. If you intersperse this Africa with a little variety—oh, Sweden perhaps, or Denmark or China—"

"I thought we were free to play as we wished."

"You are, within reasonable bounds."

"What's wrong with Africa, Father?"

"Oh, so now you admit you have been conjuring up Africa, do you?"

"I wouldn't want the nursery locked up," said Peter coldly. "Ever."

"Matter of fact, we're thinking of turning the whole house off for about a month. Live sort of a carefree one-for-all existence."

"That sounds dreadful! Would I have to tie my own shoes instead of letting the shoe tier do it? And brush my own teeth and comb my hair and give myself a bath?"

"It would be fun for a change, don't you think?"

"No, it would be horrid. I didn't like it when you took out the picture painter last month."

"That's because I wanted you to learn to paint all by yourself, son."

"I don't want to do anything but look and listen and smell; what else *is* there to do?"

"All right, go play in Africa."

"Will you shut off the house sometime soon?"

"We're considering it."

"I don't think you'd better consider it any more, Father."

"I won't have any threats from my son!"

"Very well." And Peter strolled off to the nursery.

"Am I on time?" said David McClean.

"Breakfast?" asked George Hadley.

"Thanks, had some. What's the trouble?"

"David, you're a psychologist."

"I should hope so."

"Well, then, have a look at our nursery. You saw it a year ago when you dropped by; did you notice anything peculiar about it then?"

"Can't say I did; the usual violences, a tendency toward a slight paranoia here or there, usual in children because they feel persecuted by parents constantly, but, oh, really nothing."

They walked down the hall. "I locked the nursery up," explained the father, "and the children broke back into it during the night. I let them stay so they could form the patterns for you to see."

There was a terrible screaming from the nursery.

"There it is," said George Hadley. "See what you make of it."

They walked in on the children without rapping.

The screams had faded. The lions were feeding.

"Run outside a moment, children," said George Hadley. "No, don't change the mental combination. Leave the walls as they are. Get!"

With the children gone, the two men stood studying the lions clustered at a distance, eating with great relish whatever it was they had caught.

"I wish I knew what it was," said George Hadley. "Sometimes I can almost see. Do you think if I brought high-powered binoculars here and—"

David McClean laughed dryly. "Hardly." He turned to study all four walls. "How long has this been going on?"

"A little over a month."

"It certainly doesn't *feel* good."

"I want facts, not feelings."

"My dear George, a psychologist never saw a fact in his life. He only hears about feelings; vague things. This doesn't feel good, I tell you. Trust my hunches and my instincts. I have a nose for something bad. This is very bad. My advice to you is to have the whole damn room torn down and your children brought to me every day during the next year for treatment."

"Is it that bad?"

"I'm afraid so. One of the original uses of these nurseries was so that we could study the patterns left on the walls by the child's mind, study at our leisure, and help the child. In this case, however, the room has become a channel toward—destructive thoughts, instead of a release away from them."

"Didn't you sense this before?"

"I sensed only that you had spoiled your children more than most. And now you're letting them down in some way. What way?"

"I wouldn't let them go to New York."

"What else?"

"I've taken a few machines from the house and threatened them, a month ago, with closing up the nursery unless they did their homework. I did close it for a few days to show I meant business."

"Ah, ha!"

"Does that mean anything?"

"Everything. Where before they had a Santa Claus now they have a Scrooge. Children prefer Santas. You've let this room and this house replace you and your wife in your children's affections. This room is their mother and father, far more important in their lives than their real parents. And now you come along and want to shut it off. No wonder there's hatred here. You can feel it coming out of the sky. Feel that sun. George, you'll have to change your life. Like too many others, you've built it around creature comforts. Why, you'd starve tomorrow if something went wrong in your kitchen. You wouldn't know how to tap an egg. Nevertheless, turn everything off. Start new. It'll take time. But we'll make good children out of bad in a year, wait and see."

"But won't the shock be too much for the children, shutting the room up abruptly, for good?"

"I don't want them going any deeper into this, that's all."

The lions were finished with their red feast.

The lions were standing on the edge of the clearing watching the two men.

"Now *I'm* feeling persecuted," said McClean. "Let's get out of here. I never have cared for these damned rooms. Make me nervous."

"The lions look real, don't they?" said George Hadley. "I don't suppose there's any way—"

"What?"

"—that they could *become* real?"

"Not that I know."

"Some flaw in the machinery, a tampering or something?"

"No."

They went to the door.

"I don't imagine the room will like being turned off," said the father.

"Nothing ever likes to die—even a room."

"I wonder if it hates me for wanting to switch it off?"

"Paranoia is thick around here today," said David McClean. "You can follow it like a spoor.⁶ Hello." He bent and picked up a bloody scarf. "This yours?"

"No." George Hadley's face was rigid. "It belongs to Lydia."

They went to the fuse box together and threw the switch that killed the nursery.

The two children were in hysterics. They screamed and pranced and threw things. They yelled and sobbed and swore and jumped at the furniture.

"You can't do that to the nursery, you can't!"

"Now, children."

The children flung themselves onto a couch, weeping.

"George," said Lydia Hadley, "turn on the nursery, just for a few moments. You can't be so abrupt."

"No."

"You can't be so cruel."

"Lydia, it's off, and it stays off. And the whole damn house dies as of here and now. The more I see of the mess we've put ourselves in, the more it

---

6 **spoor:** a track or trail left by a wild animal

sickens me. We've been contemplating our mechanical, electronic navels for too long. My God, how we need a breath of honest air!"

And he marched about the house turning off the voice clocks, the stoves, the heaters, the shoe shiners, the shoe lacers, the body scrubbers and swabbers and massagers, and every other machine he could put his hand to.

The house was full of dead bodies, it seemed. It felt like a mechanical cemetery. So silent. None of the humming hidden energy of machines waiting to function at the tap of a button.

"Don't let them do it!" wailed Peter at the ceiling, as if he was talking to the house, the nursery. "Don't let Father kill everything." He turned to his father. "Oh, I hate you!"

"Insults won't get you anywhere."

"I wish you were dead!"

"We were, for a long while. Now we're going to really start living. Instead of being handled and massaged, we're going to *live*."

Wendy was still crying and Peter joined her again. "Just a moment, just one moment, just another moment of nursery," they wailed.

"Oh, George," said the wife, "it can't hurt."

"All right—all right, if they'll only just shut up. One minute, mind you, and then off forever."

"Daddy, Daddy, Daddy!" sang the children, smiling with wet faces.

"And then we're going on a vacation. David McClean is coming back in half an hour to help us move out and get to the airport. I'm going to dress. You turn the nursery on for a minute, Lydia, just a minute, mind you."

And the three of them went babbling off while he let himself be vacuumed upstairs through the air flue and set about dressing himself. A minute later Lydia appeared.

"I'll be glad when we get away," she sighed.

"Did you leave them in the nursery?"

"I wanted to dress too. Oh, that horrid Africa. What can they see in it?"

"Well, in five minutes we'll be on our way to Iowa. Lord, how did we ever get in this house? What prompted us to buy a nightmare?"

"Pride, money, foolishness."

"I think we'd better get downstairs before those kids get engrossed with those damned beasts again."

Just then they heard the children calling, "Daddy, Mommy, come quick—quick!"

They went downstairs in the air flue and ran down the hall. The children were nowhere in sight. "Wendy? Peter!"

They ran into the nursery. The veldtland was empty save for the lions waiting, looking at them. "Peter, Wendy?"

The door slammed.

"Wendy, Peter!"

George Hadley and his wife whirled and ran back to the door.

"Open the door!" cried George Hadley, trying the knob. "Why, they've locked it from the outside! Peter!" He beat at the door. "Open up!"

He heard Peter's voice outside, against the door.

"Don't let them switch off the nursery and the house," he was saying.

Mr. and Mrs. George Hadley beat at the door. "Now, don't be ridiculous, children. It's time to go. Mr. McClean'll be here in a minute and . . ."

And then they heard the sounds.

The lions on three sides of them, in the yellow veldt grass, padding through the dry straw, rumbling and roaring in their throats.

The lions.

Mr. Hadley looked at his wife and they turned and looked back at the beasts edging slowly forward, crouching, tails stiff.

Mr. and Mrs. Hadley screamed.

And suddenly they realized why those other screams had sounded familiar.

Well, here I am," said David McClean in the nursery doorway.

"Oh, hello." He stared at the two children seated in the center of the open glade eating a little picnic lunch. Beyond them was the water hole and the yellow veldtland; above was the hot sun. He began to perspire. "Where are your father and mother?"

The children looked up and smiled. "Oh, they'll be here directly."

"Good, we must get going." At a distance Mr. McClean saw the lions fighting and clawing and then quieting down to feed in silence under the shady trees.

He squinted at the lions with his hand up to his eyes.

Now the lions were done feeding. They moved to the water hole to drink.

A shadow flickered over Mr. McClean's hot face. Many shadows flickered. The vultures were dropping down the blazing sky.

"A cup of tea?" asked Wendy in the silence.

Responding to the Story

1. **LITERARY LENS** Ray Bradbury juxtaposes numerous concepts in "The Veldt." For example, the sinister nursery is juxtaposed against innocent children's books such as *The Wizard of Oz*. Use a chart like the one below to list such opposing concepts.

Concept	Juxtaposed Concept
Images from children's books in the nursery	*The African veldt*

2. Bradbury is a master of the neologism, or newly created word. Examine the context in which "automaticity" and "odorophonics" (page 170) are used. Now write dictionary definitions for each.

3. It is probably no accident that the children in this story, Wendy and Peter, have the same names as the children in "Peter Pan." What connections are you able to make between "Peter Pan" and "The Veldt"?

4. Look at the exchange of dialogue between George and Lydia on page 172. What does this dialogue tell you about their parenting?

5. **THE AUTHOR'S STYLE** Ray Bradbury credits his interest in writing to seeing a tent magic show at a carnival when he was a child. Read the quotation below. What evidence of magic do you find in "The Veldt"?

Bradbury the Magician

People call me a science fiction writer, but I don't think that's quite true. I think that I am a magician who is capable of making things appear and disappear right in front of you and you don't know how it happened.

—Ray Bradbury

William Faulkner
1897–1962

About the Author

One of the 20th century's greatest writers, William Faulkner was a high school dropout who only briefly attended college. He grew up the eldest of four sons in Oxford, Mississippi, and found success in writing about what he knew best. He once commented, ". . . I discovered my own little postage stamp of native soil was worth writing about and that I would never live long enough to exhaust it . . ."

Drawing upon family and regional history, he created the mythical Yoknapatawpha County and populated it with a gallery of memorable characters that first appeared in his novel *Sartoris* in 1929. That same year, he married his childhood sweetheart, Estelle Oldham. The couple had two daughters.

Because he felt financially responsible for a large extended family, Faulkner couldn't make enough money on his novels alone, most of which were out of print by 1945. He wrote short stories for quick publication and for 20 years worked in Hollywood as a screenwriter. Eventually his novels came back into high regard, and by the time of his death in 1964, he had won all the major prizes. He is perhaps best remembered for *The Sound and the Fury*, *As I Lay Dying*, and *Absalom, Absalom!*

The Author's Style

Faulkner's frequent themes are the burdens of Southern history, race relations in the South, and the alienation and loneliness of 20th-century life. Much of his fiction concerns powerless people, both black and white. These characters are caught between violence and injustice at one extreme and at the other, a sense that without sympathy and equity everyone is doomed. Faulkner often spoke out against segregation.

Faulkner's fiction often involves two distinct types of people. One type is the people of a dignified pre-Civil War Southern culture that had noble convictions but was responsible for slavery. The other type is people who represent a more recent way of life that is crudely enterprising, dishonest, ruthless, and violent. He frequently uses the Sartoris and Snopes families to represent these two types.

The sense of individuals threatened by seemingly overwhelming natural and social forces is reinforced by Faulkner's prose style, which builds powerful momentum through the use of complex sentence structures. His sentences include strings of adjectives, extended figures of speech, and parenthetical statements. Another feature of Faulkner's dense style is his presentation of the thoughts of characters, such as the mentally handicapped Benjy in *The Sound and the Fury*, who have difficulty expressing themselves in a way that others can understand.

LITERARY **L**ENS Faulkner is considered a master of the "stream of consciousness" technique. This is the flow of impressions—visual, psychological, auditory, and subconscious—that show the heart and mind of a character. Watch for this in the story.

Barn Burning

William Faulkner

The store in which the Justice of the Peace's court was sitting smelled of cheese. The boy, crouched on his nail keg at the back of the crowded room, knew he smelled cheese, and more: from where he sat he could see the ranked shelves close-packed with the solid, squat, dynamic shapes of tin cans whose labels his stomach read, not from the lettering which meant nothing to his mind but from the scarlet devils and the silver curve of fish—this, the cheese which he knew he smelled and the **hermetic** meat which his intestines believed he smelled coming in intermittent gusts momentary and brief between the other constant one, the smell and sense just a little of fear because mostly of despair and grief, the old fierce pull of blood. He could not see the table where the Justice sat and before which his father and his

hermetic:
in an airtight seal

Hay Ledge, Andrew Wyeth, 1957, Greenville County Museum of Art

father's enemy (*our enemy* he thought in that despair; *ourn! mine and hisn both! He's my father!*) stood, but he could hear them, the two of them that is, because his father had said no word yet:

"But what proof have you, Mr. Harris?"

"I told you. The hog got into my corn. I caught it up and sent it back to him. He had no fence that would hold it. I told him so, warned him. The next time I put the hog in my pen. When he came to get it I gave him enough wire to patch up his pen. The next time I put the hog up and kept it. I rode down to his house and saw the wire I gave him still rolled on to the spool in his yard. I told him he could have the hog when he paid me a dollar pound fee. That evening a nigger came with the dollar and got the hog. He was a strange nigger. He said, 'He say to tell you wood and hay kin burn.' I said,

'What?' 'That whut he say to tell you,' the nigger said. 'Wood and hay kin burn.' That night my barn burned. I got the stock out but I lost the barn."

"Where is the nigger? Have you got him?"

"He was a strange nigger, I tell you. I don't know what became of him."

"But that's not proof. Don't you see that's not proof?"

"Get that boy up here. He knows." For a moment the boy thought too that the man meant his older brother until Harris said, "Not him. The little one. The boy," and, crouching, small for his age, small and wiry like his father, in patched and faded jeans even too small for him, with straight, uncombed, brown hair and eyes gray and wild as storm scud, he saw the men between himself and the table part and become a lane of grim faces, at the end of which he saw the Justice, a shabby, collarless, graying man in spectacles, beckoning him. He felt no floor under his bare feet; he seemed to walk beneath the **palpable** weight of the grim turning faces. His father, stiff in his black Sunday coat donned not for the trial but for the moving, did not even look at him. *He aims for me to lie,* he thought, again with that frantic grief and despair. *And I will have to do hit.*

palpable: solid; touchable

"What's your name, boy?" the Justice said.

"Colonel Sartoris Snopes," the boy whispered.

"Hey?" the Justice said. "Talk louder. Colonel Sartoris? I reckon anybody named for Colonel Sartoris in this country can't help but tell the truth, can they?" The boy said nothing. *Enemy! Enemy!* he thought; for a moment he could not even see, could not see that the Justice's face was kindly nor discern that his voice was troubled when he spoke to the man named Harris: "Do you want me to question this boy?" But he could hear, and during those subsequent long seconds while there was absolutely no sound in the crowded little room save that of quiet and intent breathing it was as if he had swung outward at the end of a grape vine, over a ravine, and at the top of the swing had been caught in a prolonged instant of mesmerized gravity, weightless in time.

"No!" Harris said violently, explosively. "Damnation! Send him out of here!" Now time, the fluid world, rushed beneath him again, the voices coming to him again through the smell of cheese and sealed meat, the fear and despair and the old grief of blood.

"This case is closed. I can't find against you, Snopes, but I can give you advice. Leave this country and don't come back to it."

His father spoke for the first time, his voice cold and harsh, level, without emphasis: "I aim to. I don't figure to stay in a country among people who . . ." he said something unprintable and vile, addressed to no one.

"That'll do," the Justice said. "Take your wagon and get out of this country before dark. Case dismissed."

His father turned, and he followed the stiff black coat, the wiry figure walking a little stiffly from where a Confederate provost's[1] man's musket ball had taken him in the heel on a stolen horse thirty years ago, followed the two backs now, since his older brother had appeared from somewhere in the crowd, no taller than the father but thicker, chewing tobacco steadily, between the two lines of grim-faced men and out of the store and across the worn gallery and down the sagging steps and among the dogs and half-grown boys in the mild May dust, where as he passed a voice hissed:

"Barn burner!"

Again he could not see, whirling; there was a face in a red haze, moon-like, bigger than the full moon, the owner of it half again his size, he leaping in the red haze toward the face, feeling no blow, feeling no shock when his head struck the earth, scrabbling up and leaping again, feeling no blow this time either and tasting no blood, scrabbling up to see the other boy in full flight and himself already leaping into pursuit as his father's hand jerked him back, the harsh, cold voice speaking above him: "Go get in the wagon."

It stood in a grove of locusts and mulberries across the road. His two hulking sisters in their Sunday dresses and his mother and her sister in calico[2] and sunbonnets were already in it, sitting on and among the sorry residue of the dozen and more movings which even the boy could remember—the battered stove, the broken beds and chairs, the clock inlaid with mother-of-

---

1 **provost's:** belonging to the keeper of a prison

2 **calico:** inexpensive, patterned, cotton fabric

William Faulkner

pearl,[3] which would not run, stopped at some fourteen minutes past two o'clock of a dead and forgotten day and time, which had been his mother's dowry.[4] She was crying, though when she saw him she drew her sleeve across her face and began to descend from the wagon. "Get back," the father said.

"He's hurt. I got to get some water and wash his . . ."

"Get back in the wagon," his father said. He got in too, over the tail-gate. His father mounted to the seat where the older brother already sat and struck the gaunt mules two savage blows with the peeled willow, but without heat. It was not even **sadistic**; it was exactly that same quality which in later years would cause his descendants to over-run the engine before putting a motor car into motion, striking and reining back in the same movement. The wagon went on, the store with its quiet crowd of grimly watching men dropped behind; a curve in the road hid it. *Forever* he thought. *Maybe he's done satisfied now, now that he has . . .* stopping himself, not to say it aloud even to himself. His mother's hand touched his shoulder.

"Does hit hurt?" she said.

"Naw," he said. "Hit don't hurt. Lemme be."

"Can't you wipe some of the blood off before hit dries?"

"I'll wash to-night," he said. "Lemme be, I tell you."

The wagon went on. He did not know where they were going. None of them ever did or ever asked, because it was always somewhere, always a house of sorts waiting for them a day or two days or even three days away. Likely his father had already arranged to make a crop on another farm before he . . . Again he had to stop himself. He (the father) always did. There was something about his wolflike independence and

sadistic:
taking pleasure in others' pain

*H*is father mounted to the seat where the older brother already sat and struck the gaunt mules two savage blows with the peeled willow, but without heat. It was not even sadistic; it was exactly that same quality which in later years would cause his descendants to over-run the engine before putting a motor car into motion, striking and reining back in the same movement.

---

3 **mother-of-pearl:** a hard, pearly substance that lines the inside of a mollusk shell, often used in jewelry

4 **dowry:** gift or property given to the new household by the bride's family at the time of marriage

He merely ate his supper beside it and was already half asleep over his iron plate when his father called him, and once more he followed the stiff back, the stiff and ruthless limp, up the slope and on to the starlit road…

even courage when the advantage was at least neutral which impressed strangers, as if they got from his latent ravening ferocity not so much a sense of dependability as a feeling that his ferocious conviction in the rightness of his own actions would be of advantage to all whose interest lay with his.

That night they camped, in a grove of oaks and beeches where a spring ran. The nights were still cool and they had a fire against it, of a rail lifted from a nearby fence and cut into lengths—a small fire, neat, niggard almost, a shrewd fire; such fires were his father's habit and custom always, even in freezing weather. Older, the boy might have remarked this and wondered why not a big one; why should not a man who had not only seen the waste and extravagance of war, but who had in his blood an inherent **voracious** prodigality[5] with material not his own, have burned everything in sight? Then he might have gone a step father and thought that that was the reason: that niggard blaze was the living fruit of nights passed during those four years in the woods hiding from all men, blue or gray, with his strings of horses (captured horses, he called them). And older still, he might have **divined** the true reason: that the element of fire spoke to some deep mainspring of his father's being, as the element of steel or of powder spoke to other men, as the one weapon for the preservation of integrity, else breath were not worth the breathing, and hence to be regarded with respect and used with discretion.

But he did not think this now and he had seen those same niggard blazes all his life. He merely ate his supper beside it and was already half asleep over his iron plate when his father called him, and once more he followed the stiff back, the stiff and ruthless limp, up the slope and on to the starlit road where, turning, he could see his father against the stars but without face or depth—a shape black, flat, and bloodless as though cut from tin in the iron folds of the frockcoat which had not been made for him, the voice harsh like tin and without heat like tin:

"You were fixing to tell them. You would have told him." He didn't answer. His father struck him with the flat of his hand on the side of the

voracious:
greedy; insatiable

divined:
guessed;
figured out

---

5 **prodigality:** extravagance

William Faulkner

head, hard but without heat, exactly as he had struck the two mules at the store, exactly as he would strike either of them with any stick in order to kill a horse fly, his voice still without heat or anger: "You're getting to be a man. You got to learn. You got to learn to stick to your own blood or you ain't going to have any blood to stick to you. Do you think either of them, any man there this morning, would? Don't you know all they wanted was a chance to get at me because they knew I had them beat? Eh?" Later, twenty years later, he was to tell himself, "If I had said they wanted only truth, justice, he would have hit me again." But now he said nothing. He was not crying. He just stood there. "Answer me," his father said.

"Yes," he whispered. His father turned.

"Get on to bed. We'll be there tomorrow."

To-morrow they were there. In the early afternoon the wagon stopped before a paintless two-room house identical almost with the dozen others it had stopped before even in the boy's ten years, and again, as on the other dozen occasions, his mother and aunt got down and began to unload the wagon, although his two sisters and his father and brother had not moved.

"Likely hit ain't fitten for hawgs," one of the sisters said.

"Nevertheless, fit it will and you'll hog it and like it," his father said. "Get out of them chairs and help your Ma unload."

The two sisters got down, big, **bovine**, in a flutter of cheap ribbons; one of them drew from the jumbled wagon bed a battered lantern, the other a worn broom. His father handed the reins to the older son and began to climb stiffly over the wheel. "When they get unloaded, take the team to the barn and feed them." Then he said, and at first the boy thought he was still speaking to his brother: "Come with me."

"Me?" he said.

"Yes," his father said. "You."

"Abner," his mother said. His father paused and looked back—the harsh level stare beneath the shaggy, graying, **irascible** brows.

"I reckon I'll have a word with the man that aims to begin to-morrow owning me body and soul for the next eight months."

They went back up the road. A week ago—or before last night, that is—he would have asked where they were going, but not now. His father had struck him before last night but never before had he paused afterward to explain why; it was as if the blow and the following calm, outrageous voice still rang, repercussed, divulging nothing to him save the terrible handicap of

bovine: cowlike

irascible: grumpy; bad-tempered

being young, the light weight of his few years, just heavy enough to prevent his soaring free of the world as it seemed to be ordered but now heavy enough to keep him footed solid in it, to resist it and try to change the course of its events.

Presently he could see the grove of oaks and cedars and the other flowering trees and shrubs where the house would be, though not the house yet. They walked beside a fence massed with honeysuckle and Cherokee roses and came to a gate swinging open between two brick pillars, and now, beyond a sweep of drive, he saw the house for the first time and at that instant he forgot his father and the terror and despair both, and even when he remembered his father again (who had not stopped) the terror and despair did not return. Because, for all the twelve movings, they had **sojourned** until now in a poor country, a land of small farms and fields and houses, and he had never seen a house like this before. *Hit's big as a courthouse* he thought quietly, with a surge of peace and joy whose reason he could not have thought into words, being too young for that: *They are safe from him. People whose lives are a part of this peace and dignity are beyond his touch, he no more to them than a buzzing wasp: capable of stinging for a little moment but that's all; the spell of this peace and dignity rendering even the barns and stable and cribs which belong to it **impervious** to the puny flames he might contrive* . . . this, the peace and joy, ebbing for an instant as he looked again at the stiff black back, the stiff and **implacable** limp of the figure which was not dwarfed by the house, for the reason that it had never looked big anywhere and which now, against the serene columned backdrop, had more than ever that impervious quality of something cut ruthlessly from tin, depthless, as though, sidewise to the sun, it would cast no shadow. Watching him, the boy remarked the absolutely undeviating course which his father held and saw the stiff foot come squarely down in a pile of fresh

> *W*atching him, the boy remarked the absolutely undeviating course which his father held and saw the stiff foot come squarely down in a pile of fresh droppings where a horse had stood in the drive and which his father could have avoided by a simple change of stride.

sojourned: wandered

impervious: invulnerable; impenetrable

implacable: relentless; uncompromising

192   William Faulkner

droppings where a horse had stood in the drive and which his father could have avoided by a simple change of stride. But it ebbed only for a moment, though he could not have thought this into words either, walking on in the spell of the house, which he could even want but without envy, without sorrow, certainly never with that ravening and jealous rage which unknown to him walked in the ironlike black coat before him: *Maybe he will feel it too. Maybe it will even change him now from what maybe he couldn't help but be.*

They crossed the portico.[6] Now he could hear his father's stiff foot as it came down on the boards with clocklike finality, a sound out of all proportion to the displacement of the body it bore and which was not dwarfed either by the white door before it, as though it had attained to a sort of vicious and ravening minimum not to be dwarfed by anything—the flat, wide, black hat, the formal coat of broadcloth which had once been black but which had now that friction-glazed greenish cast of the bodies of old house flies, the lifted sleeve which was too large, the lifted hand like a curled claw. The door opened so promptly that the boy knew the Negro must have been watching them all the time, an old man with neat grizzled hair, in a linen jacket, who stood barring the door with his body, saying, "Wipe yo foots, white man, fo you come in here. Major ain't home nohow."

"Get out of my way, nigger," his father said, without heat too, flinging the door back and the Negro also and entering, his hat still on his head. And now the boy saw the prints of the stiff foot on the doorjamb and saw them appear on the pale rug behind the machinelike deliberation of the foot which seemed to bear (or transmit) twice the weight which the body compassed. The Negro was shouting "Miss Lula! Miss Lula!" somewhere behind them, then the boy, **deluged** as though by a warm wave by a suave turn of carpeted stair and a pendant glitter of chandeliers and a mute gleam of gold frames, heard the swift feet and saw her too, a lady—perhaps he had never seen her like before either—in a gray, smooth gown with lace at the throat and an apron tied at the waist and the sleeves turned back, wiping cake or biscuit dough from her hands with a towel as she came up the hall, looking not at his father at all but at the tracks on the blond rug with an expression of incredulous amazement.

deluged: flooded; overwhelmed

"I tried," the Negro cried. "I tole him to . . ."

"Will you please go away?" she said in a shaking voice. "Major de Spain is not at home. Will you please go away?"

---

6 **portico:** a covered porch, often at the entrance to a house

His father had not spoken again. He did not speak again. He did not even look at her. He just stood stiff in the center of the rug, in his hat, the shaggy iron-gray brows twitching slightly above the pebble-colored eyes as he appeared to examine the house with brief deliberation. Then with the same deliberation he turned; the boy watched him pivot on the good leg and saw the stiff foot drag round the arc of the turning, leaving a final long and fading smear. His father never looked at it, he never once looked down at the rug. The Negro held the door. It closed behind them, upon the hysteric and indistinguishable woman-wail. His father stopped at the top of the steps and scraped his boot clean on the edge of it. At the gate he stopped again. He stood for a moment, planted stiffly on the stiff foot, looking back at the house. "Pretty and white, ain't it?" he said. "That's sweat. Nigger sweat. Maybe it ain't white enough yet to suit him. Maybe he wants to mix some white sweat with it."

Two hours later the boy was chopping wood behind the house within which his mother and aunt and the two sisters (the mother and aunt, not the two girls, he knew that; even at this distance and muffled by walls the flat loud voices of the two girls emanated an **incorrigible** idle **inertia**) were setting up the stove to prepare a meal, when he heard the hooves and saw the linen-clad man on a fine **sorrel** mare, whom he recognized even before he saw the rolled rug in front of the Negro youth following on a fat bay carriage horse—a **suffused**, angry face vanishing, still at full gallop, beyond the corner of the house where his father and brother were sitting in the two tilted chairs; and a moment later, almost before he could have put the axe down, he heard the hooves again and watched the sorrel mare go back out of the yard, already galloping again. Then his father began to shout one of the sisters' names, who presently emerged backward from the kitchen door dragging the rolled rug along the ground by one end while the other sister walked behind it.

"If you ain't going to tote, go on and set up the wash pot," the first said.

"You, Sarty!" the second shouted. "Set up the wash pot!" His father appeared at the door, framed against that shabbiness, as he had been against that other bland perfection, impervious to either, the mother's anxious face at his shoulder.

"Go on," the father said. "Pick it up." The two sisters stooped, broad, **lethargic**; stooping, they presented an incredible expanse of pale cloth and a flutter of **tawdry** ribbons.

incorrigible: unruly; incurable

inertia: tendency to remain in motion or at rest

sorrel: brownish-orange

suffused: flushed

lethargic: lazy; sluggish

tawdry: cheap; tasteless

"If I thought enough of a rug to have to git hit all the way from France I wouldn't keep hit where folks coming in would have to tromp on hit," the first said. They raised the rug.

"Abner," the mother said. "Let me do it."

"You go back and git dinner," his father said. "I'll tend to this."

From the woodpile through the rest of the afternoon the boy watched them, the rug spread flat in the dust beside the bubbling wash-pot, the two sisters stooping over it with that profound and lethargic reluctance, while the father stood over them in turn, implacable and grim, driving them though never raising his voice again. He could smell the harsh homemade lye they were using; he saw his mother come to the door once and look toward them with an expression not anxious now but very like despair; he saw his father turn, and he fell to with the axe and saw from the corner of his eye his father raise from the ground a flattish fragment of field stone and examine it and return to the pot, and this time his mother actually spoke: "Abner. Abner. Please don't. Please, Abner."

Then he was done too. It was dusk; the whippoorwills[7] had already begun. He could smell coffee from the room where they would presently eat the cold food remaining from the mid-afternoon meal, though when he entered the house he realized they were having coffee again probably because there was a fire on the hearth, before which the rug now lay spread over the backs of the two chairs. The tracks of his father's foot were gone. Where they had been were now long, water-cloudy **scoriations** resembling the sporadic course of a lilliputian[8] mowing machine.

scoriations: grooves; furrows

It still hung there while they ate the cold food and then went to bed, scattered without order or claim up and down the two rooms, his mother in one bed, where his father would later lie, the older brother in the other, himself, the aunt, and the two sisters on pallets on the floor. But his father was not in bed yet. The last thing the boy remembered was the depthless, harsh silhouette of

> *The tracks of his father's foot were gone. Where they had been were now long, water-cloudy scoriations resembling the sporadic course of a lilliputian mowing machine.*

---

7 **whippoorwills:** nocturnal birds named for the sound of their call

8 **lilliputian:** of or relating to the miniature people on the island of Lilliput, from Jonathan Swift's *Gulliver's Travels*

the hat and coat bending over the rug and it seemed to him that he had not even closed his eyes when the silhouette was standing over him, the fire almost dead behind it, the stiff foot prodding him awake. "Catch up the mule," his father said.

When he returned with the mule his father was standing in the black door, the rolled rug over his shoulder. "Ain't you going to ride?" he said.

"No. Give me your foot."

He bent his knee into his father's hand, the wiry, surprising power flowed smoothly, rising, he rising with it, on to the mule's bare back (they had owned a saddle once; the boy could remember it though not when or where) and with the same effortlessness his father swung the rug up in front of him. Now in the starlight they retraced the afternoon's path, up the dusty road rife with honeysuckle, through the gate and up the black tunnel of the drive to the lightless house, where he sat on the mule and felt the rough warp of the rug drag across his thighs and vanish.

"Don't you want me to help?" he whispered. His father did not answer and now he heard again that stiff foot striking the hollow portico with that wooden and clocklike deliberation, that outrageous overstatement of the weight it carried. The rug, hunched, not flung (the boy could tell that even in the darkness) from his father's shoulder struck the angle of wall and floor with a sound unbelievably loud, thunderous, then the foot again, unhurried and enormous; a light came on in the house and the boy sat, tense, breathing steadily and quietly and just a little fast, though the foot itself did not increase its beat at all, descending the steps now; now the boy could see him.

"Don't you want to ride now?" he whispered. "We kin both ride now," the light within the house altering now, flaring up and sinking. *He's coming down the stairs now,* he thought. He had already ridden the mule up beside the horse block; presently his father was up behind him and he doubled the reins over and slashed the mule across the neck, but before the animal could begin to trot the hard, thin arm came round him, the hard knotted hand jerking the mule back to a walk.

In the first red rays of the sun they were in the lot, putting plow gear on the mules. This time the sorrel mare was in the lot before he heard it at all, the rider collarless and even bareheaded, trembling, speaking in a shaking voice as the woman in the house had done, his father merely looking up once before stooping again to the hame he was buckling, so that the man on the mare spoke to his stooping back:

"You must realize you have ruined that rug. Wasn't there anybody here, any of your women . . ." he ceased, shaking, the boy watching him, the older brother leaning now in the stable door, chewing, blinking slowly and steadily at nothing apparently. "It cost a hundred dollars. But you never had a hundred dollars. You never will. So I'm going to charge you twenty bushels of corn against your crop. I'll add it in your contract and when you come to the commissary[9] you can sign it. That won't keep Mrs. de Spain quiet but maybe it will teach you to wipe your feet off before you enter her house again."

Then he was gone. The boy looked at his father, who still had not spoken or even looked up again, who was now adjusting the logger-head in the hame.[10]

"Pap," he said. His father looked at him—the inscrutable face, the shaggy brows beneath which the gray eyes glinted coldly. Suddenly the boy went toward him, fast, stopping as suddenly. "You done the best you could!" he cried. "If he wanted hit done different why didn't he wait and tell you how? He won't git no twenty bushels! He won't get none! We'll gether hit and hide it! I kin watch . . ."

"Did you put the cutter back in that straight stock like I told you?"

"No, sir," he said.

"Then go do it."

That was Wednesday. During the rest of that week he worked steadily, at what was within his scope and some which was beyond it, with an industry that did not need to be driven nor even commanded twice; he had this from his mother, with the difference that some at least of what he did he liked to do, such as splitting wood with the half-size axe which his mother and aunt had earned, or saved money somehow, to present him with at Christmas. In

---

9 **commissary:** a general store for food and supplies

10 **logger-head . . . hame:** parts of a horse's bridle

company with the two older women (and on one afternoon, even one of the sisters), he built pens for the shoat[11] and the cow which were a part of his father's contract with the landlord, and one afternoon, his father being absent, gone somewhere on one of the mules, he went to the field.

They were running a middle buster[12] now, his brother holding the plow straight while he handled the reins, and walking beside the straining mule, the rich black soil shearing cool and damp against his bare ankles, he thought *Maybe this is the end of it. Maybe even that twenty bushels that seems hard to have to pay for just a rug will be a cheap price for him to stop forever and always from being what he used to be;* thinking, dreaming now, so that his brother had to speak sharply to him to mind the mule: *Maybe he even won't collect the twenty bushels. Maybe it will all add up and balance and vanish—corn, rug, fire; the terror and grief, the being pulled two ways like between two teams of horses—gone, done with for ever and ever.*

> *Maybe this is the end of it. Maybe even that twenty bushels that seems hard to have to pay for just a rug will be a cheap price for him to stop forever and always from being what he used to be...*

Then it was Saturday; he looked up from beneath the mule he was harnessing and saw his father in the black coat and hat. "Not that," his father said. "The wagon gear." And then, two hours later, sitting in the wagon bed behind his father and brother on the seat, the wagon accomplished a final curve, and he saw the weathered paintless store with its tattered tobacco- and patent-medicine posters and the tethered wagons and saddle animals below the gallery. He mounted the gnawed steps behind his father and brother, and there again was the lane of quiet, watching faces for the three of them to walk through. He saw the man in spectacles sitting at the plank table and he did not need to be told this was a Justice of the Peace; he sent one glare of fierce, exultant, **partisan** defiance at the man in collar and cravat[13] now, whom he had seen but twice before in his life, and that on a galloping horse, who now wore on his face an expression not of rage but of amazed unbelief which the boy could not have known was at the incredible circumstance of being sued by one of his own tenants,

partisan: biased; loyal to a cause

---

11 **shoat:** a young hog

12 **buster:** a plow

13 **cravat:** a necktie

William Faulkner

and came and stood against his father and cried at the Justice: "He ain't done it! He ain't burnt . . ."

"Go back to the wagon," his father said.

"Burnt?" the Justice said. "Do I understand this rug was burned too?"

"Does anybody here claim it was?" his father said. "Go back to the wagon." But he did not, he merely retreated to the rear of the room, crowded as that other had been, but not to sit down this time, instead, to stand pressing among the motionless bodies, listening to the voices:

"And you claim twenty bushels of corn is too high for the damage you did to the rug?"

"He brought the rug to me and said he wanted the tracks washed out of it. I washed the tracks out and took the rug back to him."

"But you didn't carry the rug back to him in the same condition it was in before you made the tracks on it."

His father did not answer, and now for perhaps half a minute there was no sound at all save that of breathing, the faint steady **suspiration** of complete and intent listening.

**suspiration:** deep breath; sigh

"You decline to answer that, Mr. Snopes?" Again his father did not answer. "I'm going to find against you, Mr. Snopes. I'm going to find that you were responsible for the injury to Major de Spain's rug and hold you liable for it. But twenty bushels of corn seems a little high for a man in your circumstances to have to pay. Major de Spain claims it cost a hundred dollars. October corn will be worth about fifty cents. I figure that if Major de Spain can stand a ninety-five dollar loss on something he paid cash for, you can stand a five-dollar loss you haven't earned yet. I hold you in damages to Major de Spain to the amount of ten bushels of corn over and above your contract with him, to be paid to him out of your crop at gathering time. Court adjourned."

It had taken no time hardly, the morning was but half begun. He thought they would return home and perhaps back to the field, since they were late, far behind all other farmers. But instead his father passed on behind the wagon, merely indicating with his hand for the older brother to follow with it, and crossed the road toward the blacksmith shop opposite, pressing on after his father, overtaking him, speaking, whispering up at the harsh, calm face beneath the weathered hat: "He won't git no ten bushels neither. He won't git one. We'll . . ." until his father glanced for an instant down at him, the face absolutely calm, the grizzled eyebrows tangled above the cold eyes, the voice almost pleasant, almost gentle:

"You think so? Well, we'll wait til October anyway."

The matter of the wagon—the setting of a spoke or two and the tightening of the tires—did not take long either, the business of the tires accomplished by driving the wagon into the spring branch behind the shop and letting it stand there, the mules nuzzling into the water from time to time, and the boy on the seat with the idle reins, looking up the slope and through the sooty tunnel of the shed where the slow hammer rang and where his father sat on an upended cypress bolt, easily, either talking or listening, still sitting there when the boy brought the dripping wagon up out of the branch and halted it before the door.

"Take them on to the shade and hitch," his father said. He did so and returned. His father and the smith and a third man squatting on his heels inside the door were talking, about crops and animals; the boy, squatting too in the **ammoniac** dust and hoof-parings[14] and scales of rust, heard his father tell a long and unhurried story out of the time before the birth of the older brother even when he had been a professional horsetrader. And then his father came up beside him where he stood before a tattered last year's circus poster on the other side of the store, gazing **rapt** and quiet at the scarlet horses, the incredible poisings and **convolutions** of tulle[15] and tights and the painted leers of comedians, and said, "It's time to eat."

But not at home. Squatting beside his brother against the front wall, he watched his father emerge from the store and produce from a paper sack a segment of cheese and divide it carefully and deliberately into three with his pocket knife and produce crackers from the same sack. They all three squatted on the gallery and ate, slowly, without talking; then in the store again, they drank from a tin dipper tepid water smelling of the cedar bucket and of living beech trees. And still they did not go home. It was a horse lot this time, a tall rail fence upon and along which men stood and sat and out of which one by one horses were led, to be walked and trotted and then **cantered** back and forth along the road while the slow swapping and buying went on and the sun began to slant westward, they—the three of them—watching and listening, the older brother with his muddy eyes and his steady, inevitable tobacco, the father commenting now and then on certain of the animals, to no one in particular.

It was after sundown when they reached home. They ate supper by lamplight, then, sitting on the doorstep, the boy watched the night fully accom-

---

ammoniac: foul-smelling; cough-inducing

rapt: enchanted

convolutions: twists; intricate designs

cantered: loped; trotted

---

14 **hoof-parings:** clippings that are pared away from a horse's hoof during shoeing

15 **tulle:** a netted fabric

plish, listening to the whippoorwills and the frogs, when he heard his mother's voice: "Abner! No! No! Oh, God. Oh, God. Abner!" and he rose, whirled, and saw the altered light through the door where a candle stub now burned in a bottle neck on the table and his father, still in the hat and coat, at once formal and **burlesque** as though dressed carefully for some shabby and cer-emonial violence, emptying the reservoir of the lamp back into the five-gal-lon kerosene can from which it had been filled, while the mother tugged at his arm until he shifted the lamp to the other hand and flung her back, not savagely or viciously, just hard, into the wall, her hands flung out against the wall for balance, her mouth open and in her face the same quality of hopeless despair as had been in her voice. Then his father saw him standing in the door.

burlesque: comic; ridiculous

I could run on and on and never look back, never need to see his face again.

"Go to the barn and get that can of oil we were oiling the wagon with," he said. The boy did not move. Then he could speak.

"What . . ." he cried. "What are you . . ."

"Go get that oil," his father said. "Go."

Then he was moving, running, outside the house, toward the stable: this the old habit, the old blood which he had not been permitted to choose for himself, which had been **bequeathed** him willy nilly and which had run for so long (and who knew where, battening on what of outrage and savagery and lust) before it came to him. *I could keep on,* he thought. *I could run on and on and never look back, never need to see his face again. Only I can't. I can't,* the rusted can in his hand now, the liquid sploshing in it as he ran back to the house and into it, into the sound of his mother's weeping in the next room, and handed the can to his father.

bequeathed: handed down

"Ain't you going to even send a nigger?" he cried. "At least you sent a nig-ger before!"

This time his father didn't strike him. The hand came even faster than the blow had, the same hand which had set the can on the table with almost excruciating care flashing from the can toward him too quick for him to fol-low it, gripping him by the back of his shirt and on to tiptoe before he had seen it quit the can, the face stooping at him in breathless and frozen feroc-ity, the cold, dead voice speaking over him to the older brother who leaned against the table, chewing with that steady, curious, sidewise motion of cows:

"Empty the can into the big one and go on. I'll catch up with you."

"Better tie him up to the bedpost," the brother said.

"Do like I told you," the father said. Then the boy was moving, his bunched shirt and the hard, bony hand between his shoulder-blades, his toes just touching the floor, across the room and into the other one, past the sisters sitting with spread heavy thighs in the two chairs over the cold hearth, and to where his mother and aunt sat side by side on the bed, the aunt's arms about his mother's shoulders.

"Hold him," the father said. The aunt made a startled movement. "Not you," the father said. "Lennie. Take hold of him. I want to see you do it." His mother took him by the wrist. "You'll hold him better than that. If he gets loose don't you know what he is going to do? He will go up yonder." He jerked his head toward the road. "Maybe I'd better tie him."

"I'll hold him," his mother whispered.

"See you do then." Then his father was gone, the stiff foot heavy and measured upon the boards, ceasing at last.

Then he began to struggle. His mother caught him in both arms, he jerking and wrenching at them. He would be stronger in the end, he knew that. But he had no time to wait for it. "Lemme go!" he cried. "I don't want to have to hit you!"

"Let him go!" the aunt said. "If he don't go, before God, I am going up there myself!"

"Don't you see I can't?" his mother cried. "Sarty! Sarty! No! No! Help me, Lizzie!"

Then he was free. His aunt grasped at him but it was too late. He whirled, running, his mother stumbled forward on to her knees behind him, crying to the nearest sister: "Catch him, Net! Catch him!" But that was too late too, the sister (the sisters were twins, born at the same time, yet either of them now gave the impression of being, encompassing as much living meat and volume and weight as any other two of the family) not yet having begun to rise from the chair, her head, face, alone merely turned, presenting to him in the flying instant an astonishing expanse of young female features untroubled by any surprise even, wearing only an expression of bovine interest. Then he was out of the room, out of the house, in the mild dust of the starlit road and the heavy **rifeness** of honeysuckle, the pale ribbon unspooling with terrific

rifeness: abundance

> *He* whirled, running, his mother stumbled forward on to her knees behind him, crying to the nearest sister: "Catch him, Net! Catch him!"

slowness under his running feet, reaching the gate at last and turning in, running, his heart and lungs drumming, on up the drive toward the lighted house, the lighted door. He did not knock, he burst in, sobbing for breath, incapable for the moment of speech; he saw the astonished face of the Negro in the linen jacket without knowing when the Negro had appeared.

"De Spain!" he cried, panted. "Where's. . . ." then he saw the white man too emerging from a white door down the hall. "Barn!" he cried. "Barn!"

"What?" the white man said. "Barn?"

"Yes!" the boy cried. "Barn!"

"Catch him!" the white man shouted.

But it was too late this time too. The Negro grasped his shirt, but the entire sleeve, rotten with washing, carried away, and he was out that door too and in the drive again, and had actually never ceased to run even while he was screaming into the white man's face.

Behind him the white man was shouting, "My horse! Fetch my horse!" and he thought for an instant of cutting across the park and climbing the fence into the road, but he did not know the park nor how high the vine-massed fence might be and he dared not risk it. So he ran on down the drive, blood and breath roaring; presently he was in the road again though he could not see it. He could not hear either: the galloping mare was almost upon him before he heard her, and even then he held his course, as if the very urgency of his wild grief and need must in a moment more find him wings, waiting until the ultimate instant to hurl himself aside and into the weed-choked roadside ditch as the horse thundered past and on, for an instant in furious silhouette against the stars, the tranquil early summer night sky which, even before the shape of the horse and rider vanished, stained abruptly and violently upward: a long, swirling roar incredible and soundless, blotting the stars, and he springing up and into the road again, running again, knowing it was too late yet still running even after he heard the shot and, an instant later, two shots, pausing now without knowing he had ceased to run, crying "Pap! Pap!", running again before he knew he had begun to run, stumbling, tripping over something and scrabbling up again without ceasing to run, looking

*W*hat?" the white man said. "Barn?"

"Yes!" the boy cried. "Barn!"

"Catch him!" the white man shouted.

backward over his shoulder at the glare as he got up, running on among the invisible trees, panting, sobbing, "Father! Father!"

At midnight he was sitting on the crest of a hill. He did not know it was midnight and he did not know how far he had come. But there was no glare behind him now and he sat now, his back toward what he had called home for four days anyhow, his face toward the dark woods which he would enter when breath was strong again, small, shaking steadily in the chill darkness, hugging himself into the remainder of his thin, rotten shirt, the grief and despair now no longer terror and fear but just grief and despair. *Father. My father*, he thought. "He was brave!" he cried suddenly, aloud but not loud, no more than a whisper: "He was! He was in the war! He was in Colonel Sartoris' cav'ry!"[16] not knowing that his father had gone to that war a private in the fine old European sense, wearing no uniform, admitting the authority of and giving fidelity to no man or army or flag, going to war as Malbrouck[17] himself did: for **booty**—it meant nothing and less than nothing to him if it were enemy booty or his own.

The slow constellations wheeled on. It would be dawn and then sun-up after a while and he would be hungry. But that would be to-morrow and now he was only cold, and walking would cure that. His breathing was easier now and he decided to get up and go on, and then he found that he had been asleep because he knew it was almost dawn, the night almost over. He could tell that from the whippoorwills. They were everywhere now among the dark trees below him, constant and inflectioned and ceaseless, so that, as the instant for giving over to the day birds drew nearer and nearer, there was no interval at all between them. He got up. He was a little stiff, but walking would cure that too as it would the cold, and soon there would be the sun. He went on down the hill, toward the dark woods within which the liquid silver voices of the birds called unceasing—the rapid and urgent beating of the urgent and **quiring** heart of the late spring night. He did not look back.

booty:
plunder; winnings

quiring:
questioning

---

16 **cav'ry:** cavalry, or soldiers mounted on horseback

17 **Malbrouck:** John Churchill, Duke of Marlborough, (1650–1722); successful English general whose name evolved into Malbrough and Malbrouch in popular English and French songs

Responding to the Story

1. **LITERARY LENS** Based on what you learned from following his stream of consciousness, write a one-paragraph description of the boy.

2. The boy views the father's clothing and even his face and body as "ironlike." In what ways is the father like iron?

3. Reread the second sentence of the story. What do you think is meant by "the old, fierce pull of blood"?

4. What do you think drives the father's need to burn things?

5. **THE AUTHOR'S STYLE** Faulkner is known for making time stand still during crystallized moments in his fiction. Identify a passage in which motion is arrested. What "artificial means," or techniques of literature, does he use to accomplish this?

Arrested Motion

The aim of every artist is to arrest motion, which is life, by artificial means.

—William Faulkner
Lion in the Garden: Interviews with William Faulkner 1926–1962

Bernard Malamud

1914–1986

About the Author

Born to parents who were part of the Russian Jewish immigrant community that he would grow up to write about, Bernard Malamud spent his formative years in Brooklyn. He studied at City College of New York, which was then a school for poor but bright students, and went on to earn a master's degree in English at Columbia University.

Always a careful writer, Malamud then worked for eight years as a clerk in the Bureau of Census in Washington, D.C., perfecting his writing at night. During this time he published his first short stories. Like many writers, Malamud used teaching as well as writing to support his family, returning to his alma mater, Erasmus Hall High School, to teach evening classes. He went on to teach at prestigious schools such as Harvard as his literary reputation grew.

An enthusiastic world traveler, Malamud sometimes used the places he visited as settings in his fiction. Among his best-known works are a collection of stories, *The Magic Barrel*, and his novels *The Natural* and *The Fixer*.

****

The Author's Style

"Life is a tragedy full of joy," Malamud said in an interview with the *New York Times*. This paradox can be seen in his characters that weep and pray, curse and rejoice. Malamud was one of several Jewish writers whose stories about exiled, vulnerable people were acclaimed by wide audiences in the decades following the Holocaust. His characters are realistic and usually unremarkable in personality and occupation. They are not always Jewish, but their drab, everyday suffering can be seen as symbolic of a struggling humanity.

Malamud's plots are fairly straightforward, and often have the tone of a fable or folktale. This fable-like quality owes something to the rhythm and flavor of Yiddish speech that Malamud captures in both third-person narration and dialogue. Many of his stories have to do with questions raised by Jews who find themselves in conflict with non-Jews. More generally, though, his characters are simply trying to live in a world where they have to pay too much for making bad choices and having bad luck.

It is not uncommon for Malamud to use dreams and miracles to enable his characters to transcend their usual ways of thinking and find dignity and hope despite their constant burden of suffering. In his novel, *The Natural*, one character says to another, "We have two lives . . . the life we learn with and the life we live with after that. Suffering is what brings us toward happiness."

LITERARY LENS Malamud's stories often have the flavor of a folktale. Watch for elements of a folktale in this story.

ANGEL LEVINE

BERNARD MALAMUD

anischevitz, a tailor, in his fifty-first year suffered many reverses and indignities. Previously a man of comfortable means, he overnight lost all he had when his establishment caught fire, after a metal container of cleaning fluid exploded, and burned to the ground. Although Manischevitz was insured against fire, damage suits by two customers who had been hurt in the flames deprived him of every penny he had saved. At almost the same time, his son, of much promise, was killed in the war, and his daughter, without so much as a word of warning, married a lout and disappeared with him as off the face of the earth. Thereafter Manischevitz was victimized by excruciating backaches and found himself unable to work even as a presser—the only kind of work available to him—

The bedroom was the warmest room in the house and it was here, after his outburst to God, that Manischevitz, by the light of two small bulbs overhead, sat reading his Jewish newspaper.

for more than an hour or two daily, because beyond that the pain from standing was maddening. His Fanny, a good wife and mother, who had taken in washing and sewing, began before his eyes to waste away. Suffering shortness of breath, she at last became seriously ill and took to her bed. The doctor, a former customer of Manischevitz, who out of pity treated them, at first had difficulty diagnosing her ailment, but later put it down as hardening of the arteries at an advanced stage. He took Manischevitz aside, prescribed complete rest for her, and in whispers gave him to know there was little hope.

Throughout his trials Manischevitz had remained somewhat stoic, almost unbelieving that all this had descended on his head, as if it were happening, let us say, to an acquaintance or some distant relative; it was, in sheer quantity of woe, incomprehensible. It was also ridiculous, unjust, and because he had always been a religious man, an **affront** to God. Manischevitz believed this in all his suffering. When his burden had grown too crushingly heavy to be borne he prayed in his chair with shut hollow eyes: "My dear God, sweetheart, did I deserve that this should happen to me?" Then recognizing the worthlessness of it, he set aside the complaint and prayed humbly for assistance: "Give Fanny back her health, and to me for myself that I shouldn't feel pain in every step. Help now or tomorrow is too late." And Manischevitz wept.

affront:
insult

Manischevitz's flat, which he had moved into after the disastrous fire, was a **meager** one, furnished with a few sticks of chairs, a table, and bed, in one of the poorer sections of the city. There were three rooms: a small, poorly papered living room; an apology for a kitchen with a wooden icebox; and the comparatively large bedroom where Fanny lay in a sagging secondhand bed, gasping for breath. The bedroom was the warmest room in the house and it was here, after his outburst to God, that Manischevitz, by the light of two small bulbs overhead, sat reading his Jewish newspaper. He was not truly reading because his thoughts were everywhere; however the print offered a convenient resting place for his eyes, and a word

meager:
poor; simple

or two, when he permitted himself to comprehend them, had the momentary effect of helping him forget his troubles. After a short while he discovered, to his surprise, that he was actively scanning the news, searching for an item of great interest to him. Exactly what he thought he would read he couldn't say—until he realized, with some astonishment, that he was expecting to discover something about himself. Manischevitz put his paper down and looked up with the distinct impression that someone had come into the apartment, though he could not remember having heard the sound of the door opening. He looked around: the room was very still, Fanny sleeping, for once, quietly. Half frightened, he watched her until he was satisfied she wasn't dead; then, still disturbed by the thought of an unannounced visitor, he stumbled into the living room and there had the shock of his life, for at the table sat a black man reading a newspaper he had folded up to fit into one hand.

"What do you want here?" Manischevitz asked in fright.

The Negro put down the paper and glanced up with a gentle expression. "Good evening." He seemed not to be sure of himself, as if he had got into the wrong house. He was a large man, bonily built, with a heavy head covered by a hard derby,[1] which he made no attempt to remove. His eyes seemed sad, but his lips, above which he wore a slight mustache, sought to smile; he was not otherwise **prepossessing**. The cuffs of his sleeves, Manischevitz noted, were frayed to the lining, and the dark suit was badly fitted. He had very large feet. Recovering from his fright, Manischevitz guessed he had left the door open and was being visited by a case worker from the Welfare Department—some came at night—for he had recently applied for welfare. Therefore he lowered himself into a chair opposite the Negro, trying, before the man's uncertain smile, to feel comfortable. The former tailor sat stiffly but patiently at the table, waiting for the investigator to take out his pad and pencil and begin asking questions; but before long he became convinced the man intended to do nothing of the sort.

"Who are you?" Manischevitz at last asked uneasily.

"If I may, insofar as one is able to, identify myself, I bear the name of Alexander Levine."

prepossessing: impressive

> *W*hat do you want here?" Manischevitz asked in fright.

---

1 **derby:** a stiff felt hat with a narrow brim

In spite of his troubles Manischevitz felt a smile growing on his lips. "You said Levine?" he politely inquired.

The Negro nodded. "That is exactly right."

Carrying the jest further, Manischevitz asked, "You are maybe Jewish?"

"All my life I was, willingly."

The tailor hesitated. He had heard of black Jews but had never met one. It gave an unusual sensation.

Recognizing in afterthought something odd about the tense of Levine's remark, he said doubtfully, "You ain't Jewish anymore?"

Levine at this point removed his hat, revealing a very white part in his black hair, but quickly replaced it. He replied, "I have recently been disincarnated into an angel. As such, I offer you my humble assistance, if to offer is within my province and power—in the best sense." He lowered his eyes in apology. "Which calls for added explanation: I am what I am granted to be, and at present the completion is in the future."

"What kind of angel is this?" Manischevitz gravely asked.

"A bona fide angel of God, within prescribed limitations," answered Levine, "not to be confused with the members of any particular sect, order, or organization here on earth operating under a similar name."

Manischevitz was thoroughly disturbed. He had been expecting something, but not this. What sort of mockery was it—provided that Levine was an angel—of a faithful servant who had from childhood lived in the synagogues, concerned with the word of God?

To test Levine he asked, "Then where are your wings?"

The Negro blushed as well as he could. Manischevitz understood this from his altered expression. "Under certain circumstances we lose privileges and **prerogatives** upon returning to earth, no matter for what purpose or endeavoring to assist whomsoever."

prerogatives: rights; options

"So tell me," Manischevitz said triumphantly, "how did you get here?"

"I was translated."

Still troubled, the tailor said, "If you are a Jew, say the blessing for bread."

Levine recited it in **sonorous** Hebrew.

sonorous: full sounding; resonant

Although moved by the familiar words Manischevitz still felt doubt he was dealing with an angel.

"If you are an angel," he demanded somewhat angrily, "give me the proof."

Levine wet his lips. "Frankly, I cannot perform either miracles or near-miracles, due to the fact that I am in a condition of probation. How long that will persist or even consist depends on the outcome."

Manischevitz racked his brains for some means of causing Levine positively to reveal his true identity, when the Negro spoke again:

"It was given me to understand that both your wife and you require assistance of a **salubrious** nature?"

The tailor could not rid himself of the feeling that he was the butt of a jokester. Is this what a Jewish angel looks like? he asked himself. This I am not convinced.

He asked a last question. "So if God sends to me an angel, why a black? Why not a white that there are so many of them?"

"It was my turn to go next," Levine explained.

Manischevitz could not be persuaded. "I think you are a faker."

Levine slowly rose. His eyes indicated disappointment and worry. "Mr. Manischevitz," he said tonelessly, "if you should desire me to be of assistance to you any time in the near future, or possibly before, I can be found"—he glanced at his fingernails—"in Harlem."

He was by then gone.

The next day Manischevitz felt some relief from his backache and was able to work four hours at pressing. The day after, he put in six hours; and the third day four again. Fanny sat up a little and asked for some halvah[2] to suck. But after the fourth day the stabbing, breaking ache afflicted his back, and Fanny again lay **supine**, breathing with blue-lipped difficulty.

Manischevitz was profoundly disappointed at the return of his active pain and suffering. He had hoped for a longer interval of easement, long enough to have a thought other than of himself and his troubles. Day by day, minute after minute, he lived in pain, pain his only memory, questioning the necessity of it, **inveighing**, though with affection, against God. Why *so much*, Gottenyu?[3] If He wanted to teach His servant a lesson for some reason, some cause—the nature of His nature—to teach him, say, for reasons of his weakness, his pride, perhaps, during his years of prosperity, his frequent neglect of God—to give him a little lesson, why then any of the tragedies that had happened to him, any *one* would have sufficed to chasten him. But *all together*—

salubrious:
health-promoting;
wholesome

supine:
passively; listlessly

inveighing:
protesting

---

2 **halvah:** a sweet sesame candy

3 **Gottenyu:** Hebrew for "dear God"

the loss of both his children, his means of livelihood, Fanny's health and his—that was too much to ask one frail-boned man to endure. Who, after all, was Manischevitz that he had been given so much to suffer? A tailor. Certainly not a man of talent. Upon him suffering was largely wasted. It went nowhere, into nothing: into more suffering. His pain did not earn him bread, nor fill the cracks in the wall, nor lift, in the middle of the night, the kitchen table; only lay upon him, sleepless, so sharply oppressive that he could many times have cried out yet not heard himself this misery.

In this mood he gave no thought to Mr. Alexander Levine, but at moments when the pain wavered, slightly diminishing, he sometimes wondered if he had been mistaken to dismiss him. A black Jew and angel to boot—very hard to believe, but suppose he *had* been sent to **succor** him, and he, Manischevitz, was in his blindness too blind to understand? It was this thought that put him on the knife-point of agony.

succor: relieve; rescue

> *W*ho, after all, was Manischevitz that he had been given so much to suffer? A tailor. Certainly not a man of talent. Upon him suffering was largely wasted.

Therefore the tailor, after much self-questioning and continuing doubt, decided he would seek the self-styled angel in Harlem. Of course he had great difficulty because he had not asked for specific directions, and movement was tedious to him. The subway took him to 116th Street, and from there he wandered in the open dark world. It was vast and its lights lit nothing. Everywhere were shadows, often moving. Manischevitz hobbled along with the aid of a cane and, not knowing where to seek in the blackened tenement[4] buildings, would look fruitlessly through store windows. In the stores he saw people and everybody was black. It was an amazing thing to observe. When he was too tired, too unhappy to go farther, Manischevitz stopped in front of a tailor's shop. Out of familiarity with the appearance of it, with some sadness he entered. The tailor, an old skinny man with a mop of woolly gray hair, was sitting cross legged on his workbench, sewing a pair of tuxedo pants that had a razor slit all the way down the seat.

"You'll excuse me, please, gentleman," said Manischevitz, admiring the tailor's deft thimbled fingerwork, "but you know maybe somebody by the name Alexander Levine?"

---

4 **tenement:** low-quality apartment housing

The tailor, who, Manischevitz thought, seemed a little **antagonistic** to him, scratched his scalp.

antagonistic: hostile

"Cain't say I ever heared dat name."

"Alex-ander Lev-ine," Manischevitz repeated it.

The man shook his head. "Cain't say I heared."

Manischevitz remembered to say: "He is an angel, maybe."

"Oh, *him*," said the tailor, clucking. "He hang out in dat honky tonk down here a ways." He pointed with his skinny finger and returned to sewing the pants.

Manischevitz crossed the street against a red light and was almost run down by a taxi. On the block after the next, the sixth store from the corner was a cabaret, and the name in sparkling lights was Bella's. Ashamed to go in, Manischevitz gazed through the neon lit window, and when the dancing couples had parted and drifted away, he discovered at a table on the side, toward the rear, Alexander Levine.

He was sitting alone, a cigarette butt hanging from the corner of his mouth, playing solitaire with a dirty pack of cards, and Manischevitz felt a touch of pity for him, because Levine had deteriorated in appearance. His derby hat was dented and had a gray smudge. His ill fitting suit was shabbier, as if he had been sleeping in it. His shoes and trouser cuffs were muddy, and his face covered with an impenetrable stubble the color of licorice. Manischevitz, though deeply disappointed, was about to enter, when a bigbreasted Negress in a purple evening gown appeared before Levine's table, and with much laughter through many white teeth, broke into a vigorous shimmy. Levine looked at Manischevitz with a haunted expression, but the tailor was too paralyzed to move or acknowledge it. As Bella's gyrations continued Levine rose, his eyes lit in excitement. She embraced him with vigor, both his hands clasped around her restless buttocks, and they tangoed together across the floor, loudly applauded by the customers. She seemed to have lifted Levine off his feet and his large shoes hung limp as they danced. They slid past the windows where Manischevitz, white faced, stood staring in. Levine winked slyly and the tailor left for home.

Fanny lay at death's door. Through shrunken lips she muttered concerning her childhood, the sorrow of the marriage bed, the loss of her children; yet wept to live. Manischevitz tried not to listen, but even without ears he would have heard. It was not a gift. The doctor panted up the stairs, a broad but bland, unshaven man (it was Sunday), and soon

BLUES, Archibald Motley Jr., 1929

shook his head. A day at most, or two. He left at once to spare himself Manischevitz's multiplied sorrow; the man who never stopped hurting. He would someday get him into a public home.

Manischevitz visited a synagogue and there spoke to God, but God had absented Himself. The tailor searched his heart and found no hope. When she died, he would live dead. He considered taking his life although he knew he wouldn't. Yet it was something to consider. Considering, you existed. He railed against God—Can you love a rock, a broom, an emptiness? Baring his chest, he smote the naked bones, cursing himself for having, beyond belief, believed.

Asleep in a chair that afternoon, he dreamed of Levine. He was standing before a faded mirror, preening small decaying **opalescent** wings. "This means," mumbled Manischevitz, as he broke out of sleep, "that it is possible he could be an angel." Begging a neighbor lady to look in on Fanny and occasionally wet her lips with water, he drew on his thin coat, gripped his walking stick, exchanged some pennies for a subway token, and rode to Harlem. He knew this act was the last desperate one of his woe: to go seeking a black magician to restore his wife to **invalidism**. Yet if there was no choice, he did at least what was chosen.

He hobbled to Bella's, but the place seemed to have changed hands. It was now, as he breathed, a synagogue in a store. In the front, toward him, were several rows of empty wooden benches. In the rear stood the Ark, its portals of rough wood covered with rainbows of sequins; under it a long table on which lay the sacred scroll unrolled, illuminated by the dim light from a bulb on a chain overhead. Around the table, as if frozen to it and the scroll, which they all touched with their fingers, sat four Negroes wearing skullcaps.[5] Now as they read the Holy Word, Manischevitz could, through the plate-glass window, hear the singsong chant of their voices. One of them was old, with a gray beard. One was bubble-eyed. One was humpbacked. The fourth was a boy, no older than thirteen. Their heads moved in rhythmic swaying. Touched by this sight from his childhood and youth, Manischevitz entered and stood silent in the rear.

"Neshoma," said bubble eyes, pointing to the word with a stubby finger. "Now what dat mean?"

"That's the word that means soul," said the boy. He wore eyeglasses.

"Let's git on wid de commentary," said the old man.

"Ain't necessary," said the humpback. "Souls is immaterial substance. That's all. The soul is derived in that manner. The immateriality is derived from the substance, and they both, causally an otherwise, derived from the soul. There can be no higher."

"That's the highest."

"Over de top."

"Wait a minute," said bubble eyes. "I don't see what is dat immaterial

opalescent:
reflecting rainbow-colored light

invalidism:
a disabled condition

---

5 **skullcaps:** close-fitting caps without brims, worn by many Jews

substance. How come de one gits hitched up to de odder?" He addressed the humpback.

"Ask me something hard. Because it is substanceless immateriality. It couldn't be closer together, like all the parts of the body under one skin—closer."

"Hear now," said the old man.

"All you done is switched de words."

"It's the primum mobile, the substanceless substance from which comes all things that were incepted in the idea—you, me, and every thing and -body else."

"Now how did all dat happen? Make it sound simple."

"It de speerit," said the old man. "On the face of de water moved de speerit. An dat was good. It say so in the Book. From de speerit ariz de man."

"But now listen here. How come it become substance if it all de time a spirit?"

"God alone done dat."

"Holy! Holy! Praise His Name."

"But has dis spirit got some kind of a shade or color?" asked bubble eyes, deadpan.

"Man, of course not. A spirit is a spirit."

"Then how come we is colored?" he said with a triumphant glare.

"Ain't got nothing to do wid dat."

"I still like to know."

"God put the spirit in all things," answered the boy. "He put it in the green leaves and the yellow flowers. He put it with the gold in the fishes and the blue in the sky. That's how come it came to us."

"Amen."

"Praise Lawd and utter loud His speechless Name."

"Blow de bugle till it bust the sky."

They fell silent, intent upon the next word. Manischevitz, with doubt, approached them.

"You'll excuse me," he said. "I am looking for Alexander Levine. You know him maybe?"

"That's the angel," said the boy.

"Oh, *him*," snuffed bubble eyes.

"You'll find him at Bella's. It's the establishment right down the street," the humpback said.

Manischevitz said he was sorry that he could not stay, thanked them, and limped across the street. It was already night. The city was dark and he could barely find his way.

But Bella's was bursting with jazz and the blues. Through the window Manischevitz recognized the dancing crowd and among them sought Levine. He was sitting loose-lipped at Bella's side table. They were **tippling** from an almost empty whiskey fifth.[6] Levine had shed his old clothes, wore a shiny new checkered suit, pearl-gray derby hat, cigar, and big, two-tone, button shoes. To the tailor's dismay, a drunken look had settled upon his formerly dignified face. He leaned toward Bella, tickled her earlobe with his pinky while whispering words that sent her into **gales** of raucous laughter. She fondled his knee.

tippling: drinking liquor

Manischevitz, **girding** himself, pushed open the door and was not welcomed.

"This place reserved."

"Beat it, pale puss."

"Exit, Yankel, Semitic trash."

But he moved toward the table where Levine sat, the crowd breaking before him as he hobbled forward.

"Mr. Levine," he spoke in a trembly voice. "Is here Manischevitz."

Levine glared blearily. "Speak yo piece, son."

Manischevitz shivered. His back plagued him. Tremors tormented his legs. He looked around, everybody was all ears.

"You'll excuse me. I would like to talk to you in a private place."

"Speak, Ah is a private pusson."

Bella laughed piercingly. "Stop it, boy, you killin me."

Manischevitz, no end disturbed, considered fleeing, but Levine addressed him:

"Kindly state the pu'pose of yo communication with yo's truly."

The tailor wet cracked lips. "You are Jewish. This I am sure."

Levine rose, nostrils flaring. "Anythin else yo got to say?"

Manischevitz's tongue lay like a slab of stone.

"Speak now or fo'ever hold off."

> *L*evine had shed his old clothes, wore a shiny new checkered suit, pearl-gray derby hat, cigar, and big, two-tone, button shoes. To the tailor's dismay, a drunken look had settled upon his formerly dignified face.

gales: bursts

girding: strengthening; preparing

---

6 **whiskey fifth:** one-fifth of a gallon of whiskey

Tears blinded the tailor's eyes. Was ever man so tried? Should he say he believed a half-drunk Negro was an angel?

The silence slowly petrified.

Manischevitz was recalling scenes of his youth as a wheel in his mind whirred: believe, do not, yes, no, yes, no. The pointer pointed to yes, to between yes and no, to no, no it was yes. He sighed. It moved but one still had to make a choice.

"I think you are an angel from God." He said it in a broken voice, thinking, If you said it, it was said. If you believed it, you must say it. If you believed, you believed.

The hush broke. Everybody talked but the music began and they went on dancing. Bella, grown bored, picked up the cards and dealt herself a hand.

Levine burst into tears. "How you have humiliated me."

Manischevitz apologized.

"Wait'll I freshen up." Levine went to the men's room and returned in his old suit.

No one said goodbye as they left.

They rode to the flat via subway. As they walked up the stairs Manischevitz pointed with his cane at his door.

"That's all been taken care of," Levine said. "You go in while I take off."

Disappointed that it was so soon over, but torn by curiosity, Manischevitz followed the angel up three flights to the roof. When he got there the door was already padlocked.

Luckily he could see through a small broken window. He heard an odd noise, as though of a whirring of wings, and, when he strained for a wider view, could have sworn he saw a dark figure borne aloft on a pair of strong black wings.

A feather drifted down. Manischevitz gasped as it turned white, but it was only snowing.

He rushed downstairs. In the flat Fanny wielded a dust mop under the bed, and then upon the cobwebs on the wall.

"A wonderful thing, Fanny," Manischevitz said. "Believe me, there are Jews everywhere."

Responding to the Story

1. **LITERARY LENS** List some of the ways that Malamud gives this story the feel of a folktale.

2. In what ways is Angel Levine like and unlike the usual depiction of an angel?

3. What is implied by the fact that at the conclusion of the story, Fanny is out of her sickbed and cleaning the Manischevitz's flat?

4. Angel Levine's appearance changes every time Manischevitz sees him. You might want to use a chart like the one below to track the changes in Angel Levine's appearance. What do you think are the reasons for these changes?

Angel Levine's Appearance	Description
In the Manischevitz's living room	
At Bella's the first time	
At Bella's the second time, before going to the men's room	
After going to the men's room at Bella's	
While ascending	

5. **THE AUTHOR'S STYLE** Malamud's fiction has these qualities:

   • the spare prose is occasionally interrupted by sudden bursts of emotional or metaphorical language.
   • miraculous events take place in grim city neighborhoods.

   Identify an example of these two aspects of Malamud's style and tell what impact or meaning each gives to the story.

✶✶

John Cheever
1912–1982

About the Author

"I can't write without a reader," John Cheever once said. "It's precisely like a kiss, you can't do it alone" (*Christian Science Monitor*).

The author began his relationship with readers early in life. In 1930, when he was 18, his first short story, "Expulsion," was published in *New Republic*. The story was based on a real life incident; the year before, Cheever had been expelled from Thayer Academy in Massachusetts, a prestigious boarding school. That same year his affluent East Coast family had lost its wealth in the stock market crash. The author went on to write dozens of short stories and several novels, but before he was able to devote himself to fiction full time,

Cheever wrote synopses of films for MGM and taught in a New York State prison. Throughout his life, he suffered from alcoholism, which resulted in a stay in a rehabilitation clinic in 1975.

Cheever is best known as a writer of short stories, many of which were first published in *The New Yorker* and later collected into *The Stories of John Cheever*, which won the Pulitzer Prize, the National Book Critics Circle Award, and the American Book Award in 1978. His 1957 novel *The Wapshot Chronicle* is on the Modern Library's list of the 100 Best Novels of the 20th Century.

✶✶✶✶✶✶✶✶✶✶✶

The Author's Style

Many of Cheever's stories offer a glimpse of the moral and emotional lives of upper-middle class people from New York City or its suburbs. Using his hometown of Quincy, Massachusetts, as a model, the author lifts the veil off suburban life, revealing the sadness and dissatisfaction beneath prosperity and success.

Cheever's characters are often extremely odd and detached from reality; generally we don't learn much about how they make a living, but the author pays close attention to how they behave socially and at home. Usually they are devoted to tradition and habit, partly because of a desperate need for status and

security. Often their behavior is exaggerated both individually and in groups. The characters' obsessions—which are revealed in fantasies or dreams as well as quirky behavior—are the author's way of enabling us to understand them even when they can't understand themselves.

Cheever conveys all of this in a polite and elegant prose style. His style includes sophisticated vocabulary and complex sentences with subordinate clauses and qualifying phrases. An ironic tone satirizes both the characters and their way of life, revealing them to be both ridiculous and sad in the end.

LITERARY LENS Cheever was an accomplished practitioner of satire, which is the exposure of vices and shortcomings through humor or exaggeration. Watch for examples of satire in this story.

THE
WRYSONS

JOHN CHEEVER

The Wrysons wanted things in the suburb of Shady Hill to remain exactly as they were. Their dread of change—of irregularity of any sort—was acute, and when the Larkin estate was sold for an old people's rest home, the Wrysons went to the Village Council meeting and demanded to know what sort of old people these old people were going to be. The Wrysons' civic activities were confined to upzoning,[1] but they were very active in this field, and if you were invited to their a house for cocktails, the chances were that you would be asked to sign an upzoning petition before you got away. This was something more than a natural desire to preserve the character of the community. They seemed

---

[1] **upzoning:** allowing an increased population density in an area; in this case, the construction of a retirement community that houses many people as opposed to a single-family dwelling that only houses a few

> *There* was hardly a book in their house, and, in a place where even cooks were known to have Picasso reproductions hanging above their washstands, the Wrysons' taste in painting stopped at marine sunsets and bowls of flowers.

to sense that there was a stranger at the gates—unwashed, tirelessly scheming, foreign, the father of disorderly children who would ruin their rose garden and depreciate their real-estate investment, a man with a beard, a garlic breath, and a book. The Wrysons took no part in the intellectual life of the community. There was hardly a book in their house, and, in a place where even cooks were known to have Picasso reproductions hanging above their washstands, the Wrysons' taste in painting stopped at marine sunsets and bowls of flowers. Donald Wryson was a large man with thinning fair hair and the cheerful air of a bully,

rectitude:
righteousness;
propriety

contentious:
argumentative

but he was a bully only in the defense of **rectitude**, class distinctions, and the orderly appearance of things. Irene Wryson was not a totally unattractive woman, but she was both shy and **contentious**—especially contentious on the subject of upzoning. They had one child, a little girl named Dolly, and they lived in a pleasant house on Alewives Lane, and they went in for gardening. This was another way of keeping up the appearance of things, and Donald Wryson was very critical of a neighbor who had ragged syringa bushes and a bare spot on her front lawn. They led a limited social life; they seemed to have no ambitions or needs in this direction, although at Christmas each year they sent out about six hundred cards. The preparation and addressing of these must have occupied their evenings for at least two weeks. Donald had a laugh like a jackass, and people who did not like him were careful not to sit in the same train coach with him. The Wrysons were stiff; they were inflexible. They seemed to experience not distaste but alarm when they found quack grass in their lawn or heard of a contemplated divorce among their neighbors. They were odd, of course. They were not as odd as poor, dizzy Flossie Dolmetch, who was caught forging drug prescriptions and was discovered to have been under the influence of morphine for three years. They were not as odd as Caruthers Mason, with his collection of two thousand **lewd** photographs, or as odd as Mrs. Temon, who, with those two lovely children in the next room—But why go on? They were odd.

lewd:
obscene

Irene Wryson's oddness centered on a dream. She dreamed once or twice a month that someone—some enemy or **hapless** American pilot—had exploded a hydrogen bomb. In the light of day, her dream was inadmissible, for she could not relate it to her garden, her interest in upzoning, or her comfortable way of life. She could not bring herself to tell her husband at breakfast that she had dreamed about the hydrogen bomb. Faced with the pleasant table

hapless: unlucky

and its view of the garden—faced even with rain and snow—she could not find it in herself to explain what had troubled her sleep. The dream cost her much in energy and composure, and often left her deeply depressed. Its sequence of events varied, but it usually went like this.

The dream was set in Shady Hill—she dreamed that she woke in her own bed. Donald was always gone. She was at once aware of the fact that the bomb had exploded. Mattress stuffing and a trickle of brown water were coming through a big hole in the ceiling. The sky was gray—lightless—although there were in the west a few threads of red light, like those charming vapor trails we see in the air after the sun has set. She didn't know if these

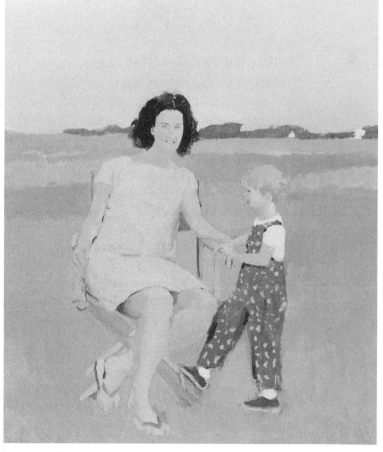

JANE AND ELIZABETH, Fairfield Porter, 1967, The Parrish Art Museum

were vapor trails or some part of that force that would destroy the marrow in her bones. The gray air seemed final. The sky would never shine with light

auxiliary:
assisting;
supplementary

din:
loud, persistent
noise

palliative:
remedy

again. From her window she could see a river, and now, as she watched, boats began to come upstream. At first, there were only two or three. Then there were tens, and then there were hundreds. There were outboards, excursion boats, yachts, schooners with **auxiliary** motors; there were even rowboats. The number of boats grew until the water was covered with them, and the noise of motors rose to a loud **din**. The jockeying for position in this retreat up the river became aggressive and then savage. She saw men firing pistols at one another, and a rowboat, in which there was a family with little children, smashed and sunk by a cruiser. She cried, in her dream, to see this inhumanity as the world was ending. She cried, and she went on watching, as if some truth was being revealed to her—as if she had always known this to be the human condition, as if she had always known the world to be dangerous and the comforts of her life in Shady Hill to be the merest **palliative**.

*A*nd how could she lean across the breakfast table and explain her pallor to her husky husband with this detailed vision of the end of the world? He would have laughed his jackass laugh.

Then in her dream she turned away from the window and went through the bathroom that connected their room and Dolly's. Her daughter was sleeping sweetly, and she woke her. At this point, her emotions were at their strongest. The force and purity of the love that she felt toward this fragrant child was an agony. She dressed the little girl and put a snowsuit on her and led her into the bathroom. She opened the medicine cabinet, the one place in the house that the Wrysons, in their passion for neatness, had not put in order. It was crowded with leftover medicines from Dolly's trifling illnesses—cough syrups, calamine lotion for poison ivy, aspirin, and physics. And the mild perfume of these remnants and the tenderness she had felt for her daughter when she was ill—as if the door of the medicine cabinet had been a window opening onto some dazzling summer of the emotions—made her cry again. Among the bottles was one that said "Poison," and she reached for this and unscrewed the top, and shook into her left hand a pill for herself and one for the girl. She told the trusting child some gentle lie, and was about to put the pill between her lips when the ceiling of the bathroom collapsed and they stood knee deep in plaster and dirty water She groped around in the water for the poison, but it was lost, and the dream usually ended in this way. And

224   John Cheever

how could she lean across the breakfast table and explain her **pallor** to her husky husband with this detailed vision of the end of the world? He would have laughed his jackass laugh.

pallor: paleness

Donald Wryson's oddness could be traced easily enough to his childhood. He had been raised in a small town in the Middle West that couldn't have had much to recommend it, and his father, an old-fashioned commercial traveler, with a hothouse rose in his buttonhole and buff-colored spats,[2] had abandoned his wife and his son when the boy was young. Mrs. Wryson had few friends and no family. With her husband gone, she got a job as a clerk in an insurance office, and took up, with her son, a life of **unmitigated melancholy** and need. She never forgot the horror of her abandonment, and she leaned so heavily for support on her son that she seemed to threaten his animal spirits. Her life was a Calvary,[3] as she often said, and the most she could do was to keep body and soul together.

unmitigated: unrelieved

melancholy: sadness

She had been young and fair and happy once, and the only way she had of evoking these lost times was by giving her son baking lessons. When the nights were long and cold and the wind whistled around the four-family house where they lived, she would light a fire in the kitchen range and drop an apple peel onto the stove lid for the fragrance. Then Donald would put on an apron and scurry around, getting out the necessary bowls and pans, measuring out flour and sugar, separating eggs. He learned the contents of every cupboard. He knew where the spices and the sugar were kept, the nutmeats and the citron, and when the work was done, he enjoyed washing the bowls and pans and putting them back where they belonged. Donald loved these hours himself, mostly because they seemed to dispel the oppression that stood unlifted over those years of his mother's life—and was there any reason why a lonely boy should rebel against the feeling of security that he found in the kitchen on a stormy night? She taught him how to make cookies and muffins and banana bread and, finally, a Lady Baltimore cake.[4] It was sometimes after eleven

> *S*he never forgot the horror of her abandonment, and she leaned so heavily for support on her son that she seemed to threaten his animal spirits.

---

2 **spats:** fancy, old-fashioned shoes or leg coverings

3 **Calvary:** an experience of intense mental suffering; also the place in the Bible where Jesus was crucified

4 **Lady Baltimore cake:** a fluffy, layered cake filled with raisins, nuts, cherries, and sherry

o'clock when their work was done. "We do have a good time together, don't we, son?" Mrs. Wryson would ask. "We have a lovely time together, don't we, you and me? Oh, hear that wind howling! Think of the poor sailors at sea." Then she would embrace him, she would run her fingers through his light hair, and sometimes, although he was much too big, she would draw him onto her lap.

All of that was long ago. Mrs. Wryson was dead, and when Donald stood at the edge of her grave he had not felt any very great grief. She had been **reconciled** to dying years before she did die, and her conversation had been full of **gallant** references to the grave. Years later, when Donald was living alone in New York, he had been overtaken suddenly, one spring evening, by a depression as keen as any in his adolescence. He did not drink, he did not enjoy books or movies or the theatre, and, like his mother, he had few friends. Searching desperately for some way to take himself out of this misery, he hit on the idea of baking a Lady Baltimore cake. He went out and bought the ingredients—deeply ashamed of himself—and sifted the flour and chopped the nuts and citron in the kitchen of the little walk-up apartment where he lived. As he stirred the cake batter, he felt his depression vanish. It was not until he had put the cake in the oven and sat down to wipe his hands on his apron that he realized how successful he had been in summoning the ghost of his mother and the sense of security he had experienced as a child in her kitchen on stormy nights. When the cake was done he iced it, ate a slice, and dumped the rest into the garbage.

The next time he felt troubled, he resisted the temptation to bake a cake, but he was not always able to do this, and during the eight or nine years he had been married to Irene he must have baked eight or nine cakes. He took extraordinary precautions, and she knew nothing of this. She believed him to be a complete stranger to the kitchen. And how could he at the breakfast table—all two hundred and sixteen pounds of him—explain that he looked sleepy because he had been up until three baking a Lady Baltimore cake, which he had hidden in the garage?

Given these unpleasant facts, then, about these not attractive people, we can dispatch them brightly enough, and who but Dolly would ever miss them? Donald Wryson, in his crusading zeal for upzoning, was out in all kinds of weather, and let's say that one night, when he was returning from a referendum in an ice storm, his car skidded down

reconciled: accepting of; ready for

gallant: noble; self-sacrificing

Hill Street, struck the big elm at the corner, and was demolished. Finis.[5] His poor widow, either through love or dependence, was inconsolable. Getting out of bed one morning, a month or so after the loss of her husband, she got her feet caught in the dust ruffle and fell and broke her hip. Weakened by a long convalescence, she contracted pneumonia and departed this life. This leaves us with Dolly to account for, and what a sad tale we can write for this little girl. During the months in which her parents' will is in probate,[6] she lives first on the charity and then on the **forbearance** of her neighbors. Finally, she is sent to live with her only relative, a cousin of her mother's, who is a schoolteacher in Los Angeles. How many hundreds of nights will she cry herself to sleep in bewilderment and loneliness. How strange and cold the world will seem. There is little to remind her of her parents except at Christmas, when, forwarded from Shady Hill, will come Greetings from Mrs. Sallust Trevor, who has been living in Paris and does not know about the accident; Salutations from the Parkers, who live in Mexico and never did get their lists straight; Season's Greetings from Meyers' Drugstore; Merry Christmas from the Perry Browns; Santissimas from the Oak Tree Italian Restaurant; A Joyeux Noël from Dodie Smith. Year after year, it will be this little girl's responsibility to throw into the wastebasket these cheerful holiday greetings that have followed her parents to and beyond the grave. . . . But this did not happen, and if it had, it would have thrown no light on what we know.

forbearance: patience; leniency

The air smelled sweet. Sweating suddenly, the beating of her heart strained with terror, she realized that the end had come. What could that sweetness in the air be but atomic ash?

What happened was this: Irene Wryson had her dream one night. When she woke, she saw that her husband was not in bed. The air smelled sweet. Sweating suddenly, the beating of her heart strained with terror, she realized that the end had come. What could that sweetness in the air be but atomic ash? She ran to the window, but the river was empty. Half asleep and feeling cruelly lost as she was, she was kept from waking Dolly only by a healthy curiosity. There was smoke in the hallway, but it was not the smoke of any common fire. The sweetness made her feel sure that this was lethal ash. Led

---

5 **Finis:** Middle English for "the end"

6 **probate:** the process of legally determining if a last will and testament is genuine

on by the smell, she went on down the stairs and through the dining room into the lighted kitchen. Donald was asleep with his head on the table and the room was full of smoke. "Oh, my darling," she cried, and woke him.

"I burned it," he said when he saw the smoke pouring from the oven. "I burned the damned thing."

"I thought it was the hydrogen bomb," she said.

"It's a cake," he said. "I burned it. What made you think it was the hydrogen bomb?"

"If you wanted something to eat, you should have waked me," she said.

She turned off the oven, and opened the window to let out the smell of smoke and let in the smell of nicotiana and other night flowers. She may have hesitated for a moment, for what would the stranger at the gates—that intruder with his beard and his book—have made of this couple, in their nightclothes, in the smoke-filled kitchen at half past four in the morning? Some comprehension—perhaps momentary—of the complexity of life must have come to them, but it was only momentary. There were no further explanations. He threw the cake, which was burned to a cinder, into the garbage, and they turned out the lights and climbed the stairs, more mystified by life than ever, and more interested than ever in a good appearance.

Responding to the Story

1. **LITERARY LENS** What human vices and follies does Cheever satirize in this story?

2. Reread the three paragraphs that concern Irene Wryson's dream beginning on page 223. What can you conclude about her fears and obsessions?

3. The word "wry" means ironically or grimly humorous. It is probably not an accident that the word is embedded in the Wrysons' name. In what way is the meaning of their name played out in the Wrysons' story?

4. In her dream, Irene Wryson checks on her sleeping daughter and "the force and purity of the love that she felt toward this fragrant child was an agony." What do you think can make a pure and strong love feel agonizing?

5. Why is Donald Wryson so secretive about baking cakes?

6. **THE AUTHOR'S STYLE** Cheever has the gift for revealing the psychology of characters, especially when the characters don't understand themselves. Choose either Irene or Donald Wryson and tell what you have come to understand about them that they don't understand themselves. Consider personality traits, fears, motivations, mannerisms, and attitudes.

★★★

Kurt Vonnegut
1922

About the Author

"As a kid I was a jokemaker," Kurt Vonnegut recalls of his boyhood in Indianapolis. "I was the youngest member of my family, and the youngest child in any family is always a jokemaker because a joke is the only way he can enter into adult conversation" (*Christian Century*).

The author's rollicking but edgy humor is one reason he is not only praised by critics but also popular with readers. Although much of what he writes can be considered science fiction, an overall tone of black humor, absurdism, and satire transcends that label and puts his writing in the literary mainstream.

Before becoming a freelance writer in 1950, Vonnegut served as a soldier in World War II and worked at General Electric Company. Awarded a Purple Heart for his military service, Vonnegut and other prisoners of war were forced to take refuge in an underground meatlocker for several days during the fire-bombing of Dresden, Germany.

That experience became the basis of his hugely successful 1969 novel, *Slaughterhouse-Five*, which attracted a cult-like following. Other well-known works include a collection of short stories called *Welcome to the Monkey House* and the novels *Cat's Cradle* and *The Sirens of Titan*. The unpretentious writer once commented that he would rather have written the television show "Cheers" than anything he has written. Some of his works have been adapted for stage and screen.

★★★★★★★★★★★

The Author's Style

In many of Vonnegut's stories the narrative tone is unemotional and non-judgmental. This is a satirist's strategy for forcing us to respond to what we see because at least on the surface, the author himself isn't taking any stands.

Generally, Vonnegut's stories and novels lean in the direction of fable rather than realistic fiction. His often-exaggerated characters and fantastic plots are meant to wake us up by taking us outside our own society, whose faults and attitudes we tend to overlook. In the novel *Slaughterhouse-Five*, for example, his use of the science fiction technique of time travel enables Vonnegut to deliver a biting critique not only of contemporary culture, but also of the Vietnam War, which was going on at the time the novel was published. Frequent Vonnegut targets include consumerism, ecology, and war.

Vonnegut sometimes discusses oppression as if he were resigned to it but his ironic tone tells us that he is criticizing its tragic human cost. By making matter-of-fact statements about outrageous actions, the writer is forcing the reader to evaluate and decide what matters.

LITERARY LENS
The *absurdists* were a group of artists of the 1950s and '60s who attempted to show the absurdity of the human condition and to satirize social attitudes and institutions. These authors used extreme illogic, black humor, and dark fantasy to expose what they felt to be the futility and despair of modern society. Watch for aspects of the absurd in this short story.

HARRISON BERGERON

KURT VONNEGUT

The year was 2081, and everybody was finally equal. They weren't only equal before God and the law. They were equal every which way. Nobody was smarter than anybody else. Nobody was better looking than anybody else. Nobody was stronger or quicker than anybody else. All this equality was due to the 211th, 212th, and 213th Amendments to the Constitution, and to the unceasing **vigilance** of agents of the United States Handicapper General.

Some things about living still weren't quite right, though. April, for instance, still drove people crazy by not being springtime. And it was in that clammy month that the H-G men took George and Hazel Bergeron's fourteen-year-old son, Harrison, away.

It was tragic, all right, but George and Hazel couldn't think about it very hard. Hazel had a perfectly average intelligence, which

vigilance:
watchfulness;
caution

231

meant she couldn't think about anything except in short bursts. And George, while his intelligence was way above normal, had a little mental handicap radio in his ear. He was required by law to wear it at all times. It was tuned to a government transmitter. Every twenty seconds or so, the transmitter would send out some sharp noise to keep people like George from taking unfair advantage of their brains.

George and Hazel were watching television. There were tears on Hazel's cheeks, but she'd forgotten for the moment what they were about.

On the television screen were ballerinas.

A buzzer sounded in George's head. His thoughts fled in panic, like bandits from a burglar alarm.

"That was a real pretty dance, that dance they just did," said Hazel.

"Huh?" said George.

"That dance—it was nice," said Hazel.

"Yup," said George. He tried to think a little about the ballerinas. They weren't really very good—no better than anybody else would have been, anyway. They were burdened with sashweights[1] and bags of birdshot,[2] and their faces were masked, so that no one, seeing a free and graceful gesture or a pretty face, would feel like something the cat drug in. George was toying with the vague notion that maybe dancers shouldn't be handicapped. But he didn't get very far with it before another noise in his ear radio scattered his thoughts.

George winced. So did two out of the eight ballerinas.

Hazel saw him wince. Having no mental handicap herself, she had to ask George what the latest sound had been.

"Sounded like somebody hitting a milk bottle with a ball peen hammer,"[3] said George.

"I'd think it would be real interesting, hearing all the different sounds," said Hazel, a little envious. "All the things they think up."

"Um," said George.

"Only, if I was Handicapper General, you know what I would do?" said Hazel. Hazel, as a matter of fact, bore a strong resemblance to the Handicapper General, a woman named Diana Moon Glampers. "If I was Diana Moon Glampers," said Hazel, "I'd have chimes on Sunday—just chimes. Kind of in honor of religion."

---

1 **sashweights:** narrow lead weights

2 **birdshot:** lead that is inside shotgun shells

3 **ball peen hammer:** hammer with one rounded head, usually used for working with metal

"I could think, if it was just chimes," said George.

"Well—maybe make 'em real loud," said Hazel. "I think I'd make a good Handicapper General."

"Good as anybody else," said George.

"Who knows better'n I do what normal is?" said Hazel.

"Right," said George. He began to think **glimmeringly** about his abnormal son who was now in jail, about Harrison, but a twenty-one-gun salute in his head stopped that.

"Boy!" said Hazel, "that was a doozy, wasn't it?"

It was such a doozy that George was white and trembling and tears stood on the rims of his red eyes. Two of the eight ballerinas had collapsed to the studio floor, holding their temples.

*A*ll of a sudden you look so tired," said Hazel. "Why don't you stretch out on the sofa, so's you can rest your handicap bag on the pillows, honeybunch." She was referring to the forty-seven pounds of birdshot in a canvas bag, which was padlocked around George's neck.

glimmeringly:
intermittently;
unsteadily

"All of a sudden you look so tired," said Hazel. "Why don't you stretch out on the sofa, so's you can rest your handicap bag on the pillows, honeybunch." She was referring to the forty seven pounds of birdshot in a canvas bag, which was padlocked around George's neck. "Go on and rest the bag for a little while," she said. "I don't care if you're not equal to me for a while."

George weighed the bag with his hands. "I don't mind it," he said. "I don't notice it anymore. It's just a part of me."

"You been so tired lately—kind of wore out," said Hazel. "If there was just some way we could make a little hole in the bottom of the bag, and just take out a few of them lead balls. Just a few."

"Two years in prison and two thousand dollars fine for every ball I took out," said George. "I don't call that a bargain."

"If you could just take a few out when you came home from work," said Hazel. "I mean—you don't compete with anybody around here. You just set around."

"If I tried to get away with it," said George, "then other people'd get away with it—and pretty soon we'd be right back to the dark ages again, with everybody competing against everybody else. You wouldn't like that, would you?"

> *And she had to apologize at once for her voice, which was a very unfair voice for a woman to use. Her voice was a warm, luminous, timeless melody.*

"I'd hate it," said Hazel.

"There you are," said George. "The minute people start cheating on laws, what do you think happens to society?"

If Hazel hadn't been able to come up with an answer to this question, George couldn't have supplied one. A siren was going off in his head.

"Reckon it'd fall all apart," said Hazel.

"What would?" said George blankly.

"Society," said Hazel uncertainly. "Wasn't that what you just said?"

"Who knows?" said George.

The television program was suddenly interrupted for a news bulletin. It wasn't clear at first as to what the bulletin was about, since the announcer, like all announcers, had a serious speech impediment. For about half a minute, and in a state of high excitement, the announcer tried to say, "Ladies and gentlemen—"

He finally gave up, handed the bulletin to a ballerina to read.

"That's all right—" Hazel said of the announcer, "he tried. That's the big thing. He tried to do the best he could with what God gave him. He should get a nice raise for trying so hard."

"Ladies and gentlemen—" said the ballerina, reading the bulletin. She must have been extraordinarily beautiful, because the mask she wore was hideous. And it was easy to see that she was the strongest and most graceful of all the dancers, for her handicap bags were as big as those worn by two-hundred-pound men.

And she had to apologize at once for her voice, which was a very unfair voice for a woman to use. Her voice was a warm, luminous, timeless melody. "Excuse me—" she said, and she began again, making her voice absolutely uncompetitive. "Harrison Bergeron, age fourteen," she said in a grackle[4] squawk, "has just escaped from jail, where he was held on suspicion of plotting to overthrow the government. He is a genius and an athlete, is under-handicapped, and should be regarded as extremely dangerous."

A police photograph of Harrison Bergeron was flashed on the screen, upside down, then sideways, upside down again, then right side up. The

---

4 **grackle:** a large blackbird

picture showed the full length of Harrison against a background calibrated in feet and inches. He was exactly seven feet tall.

The rest of Harrison's appearance was Halloween and hardware. Nobody had ever borne heavier handicaps. He had outgrown **hindrances** faster than the H-G men could think them up. Instead of a little ear radio for a mental handicap, he wore a tremendous pair of earphones, and spectacles with thick wavy lenses. The spectacles were intended to make him not only half blind, but to give him **whanging** headaches besides.

Scrap metal was hung all over him. Ordinarily, there was a certain symmetry, a military neatness to the handicaps issued to strong people, but Harrison looked like a walking junkyard. In the race of life, Harrison carried three hundred pounds.

And to offset his good looks, the H-G men required that he wear at all times a red rubber ball for a nose, keep his eyebrows shaved off, and cover his even white teeth with black caps at **snaggletooth** random.

"If you see this boy," said the ballerina, "do not—I repeat, do not—try to reason with him."

There was the shriek of a door being torn from its hinges.

Screams and barking cries of consternation came from the television set. The photograph of Harrison Bergeron on the screen jumped again and again, as though dancing to the tune of an earthquake.

George Bergeron correctly identified the earthquake, and well he might have—for many was the time his own home had danced to the same crashing tune. "Oh, no—" said George, "that must be Harrison."

The realization was blasted from his mind instantly by the sound of an automobile collision in his head.

When George could open his eyes again, the photograph of Harrison was gone. A living, breathing Harrison filled the screen.

Clanking, clownish, and huge, Harrison stood in the center of the studio. The knob of the uprooted studio door was still in his hand. Ballerinas, technicians, musicians, and announcers cowered on their knees before him, expecting to die.

hindrances: handicaps; obstructions

whanging: sharp; pounding

snaggletooth: broken; irregular

> *S*creams and barking cries of consternation came from the television set. The photograph of Harrison Bergeron on the screen jumped again and again, as though dancing to the tune of an earthquake.

"I am the Emperor!" cried Harrison. "Do you hear? I am the Emperor! Everybody must do what I say at once!" He stamped his foot and the studio shook.

"Even as I stand here—" he bellowed, "crippled, hobbled, sickened—I am a greater ruler than any man who ever lived! Now watch me become what I *can* become!"

Harrison tore the straps of his handicap harness like wet tissue paper, tore straps guaranteed to support five thousand pounds.

Harrison's scrap-iron handicaps crashed to the floor.

Harrison thrust his thumbs under the bar of the padlock that secured his head harness. The bar snapped like celery. Harrison smashed his headphones and spectacles against the wall.

He flung away his rubber-ball nose, revealed a man that would have awed Thor, the god of thunder.

"I shall now select my Empress!" he said, looking down on the cowering people. "Let the first woman who dares rise to her feet claim her mate and her throne!"

A moment passed, and then a ballerina arose, swaying like a willow. Harrison plucked the mental handicap from her ear, snapped off her physical handicaps with marvelous delicacy. Last of all, he removed her mask.

She was blindingly beautiful.

"Now—" said Harrison, taking her hand, "shall we show the people the meaning of the word dance? Music!" he commanded.

The musicians scrambled back into their chairs, and Harrison stripped them of their handicaps, too. "Play your best," he told them, "and I'll make you barons and dukes and earls."

The music began. It was normal at first—cheap, silly, false. But Harrison snatched two musicians from their chairs, waved them like batons as he sang the music as he wanted it played. He slammed them back into their chairs.

The music began again and was much improved.

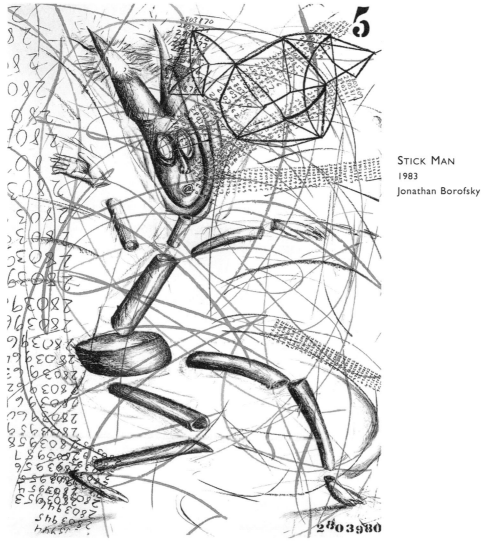

STICK MAN
1983
Jonathan Borofsky

Harrison and his Empress merely listened to the music for a while—listened gravely, as though synchronizing their heartbeats with it.

They shifted their weight to their toes.

Harrison placed his big hands on the girl's tiny waist, letting her sense the weightlessness that would soon be hers.

And then, in an explosion of joy and grace, into the air they sprang!

Not only were the laws of the land abandoned, but the law of gravity and the laws of motion as well.

gamboled:
leapt; frolicked

They reeled, whirled, swiveled, flounced, capered, **gamboled**, and spun.

They leaped like deer on the moon.

The studio ceiling was thirty feet high, but each leap brought the dancers nearer to it.

It became their obvious intention to kiss the ceiling.

They kissed it.

And then, neutralizing gravity with love and pure will, they remained suspended in air inches below the ceiling, and they kissed each other for a long, long time.

It was then that Diana Moon Glampers, the Handicapper General, came into the studio with a double-barreled ten-gauge shotgun. She fired twice, and the Emperor and the Empress were dead before they hit the floor.

Diana Moon Glampers loaded the gun again. She aimed it at the musicians and told them they had ten seconds to get their handicaps back on.

It was then that the Bergerons' television tube burned out.

Hazel turned to comment about the blackout to George. But George had gone out into the kitchen for a can of beer.

George came back in with the beer, paused while a handicap signal shook him up. And then he sat down again. "You been crying?" he said to Hazel.

"Yup," she said,

"What about?" he said.

"I forget," she said. "Something real sad on television."

"What was it?" he said.

"It's all kind of mixed up in my mind," said Hazel.

"Forget sad things," said George.

"I always do," said Hazel.

"That's my girl," said George. He winced. There was the sound of a riveting gun in his head.

"Gee—I could tell that one was a doozy," said Hazel.

"You can say that again," said George.

"Gee—" said Hazel, "I could tell that one was a doozy."

Responding to the Story

1. LITERARY LENS From the story, detail at least one example of extreme illogic, black humor, or dark fantasy. Then explain why you think Vonnegut uses the device.

2. Why do you think the Handicapper General and others in charge want everyone to be equal?

3. "All people are created equal" is a basic tenet of American democracy. How is this notion exploited in "Harrison Bergeron"?

4. Satirists are quick to identify the evils and excesses of society and those in power but they often don't have ready solutions to the problems they point out. What evil is Vonnegut satirizing and what solutions might address the problem?

5. THE AUTHOR'S STYLE A *pessimist* is a person who generally considers reality to be dismal and expects the worst outcome; an *optimist* is just the opposite. Consider the quotation by Vonnegut below along with the short story "Harrison Bergeron." Do you think Vonnegut leans more toward pessimism or optimism? Explain your response.

Laughter and Tears

Laughter and tears are both responses to frustration and exhaustion. I myself prefer to laugh, since there is less cleaning up to do afterward.

—Kurt Vonnegut
Quotations to Cheer You Up When the World Is Getting You Down

---

Flannery O'Connor
1925–1964

About the Author

When Flannery O'Connor was growing up in Milledgeville, Georgia, she lived right across the street from the looming cathedral her family attended. Her intense Catholicism was to have a strong influence on her life and work.

Also influential was her parents' encouragement in developing her talents. O'Connor was a shy and talented only child who wrote, drew cartoons, and attended an experimental private school. The author showed ingenuity and a certain fascination with freakishness at a young age, when she taught a "frizzled" chicken (one whose feathers grew inward) to walk backwards. This fascination would later turn up in her writing.

O'Connor went to college in the South and published her first story in 1946. Not long after receiving her master's degree from the well-known University of Iowa Writers' Workshop, she was stricken with lupus, the chronic inflammatory disease that had killed her father. She returned home to live with her mother and raise peacocks on her family's ancestral farm while continuing to write until her death in 1964.

Remembered primarily as a short story writer, O'Connor's best-known works include the novel *The Violent Bear It Away* and the short story collections *A Good Man Is Hard to Find* and *Everything That Rises Must Converge*.

****

The Author's Style

O'Connor was a devout Catholic who lived in the South, a region historically intolerant toward her religion. Her stories focus on the need for salvation in a world that is beset by evil. O'Connor's characters often reveal through their manners and everyday behavior how obsessed they are by race and social class. Worse, they often think their wrongful actions and attitudes make them "good people."

These characters, who speak in the idiom of rural Georgia, often fail to see the moral implications of their own words. In the end, they are often shaken out of their narrow habits of mind by shocking, even violent events.

When O'Connor's characters are saved from their meanness and shallowness, it is not through their own efforts. Instead, it is by mysterious events, sudden evidence of what O'Connor thought of as the grace of God. She is critical of the prideful and the smug—people who think they always know what is right—and these characters often pay a high price for the humbling insights they reach. O'Connor's stories sometimes read like modern parables of spiritual enlightenment. Bizarre characters, comical descriptions, and grotesque metaphors for the way things look or feel also mark her style. The physical deformities of her characters often reflect their moral shortcomings. Her stories often concern an individual's relationship to God.

LITERARY LENS In literature, recurrent images, objects, phrases, or actions are called *motifs*. The repetition of such elements tends to unify a work of literature. Watch for motifs in this story.

Everything That Rises Must Converge

Flannery O'Connor

Her doctor had told Julian's mother that she must lose twenty pounds on account of her blood pressure, so on Wednesday nights Julian had to take her downtown on the bus for a reducing class at the Y. The reducing class was designed for working girls over fifty, who weighed from 165 to 200 pounds. His mother was one of the slimmer ones, but she said ladies did not tell their age or weight. She would not ride the buses by herself at night since they had been integrated,[1] and because the reducing class was one of her few pleasures, necessary for her health, and *free*, she said Julian could at least put himself out

---

1 **since they had been integrated:** since blacks had been allowed to ride the same buses as whites

MORALITY WAS HER OWN, Daphne Confar

to take her, considering all she did for him. Julian did not like to consider all she did for him, but every Wednesday night he braced himself and took her.

She was almost ready to go, standing before the hall mirror, putting on her hat, while he, his hands behind him, appeared pinned to the door frame, waiting like Saint Sebastian for the arrows to begin piercing him.[2] The hat was new and had cost her seven dollars and a half. She kept saying, "Maybe I shouldn't have paid that for it. No, I shouldn't have. I'll take it off and return it tomorrow. I shouldn't have bought it."

Julian raised his eyes to heaven. "Yes, you should have bought it," he said. "Put it on and let's go." It was a hideous hat. A purple velvet flap came down on one side of it and stood up on the other; the rest of it was green and looked like a cushion with the stuffing out. He decided it was less comical than **jaunty** and pathetic. Everything that gave her pleasure was small and depressed him.

jaunty:
showy; stylish

She lifted the hat one more time and set it down slowly on top of her head. Two wings of gray hair protruded on either side of her **florid** face, but her eyes, sky-blue, were as innocent and untouched by experience as they must have been when she was ten. Were it not that she was a widow who had

florid:
flowery; ornate
in style

2 **Saint Sebastian . . . piercing him:** Sebastian was tied to a tree and shot with arrows for being a Christian during the reign of Roman emperor Diocletian, 284–305 B.C.

struggled fiercely to feed and clothe and put him through school and who was supporting him still, "until he got on his feet," she might have been a little girl that he had to take to town.

"It's all right, it's all right," he said. "Let's go." He opened the door himself and started down the walk to get her going. The sky was a dying violet and the houses stood out darkly against it, **bulbous** liver-colored monstrosities of a uniform ugliness though no two were alike. Since this had been a fashionable neighborhood forty years ago, his mother persisted in thinking they did well to have an apartment in it. Each house had a narrow collar of dirt around it in which sat, usually, a grubby child. Julian walked with his hands in his pockets, his head down and thrust forward and his eyes glazed with the determination to make himself completely numb during the time he would be sacrificed to her pleasure.

The door closed and he turned to find the dumpy figure, surmounted by the atrocious hat, coming toward him. "Well," she said, "you only live once and paying a little more for it, I at least won't meet myself coming and going."

bulbous: round; resembling a bulb

The door closed and he turned to find the dumpy figure, surmounted by the atrocious hat, coming toward him. "Well," she said, "you only live once and paying a little more for it, I at least won't meet myself coming and going."

"Some day I'll start making money," Julian said gloomily—he knew he never would—"and you can have one of those jokes whenever you take the fit." But first they would move. He visualized a place where the nearest neighbors would be three miles away on either side.

"I think you're doing fine," she said, drawing on her gloves. "You've only been out of school a year. Rome wasn't built in a day."

She was one of the few members of the Y reducing class who arrived in hat and gloves and who had a son who had been to college. "It takes time," she said, "and the world is in such a mess. This hat looked better on me than any of the others, though when she brought it out I said, 'Take that thing back. I wouldn't have it on my head,' and she said, 'Now wait till you see it on,' and when she put it on me, I said, 'We-ull,' and she said, 'If you ask me, that hat does something for you and you do something for the hat, and besides,' she said, 'with that hat, you won't meet yourself coming and going.'"

Julian thought he could have stood his lot better if she had been selfish, if she had been an old hag who drank and screamed at him. He walked along, saturated in depression, as if in the midst of his martyrdom he had lost his faith. Catching sight of his long, hopeless, irritated face, she stopped suddenly with a grief-stricken look, and pulled back on his arm. "Wait on me," she said. "I'm going back to the house and take this thing off and tomorrow I'm going to return it. I was out of my head. I can pay the gas bill with that seven-fifty."

He caught her arm in a vicious grip. "You are not going to take it back," he said. "I like it."

"Well," she said, "I don't think I ought. . . ."

"Shut up and enjoy it," he muttered, more depressed than ever.

"With the world in the mess it's in," she said, "it's a wonder we can enjoy anything. I tell you, the bottom rail is on the top."

Julian sighed.

"Of course," she said, "if you know who you are, you can go anywhere." She said this every time he took her to the reducing class. "Most of them in it are not our kind of people," she said, "but I can be gracious to anybody. I know who I am."

"They don't give a damn for your graciousness," Julian said savagely. "Knowing who you are is good for one generation only. You haven't the foggiest idea where you stand now or who you are."

She stopped and allowed her eyes to flash at him. "I most certainly do know who I am," she said, "and if you don't know who you are, I'm ashamed of you."

"Oh hell," Julian said.

"Your great-grandfather was a former governor of this state," she said. "Your grandfather was a prosperous landowner. Your grandmother was a Godhigh."

"Will you look around you," he said tensely, "and see where you are now?" and he swept his arm jerkily out to indicate the neighborhood, which the growing darkness at least made less dingy.

"You remain what you are," she said. "Your great-grandfather had a plantation and two hundred slaves."

"There are no more slaves," he said irritably.

"They were better off when they were," she said. He groaned to see that she was off on that topic. She rolled onto it every few days like a train on an open track. He knew every stop, every junction, every swamp along the way, and knew the exact point at which her conclusion would roll majestically into the station: "It's ridiculous. It's simply not realistic. They should rise, yes, but on their own side of the fence."

"Let's skip it," Julian said.

"The ones I feel sorry for," she said, "are the ones that are half white. They're tragic."

"Will you skip it?"

"Suppose we were half white. We would certainly have mixed feelings."

"I have mixed feelings now," he groaned.

"Well let's talk about something pleasant," she said. "I remember going to Grandpa's when I was a little girl. Then the house had double stairways that went up to what was really the second floor—all the cooking was done on the first. I used to like to stay down in the kitchen on account of the way the walls smelled. I would sit with my nose pressed against the plaster and take deep breaths. Actually the place belonged to the Godhighs but your grandfather Chestny paid the mortgage and saved it for them. They were in reduced circumstances," she said, "but reduced or not, they never forgot who they were."

"Doubtless that decayed mansion reminded them," Julian muttered. He never spoke of it without contempt or thought of it without longing. He had seen it once when he was a child before it had been sold. The double stairways had rotted and been torn down. Negroes were living in it. But it remained in his mind as his mother had known it. It appeared in his dreams regularly. He would stand on the wide porch, listening to the rustle of oak leaves, then wander through the high-ceilinged hall into the parlor that opened onto it and gaze at the worn rugs and faded draperies. It occurred to him that it was he, not she, who could have appreciated it. He preferred its threadbare elegance to anything he could name and it was because of it that all the neighborhoods they had lived in had been a torment to him—whereas she had hardly known the difference. She called her insensitivity "being adjustable."

"And I remember the old darky[3] who was my nurse, Caroline. There was

He preferred its threadbare elegance to anything he could name and it was because of it that all the neighborhoods they had lived in had been a torment to him—whereas she had hardly known the difference.

3 **darky:** derrogatory term for a black person

no better person in the world. I've always had a great respect for my colored friends," she said. "I'd do anything in the world for them and they'd. . . ."

"Will you for God's sake get off that subject?" Julian said. When he got on a bus by himself, he made it a point to sit down beside a Negro, in **reparation** as it were for his mother's sins.

reparation: compensation; atonement

"You're mighty touchy tonight," she said. "Do you feel all right?"

"Yes I feel all right," he said. "Now lay off."

She pursed her lips. "Well, you certainly are in a **vile** humor," she observed. "I just won't speak to you at all."

vile: foul; miserable

They had reached the bus stop. There was no bus in sight and Julian, his hands still jammed in his pockets and his head thrust forward, scowled down the empty street. The frustration of having to wait on the bus as well as ride on it began to creep up his neck like a hot hand. The presence of his mother was borne in upon him as she gave a pained sigh. He looked at her bleakly. She was holding herself very erect under the **preposterous** hat, wearing it like a banner of her imaginary dignity. There was in him an evil urge to break her spirit. He suddenly unloosened his tie and pulled it off and put it in his pocket.

preposterous: ridiculous

She stiffened. "Why must you look like *that* when you take me to town?" she said. "Why must you deliberately embarrass me?"

"If you'll never learn where you are," he said, "you can at least learn where I am."

"You look like a—thug," she said.

"Then I must be one," he murmured.

"I'll just go home," she said. "I will not bother you. If you can't do a little thing like that for me . . ."

Rolling his eyes upward, he put his tie back on. "Restored to my class," he muttered. He thrust his face toward her and hissed. "True culture is in the mind, the *mind*," he said, and tapped his head, "the mind."

"It's in the heart," she said, "and in how you do things and how you do things is because of who you *are*."

"Nobody in the damn bus cares who you are."

"I care who I am," she said icily.

The lighted bus appeared on top of the next hill and as it approached, they moved out into the street to meet it. He put his hand under her elbow and hoisted her up on the creaking step. She entered with a little smile, as if she were going into a drawing room where everyone had been waiting for her.

While he put in the tokens, she sat down on one of the broad front seats for three which faced the aisle. A thin woman with protruding teeth and long yellow hair was sitting on the end of it. His mother moved up beside her and left room for Julian beside herself. He sat down and looked at the floor across the aisle where a pair of thin feet in red and white canvas sandals were planted.

His mother immediately began a general conversation meant to attract anyone who felt like talking. "Can it get any hotter?" she said and removed from her purse a folding fan, black with a Japanese scene on it, which she began to flutter before her.

"I reckon it might could," the woman with the protruding teeth said, "but I know for a fact my apartment couldn't get no hotter."

"It must get the afternoon sun," his mother said. She sat forward and looked up and down the bus. It was half filled. Everybody was white. "I see we have the bus to ourselves," she said. Julian cringed.

"For a change," said the woman across the aisle, the owner of the red and white canvas sandals. "I come on one the other day and they were thick as fleas—up front and all through."

"The world is in a mess everywhere," his mother said. "I don't know how we've let it get in this fix."

"What gets my goat is all those boys from good families stealing automobile tires," the woman with the protruding teeth said. "I told my boy, I said you may not be rich but you been raised right and if I ever catch you in any such mess, they can send you on to the reformatory. Be exactly where you belong."

"Training tells," his mother said. "Is your boy in high school?"

"Ninth grade," the woman said.

"My son just finished college last year. He wants to write but he's selling typewriters until he gets started," his mother said.

The woman leaned forward and peered at Julian. He threw her such a **malevolent** look that she **subsided** against the seat. On the floor across the aisle there was an abandoned newspaper. He got up and got it and opened it out in front of him. His mother discreetly continued the conversation in a lower tone but the woman across the aisle said in a loud voice, "Well that's nice. Selling typewriters is close to writing. He can go right from one to the other."

"I tell him," his mother said, "that Rome wasn't built in a day."

Behind the newspaper Julian was withdrawing into the inner compartment of his mind where he spent most of his time. This was a kind of mental

malevolent:
evil; spiteful

subsided:
slumped; settled back

bubble in which he established himself when he could not bear to be a part of what was going on around him. From it he could see out and judge but in it he was safe from any kind of penetration from without. It was the only place where he felt free of the general idiocy of his fellows. His mother had never entered it but from it he could see her with absolute clarity.

The old lady was clever enough and he thought that if she had started from any of the right premises, more might have been expected of her. She lived according to the laws of her own fantasy world, outside of which he had never seen her set foot. The law of it was to sacrifice herself for him after she had first created the necessity to do so by making a mess of things. If he had permitted her sacrifices, it was only because her lack of foresight had made them necessary. All of her life had been a struggle to act like a Chestny without the Chestny goods, and to give him everything she thought a Chestny ought to have; but since, said she, it was fun to struggle, why complain? And when you had won, as she had won, what fun to look back on the hard times! He could not forgive her that she had enjoyed the struggle and that she thought *she* had won.

> *M*ost miraculous of all, instead of being blinded by love for her as she was for him, he had cut himself emotionally free of her and could see her with complete objectivity. He was not dominated by his mother.

What she meant when she said she had won was that she had brought him up successfully and had sent him to college and that he had turned out so well—good looking (her teeth had gone unfilled so that his could be straightened), intelligent (he realized he was too intelligent to be a success), and with a future ahead of him (there was of course no future ahead of him). She excused his gloominess on the grounds that he was still growing up and his radical ideas on his lack of practical experience. She said he didn't yet know a thing about "life," that he hadn't even entered the real world—when already he was as **disenchanted** with it as a man of fifty.

disenchanted: disillusioned; disappointed

The further irony of all this was that in spite of her, he had turned out so well. In spite of going to only a third-rate college, he had, on his own initiative, come out with a first-rate education; in spite of growing up dominated by a small mind, he had ended up with a large one; in spite of all her foolish views, he was free of prejudice and unafraid to face facts. Most miraculous of all, instead of being blinded by love for her as she was for him, he had cut himself emotionally free of her and could see her with complete objectivity. He was not dominated by his mother.

The bus stopped with a sudden jerk and shook him from his meditation. A woman from the back lurched forward with little steps and barely escaped falling in his newspaper as she righted herself. She got off and a large Negro got on. Julian kept his paper lowered to watch. It gave him a certain satisfaction to see injustice in daily operation. It confirmed his view that with a few exceptions there was no one worth knowing within a radius of three hundred miles. The Negro was well dressed and carried a briefcase. He looked around and then sat down on the other end of the seat where the woman with the red and white canvas sandals was sitting. He immediately unfolded a newspaper and obscured himself behind it. Julian's mother's elbow at once prodded insistently into his ribs. "Now you see why I won't ride on these buses by myself," she whispered.

The woman with the red and white canvas sandals had risen at the same time the Negro sat down and had gone further back in the bus and taken the seat of the woman who had got off. His mother leaned forward and cast her an approving look.

Julian rose, crossed the aisle, and sat down in the place of the woman with the canvas sandals. From this position, he looked serenely across at his mother. Her face had turned an angry red. He stared at her, making his eyes the eyes of a stranger. He felt his tension suddenly lift as if he had openly declared war on her.

He would have liked to get in conversation with the Negro and to talk with him about art or politics or any subject that would be above the comprehension of those around them, but the man remained entrenched behind his paper. He was either ignoring the change of seating or had never noticed it. There was no way for Julian to convey his sympathy.

His mother kept her eyes fixed reproachfully on his face. The woman with the protruding teeth was looking at him avidly as if he were a type of monster new to her.

"Do you have a light?" he asked the Negro.

Without looking away from his paper, the man reached in his pocket and handed him a packet of matches.

"Thanks," Julian said. For a moment he held the matches foolishly. A NO SMOKING sign looked down upon him from over the door. This alone

★★

would not have deterred him; he had no cigarettes. He had quit smoking some months before because he could not afford it. "Sorry," he muttered and handed back the matches. The Negro lowered the paper and gave him an annoyed look. He took the matches and raised the paper again.

His mother continued to gaze at him but she did not take advantage of his momentary discomfort. Her eyes retained their battered look. Her face seemed to be unnaturally red, as if her blood pressure had risen. Julian allowed no glimmer of sympathy to show on his face. Having got the advantage, he wanted desperately to keep it and carry it through. He would have liked to teach her a lesson that would last her a while, but there seemed no way to continue the point. The Negro refused to come out from behind his paper.

stolidly:
dully; without
emotion

Julian folded his arms and looked **stolidly** before him, facing her but as if he did not see her, as if he had ceased to recognize her existence. He visualized a scene in which, the bus having reached their stop, he would remain in his seat and when she said, "Aren't you going to get off?" he would look at her as at a stranger who had rashly addressed him. The corner they got off on was usually deserted, but it was well lighted and it would not hurt her to walk by herself the four blocks to the Y. He decided to wait until the time came and then decide whether or not he would let her get off by herself. He would have to be at the Y at ten to bring her back, but he could leave her wondering if he was going to show up. There was no reason for her to think she could always depend on him.

He retired again into the high-ceilinged room sparsely settled with large pieces of antique furniture. His soul expanded momentarily but then he became aware of his mother across from him and the vision shriveled. He studied her coldly. Her feet in little pumps dangled like a child's and did not quite reach the floor. She was training on him an exaggerated look of reproach. He felt completely detached from her. At that moment he could with pleasure have slapped her as he would have slapped a particularly obnoxious child in his charge.

He began to imagine various unlikely ways by which he could teach her a lesson. He might make friends with some distinguished Negro professor or lawyer and bring him home to spend the evening. He would be entirely justified but her blood pressure would rise to 300. He could not push her to the extent of making her have a stroke, and moreover, he had never been successful at making any Negro friends. He had tried to strike up an acquain-

Flannery O'Connor

tance on the bus with some of the better types, with ones that looked like professors or ministers or lawyers. One morning he had sat down next to a distinguished-looking dark brown man who had answered his questions with a sonorous **solemnity** but who had turned out to be an undertaker. Another day he had sat down beside a cigar-smoking Negro with a diamond ring on his finger, but after a few stilted pleasantries, the Negro had rung the buzzer and risen, slipping two lottery tickets into Julian's hand as he climbed over him to leave.

solemnity: seriousness; dignity

He imagined his mother lying desperately ill and his being able to secure only a Negro doctor for her. He toyed with that idea for a few minutes and then dropped it for a momentary vision of himself participating as a sympathizer in a sit-in demonstration. This was possible but he did not linger with it. Instead, he approached the ultimate horror. He brought home a beautiful suspiciously Negroid woman. Prepare yourself, he said. There is nothing you can do about it. This is the woman I've chosen. She's intelligent, dignified, even good, and she's suffered and she hasn't thought it *fun*. Now persecute us, go ahead and persecute us. Drive her out of here, but remember, you're driving me too. His eyes were narrowed and through the indignation he had generated, he saw his mother across the aisle, purple-faced, shrunken to the dwarf-like proportions of her moral nature, sitting like a mummy beneath the ridiculous banner of her hat.

She was a giant of a woman. Her face was set not only to meet opposition but to seek it out.

He was tilted out of his fantasy again as the bus stopped. The door opened with a sucking hiss and out of the dark a large, gaily dressed, sullen-looking colored woman got on with a little boy. The child, who might have been four, had on a short plaid suit and a Tyrolean hat with a blue feather in it. Julian hoped that he would sit down beside him and that the woman would push in beside his mother. He could think of no better arrangement.

As she waited for her tokens, the woman was surveying the seating possibilities—he hoped with the idea of sitting where she was least wanted. There was something familiar-looking about her but Julian could not place what it was. She was a giant of a woman. Her face was set not only to meet opposition but to seek it out. The downward tilt of her large lower lip was like a warning sign: DON'T TAMPER WITH ME. Her bulging figure was encased in

The vision of the two hats, identical, broke upon him with the radiance of a brilliant sunrise. His face was suddenly lit with joy. He could not believe that Fate had thrust upon his mother such a lesson.

a green crepe dress and her feet overflowed in red shoes. She had on a hideous hat. A purple velvet flap came down on one side of it and stood up on the other; the rest of it was green and looked like a cushion with the stuffing out. She carried a mammoth red pocketbook that bulged throughout as if it were stuffed with rocks.

To Julian's disappointment, the little boy climbed up on the empty seat beside his mother. His mother lumped all children, black and white, into the common category, "cute," and she thought little Negroes were on the whole cuter than little white children. She smiled at the little boy as he climbed on the seat.

Meanwhile the woman was bearing down upon the empty seat beside Julian. To his annoyance, she squeezed herself into it. He saw his mother's face change as the woman settled herself next to him and he realized with satisfaction that this was more objectionable to her than it was to him. Her face seemed almost gray and there was a look of dull recognition in her eyes, as if suddenly she had sickened at some awful confrontation. Julian saw that it was because she and the woman had, in a sense, swapped sons. Though his mother would not realize the symbolic significance of this, she would feel it. His amusement showed plainly on his face.

The woman next to him muttered something unintelligible to herself. He was conscious of a kind of bristling next to him, a muted growling like that of an angry cat. He could not see anything but the red pocketbook upright on the bulging green thighs. He visualized the woman as she had stood waiting for her tokens—the ponderous figure, rising from the red shoes upward over the solid hips, the mammoth bosom, the haughty face, to the green and purple hat.

His eyes widened.

The vision of the two hats, identical, broke upon him with the radiance of a brilliant sunrise. His face was suddenly lit with joy. He could not believe that Fate had thrust upon his mother such a lesson. He gave a loud chuckle so that she would look at him and see that he saw. She turned her eyes on him slowly. The blue in them seemed to have turned a bruised purple. For a moment he had an uncomfortable sense of her innocence, but it lasted only a second before principle rescued him. Justice entitled him to laugh. His grin hardened until it said to her as plainly as if he were saying aloud: Your punishment exactly fits your pettiness. This should teach you a permanent lesson.

Her eyes shifted to the woman. She seemed unable to bear looking at him and to find the woman preferable. He became conscious again of the bristling presence at his side. The woman was rumbling like a volcano about to become active. His mother's mouth began to twitch slightly at one corner. With a sinking heart, he saw **incipient** signs of recovery on her face and realized that this was going to strike her suddenly as funny and was going to be no lesson at all. She kept her eyes on the woman and an amused smile came over her face as if the woman were a monkey that had stolen her hat. The little Negro was looking up at her with large fascinated eyes. He had been trying to attract her attention for some time.

incipient: beginning

"Carver!" the woman said suddenly. "Come heah!"

When he saw that the spotlight was on him at last, Carver drew his feet up and turned himself toward Julian's mother and giggled.

"Carver!" the woman said. "You heah me? Come heah!"

Carver slid down from the seat but remained squatting with his back against the base of it, his head turned slyly around toward Julian's mother, who was smiling at him. The woman reached a hand across the aisle and snatched him back to her. He righted himself and hung backwards on her knees, grinning at Julian's mother. "Isn't he cute?" Julian's mother said to the woman with the protruding teeth.

"I reckon he is," the woman said without conviction.

The Negress yanked him upright but he eased out of her grip and shot across the aisle and scrambled, giggling wildly, onto the seat beside his love.

"I think he likes me," Julian's mother said, and smiled at the woman. It was the smile she used when she was being particularly gracious to an inferior. Julian saw everything lost. The lesson had rolled off her like rain on a roof.

The woman stood up and yanked the little boy off the seat as if she were snatching him from **contagion**. Julian could feel the rage in her at having no weapon like his mother's smile. She gave the child a sharp slap across his leg. He howled once and then thrust his head into her stomach and kicked his feet against her shins. "Be-have," she said vehemently.

contagion: spreading infection

The bus stopped and the Negro who had been reading the newspaper got off. The woman moved over and set the little boy down with a thump between herself and Julian. She held him firmly by the knee. In a moment he put his hands in front of his face and peeped at Julian's mother through his fingers.

"I see yoooooooo!" she said and put her hand in front of her face and peeped at him.

The woman slapped his hand down. "Quit yo' foolishness," she said, "before I knock the living Jesus out of you!"

Julian was thankful that the next stop was theirs. He reached up and pulled the cord. The woman reached up and pulled it at the same time. Oh my God, he thought. He had the terrible intuition that when they got off the bus together, his mother would open her purse and give the little boy a nickel. The gesture would be as natural to her as breathing. The bus stopped and the woman got up and lunged to the front, dragging the child, who wished to stay on, after her. Julian and his mother got up and followed. As they neared the door, Julian tried to relieve her of her pocketbook.

"No," she murmured, "I want to give the little boy a nickel."

"No!" Julian hissed. "No!"

She smiled down at the child and opened her bag. The bus door opened and the woman picked him up by the arm and descended with him, hanging at her hip. Once in the street she set him down and shook him.

Julian's mother had to close her purse while she got down the bus step but as soon as her feet were on the ground, she opened it again and began to rummage inside. "I can't find but a penny," she whispered, "but it looks like a new one."

"Don't do it!" Julian said fiercely between his teeth. There was a streetlight on the corner and she hurried to get under it so that she could better see into her pocketbook. The woman was heading off rapidly down the street with the child still hanging backward on her hand.

"Oh little boy!" Julian's mother called and took a few quick steps and caught up with them just beyond the lamp-post. "Here's a bright new penny for you," and she held out the coin, which shone bronze in the dim light.

The huge woman turned and for a moment stood, her shoulders lifted and her face frozen with frustrated rage, and stared at Julian's mother. Then all at once she seemed to explode like a piece of machinery that had been given one ounce of pressure too much. Julian saw the black fist swing out with the red pocketbook. He shut his eyes and cringed as he heard the woman shout, "He don't take nobody's pennies!" When he opened his eyes, the woman was disappearing down the street with the little boy staring wide-eyed over her shoulder. Julian's mother was sitting on the sidewalk.

"I told you not to do that," Julian said angrily. "I told you not to do that!"

He stood over her for a minute, gritting his teeth. Her legs were stretched out in front of her and her hat was on her lap. He squatted down and looked her in the face. It was totally expressionless. "You got exactly what you deserved," he said. "Now get up."

He picked up her pocketbook and put what had fallen out back in it. He picked the hat up off her lap. The penny caught his eye on the sidewalk and he picked that up and let it drop before her eyes into the purse. Then he stood up and leaned over and held his hands out to pull her up. She remained immobile. He sighed. Rising above them on either side were black apartment buildings, marked with irregular rectangles of light. At the end of the block a man came out of a door and walked off in the opposite direction. "All right," he said, "suppose somebody happens by and wants to know why you're sitting on the sidewalk?"

She took the hand and, breathing hard, pulled heavily up on it and then stood for a moment, swaying slightly as if the spots of light in the darkness were circling around her.

She took the hand and, breathing hard, pulled heavily up on it and then stood for a moment, swaying slightly as if the spots of light in the darkness were circling around her. Her eyes, shadowed and confused, finally settled on his face. He did not try to conceal his irritation. "I hope this teaches you a lesson," he said. She leaned forward and her eyes raked his face. She seemed trying to determine his identity. Then, as if she found nothing familiar about him, she started off with a headlong movement in the wrong direction.

"Aren't you going on to the Y?" he asked.

"Home," she muttered.

"Well, are we walking?"

For answer she kept going. Julian followed along, his hands behind him. He saw no reason to let the lesson she had had go without backing it up with an explanation of its meaning. She might as well be made to understand what had happened to her. "Don't think that was just an uppity Negro woman," he said. "That was the whole colored race which will no longer take your condescending pennies. That was your black double. She can wear the

gratuitously:
unnecessarily;
unkindly

obsolete:
outdated; useless

same hat as you, and to be sure," he added **gratuitously** (because he thought it was funny), "it looked better on her than it did on you. What all this means," he said, "is that the old world is gone. The old manners are **obsolete** and your graciousness is not worth a damn." He thought bitterly of the house that had been lost for him. "You aren't who you think you are," he said.

She continued to plow ahead, paying no attention to him. Her hair had come undone on one side. She dropped her pocketbook and took no notice. He stooped and picked it up and handed it to her but she did not take it.

"You needn't act as if the world had come to an end," he said, "because it hasn't. From now on you've got to live in a new world and face a few realities for a change. Buck up," he said, "it won't kill you."

She was breathing fast.

"Let's wait on the bus," he said.

"Home," she said thickly.

"I hate to see you behave like this," he said. "Just like a child. I should be able to expect more of you." He decided to stop where he was and make her stop and wait for a bus. "I'm not going any farther," he said, stopping. "We're going on the bus."

She continued to go on as if she had not heard him. He took a few steps and caught her arm and stopped her. He looked into her face and caught his breath. He was looking into a face he had never seen before. "Tell Grandpa to come get me," she said.

He stared, stricken.

"Tell Caroline to come get me," she said.

Stunned, he let her go and she lurched forward again, walking as if one leg were shorter than the other. A tide of darkness seemed to be sweeping her from him. "Mother!" he cried. "Darling, sweetheart, wait!" Crumpling, she fell to the pavement. He dashed forward and fell at her side, crying, "Mamma, Mamma!" He turned her over. Her face was fiercely distorted. One eye, large and staring, moved slightly to the left as if it had become **unmoored**. The other remained fixed on him, raked his face again, found nothing and closed.

unmoored
disconnected

"Wait here, wait here!" he cried and jumped up and began to run for help toward a cluster of lights he saw in the distance ahead of him. "Help, help!" he shouted, but his voice was thin, scarcely a thread of sound. The lights drifted farther away the faster he ran and his feet moved numbly as if they carried him nowhere. The tide of darkness seemed to sweep him back to her, postponing from moment to moment his entry into the world of guilt and sorrow.

Responding to the Story

1. **LITERARY LENS** What motifs did you notice in this story? In what ways do these repeated elements unify the story?

2. Reread the first paragraph of the story. What do you know about Julian's mother from the very beginning?

3. The concept of martyrdom appears several times in the story. What sacrifices are made in this story and by whom?

4. Consider the title of the story. Understanding that to converge means to come together and unite with a common focus, what in the story rises and therefore must converge?

5. It has been said that good literature raises more questions than it answers. O'Connor in particular is known for the profound questions her fiction poses. What questions do you think arise in this story?

6. **THE AUTHOR'S STYLE** Many of O'Connor's stories contain unexpected, sometimes violent, actions. Read the quotation below by O'Connor and consider "Everything That Rises Must Converge" in light of her statement. What action or gesture do you think indicates the "real heart of the story"?

O'Connor on the Unexpected

I often ask myself what makes a story work, and what makes it hold up as a story, and I have decided that it is probably some action, some gesture of a character that is unlike any other in the story, one which indicates where the real heart of the story lies. This would have to be an action or a gesture which was both totally right and totally unexpected; it would have to be one that was both in character and beyond character; it would have to suggest both the world and eternity.... It would be a gesture that somehow made contact with mystery.

—Flannery O'Connor

★★★

John Updike
1932

About the Author

As the recipient of two Pulitzer Prizes and a man who has twice been on the cover of *Time* magazine, John Updike is one of America's most celebrated authors.

Updike grew up in Shillington, Pennsylvania, on an 80-acre farm, a setting much like the American Protestant, small-town middle class he often uses as the backdrop for his work. President and co-valedictorian of his high school class, he worked summers at his hometown newspaper, *Reading Eagle*, before entering Harvard, where he wrote for the *Harvard Lampoon*. While studying art at Oxford University in England, Updike met E. B. White (author of *Charlotte's Web*). White offered him a position as a columnist at *The New Yorker*, where Updike eventually published many stories.

Among Updike's best-known work is the "Rabbit" novel series, about a former star athlete who is unable to recapture the glory he knew in school when trapped by marriage and life in a small town. Updike was quoted in *Writers on Writing* as saying, "When I write, I aim in my mind not toward New York but toward a vague spot a little to the east of Kansas. I think of the books on library shelves, without their jackets, years old, and a countryish teen-aged boy finding them, and having them speak to him. The reviews, the stacks in Brentano's, are just hurdles to get over, to place the books on that shelf."

★★★★★★★★★★★

The Author's Style

Updike's fiction typically chronicles everyday incidents from middle-class lives. His stories often reflect the eventual influence of cultural movements or historical events, such as the Civil Rights marches or the Vietnam War, on the lives of his characters. Yet he is more interested in the way personal choices affect family relationships and how personal decisions and behavior change individual lives. For this reason, Updike shows us how characters think and feel through ordinary incidents rather than confrontations with catastrophe.

Often, Updike uses humor, irony, and pathos to suggest that people are not tragic figures but works in progress—especially when they are struggling through the difficulties of adolescence. His stories are gently realistic and pay careful attention to the nuances of personality. It is not uncommon for an Updike story to end with a sense that whatever a character has learned from a particular incident, there is more to come.

LITERARY LENS Listen for the voice of the narrator in this story.

A&P

John Updike

n walks these three girls in nothing but bathing suits. I'm in the third checkout slot, with my back to the door, so I don't see them until they're over by the bread. The one that caught my eye first was the one in the plaid green two-piece. She was a chunky kid, with a good tan and a sweet broad soft-looking can with those two crescents of white just under it, where the sun never seems to hit, at the top of the backs of her legs. I stood there with my hand on a box of HiHo crackers trying to remember if I rang it up or not. I ring it up again and the customer starts giving me hell. She's one of these cash-register-watchers, a witch about fifty with rouge on her cheekbones and no eyebrows, and I know it made her day to trip me up. She'd been watching cash registers for fifty years and probably never seen a mistake before.

By the time I got her feathers smoothed and her goodies into a bag—she gives me a little snort in passing, if she'd been born at the right time they would have burned her over in Salem[1]—by the time I get her on her way the girls had circled around the bread and were coming back, without a pushcart, back my way along the counters, in the aisle between the checkouts and the Special bins. They didn't even have shoes on. There was this chunky one, with the two-piece—it was bright green and the seams on the bra were still sharp and her belly was still pretty pale so I guessed she just got it (the suit)—there was this one, with one of those chubby berry-faces, the lips all bunched together under her nose, this one, and a tall one, with black hair that hadn't quite frizzed right,

> She didn't look around, not this queen, she just walked straight on slowly, on these long white primadonna legs.

and one of these sunburns right across under the eyes, and a chin that was too long—you know, the kind of girl other girls think is very "striking" and "attractive" but never quite makes it, as they very well know, which is why they like her so much—and then the third one, that wasn't quite so tall. She was the queen. She kind of led them, the other two peeking around and making their shoulders round. She didn't look around, not this queen, she just walked straight on slowly, on these long white primadonna legs. She came down a little hard on her heels, as if she didn't walk in bare feet that much, putting down her heels and then letting the weight move along to her toes as if she was testing the floor with every step, putting a little deliberate extra action into it. You never know for sure how girls' minds work (do you really think it's a mind in there or just a little buzz like a bee in a glass jar?) but you got the idea she had talked the other two into coming here with her, and now she was showing them how to do it, walk slow and hold yourself straight.

She had on a kind of dirty-pink—beige maybe, I don't know—bathing suit with a little nubble all over it and, what got me, the straps were down. They were off her shoulders looped loose around the cool tops of her arms, and I guess as a result the suit had slipped a little on her, so all around the top of the cloth there was a shining rim. If it hadn't been there you wouldn't have known there could have been anything whiter than those shoulders. With the straps pushed off, there was nothing between the top of the suit and the top of her head except just *her*, this clean bare plane of the top of her

---

1 **burned . . . Salem:** refers to the women who were burned for alledgedly practicing witchcraft in Salem, Massachussetts, in 1692

chest down from the shoulder bones like a dented sheet of metal tilted in the light. I mean, it was more than pretty.

She had a sort of oaky hair that the sun and salt had bleached, done up in a bun that was unravelling, and a kind of prim face. Walking into the A & P with your straps down, I suppose it's the only kind of face you *can* have. She held her head so high her neck, coming up out of those white shoulders, looked kind of stretched, but I didn't mind. The longer her neck was, the more of her there was.

She must have felt in the corner of her eye me and over my shoulder Stokesie in the second slot watching, but she didn't tip. Not this queen. She kept her eyes moving across the racks, and stopped, and turned so slow it made my stomach rub the inside of my apron, and buzzed to the other two, who kind of huddled against her for relief, and then they all three of them went up the cat-and-dog food-breakfast-cereal-macaroni-rice-raisins-seasonings-spreads-spaghetti-soft drinks-crackers-and-cookies

MEASURE, Victor Maldonado

aisle. From the third slot I look straight up this aisle to the meat counter, and I watched them all the way. The fat one with the tan sort of fumbled with the cookies, but on second thought she put the package back. The sheep pushing their carts down the aisle—the girls were walking against the usual traffic (not that we have one-way signs or anything)—were pretty hilarious. You could see them,

*W*hat he meant was, our town is five miles from a beach, with a big summer colony out on the Point, but we're right in the middle of town, and the women generally put on a shirt or shorts or something before they get out of the car into the street.

when Queenie's white shoulders dawned on them, kind of jerk, or hop, or hiccup, but their eyes snapped back to their own baskets and on they pushed. I bet you could set off dynamite in an A & P and the people would by and large keep reaching and checking oatmeal off their lists and muttering "Let me see, there was a third thing, began with A, asparagus, no, ah, yes, applesauce!" or whatever it is they do mutter. But there was no doubt, this jiggled them. A few houseslaves in pin curlers even looked around after pushing their carts past to make sure what they had seen was correct.

You know, it's one thing to have a girl in a bathing suit down on the beach, where what with the glare nobody can look at each other much anyway, and another thing in the cool of the A & P, under the fluorescent lights, against all those stacked packages, with her feet paddling along naked over our checker-board green-and-cream rubber-tile floor.

"Oh Daddy," Stokesie said beside me. "I feel so faint."

"Darling," I said, "Hold me tight." Stokesie's married, with two babies chalked up on his **fuselage** already, but as far as I can tell that's the only difference. He's twenty-two, and I was nineteen this April.

fuselage: central body portion of an airplane

"Is it done?" he asks, the responsible married man finding his voice. I forgot to say he thinks he's going to be manager some sunny day, maybe in 1990 when it's called the Great Alexandrov and Petrooshki Tea Company or something.

What he meant was, our town is five miles from a beach, with a big summer colony out on the Point, but we're right in the middle of town, and the women generally put on a shirt or shorts or something before they get out of the car into the street. And anyway these are usually women with six children and varicose veins mapping their legs and nobody, including them, could care less. As I say, we're right in the middle of town, and if you stand at our front doors you can see two banks and the Congregational church and the newspaper store and three real-estate offices and about twenty-seven old freeloaders tearing up Central Street because the sewer broke again. It's not as if we're on the Cape;[2] we're north of Boston and there's people in this town haven't seen the ocean for twenty years.

The girls had reached the meat counter and were asking McMahon something. He pointed, they pointed, and they shuffled out of sight behind a pyramid of Diet Delight peaches. All that was left for us to see was old McMahon patting his mouth and looking after them sizing up their joints. Poor kids, I began to feel sorry for them, they couldn't help it.

Now here comes the sad part of the story, at least my family says it's sad, but I don't think it's so sad myself. The store's pretty empty, it being Thursday afternoon, so there was nothing much to do except lean on the register and wait for the girls to show up again. The whole store was like a pinball machine and I didn't know which tunnel they'd come out of. After a while they come around out of the far aisle, around the light bulbs, records at discount of the Caribbean Six or Tony Martin Sings or some such gunk you wonder they waste the wax on, six-packs of candy bars, and plastic toys done up in cellophane that fall apart when a kid looks at them anyway. Around they come, Queenie still leading the way, and holding a little gray jar in her hand. Slots Three through Seven are unmanned and I could see her wondering between Stokes and me, but Stokesie with his usual luck draws an old party in baggy gray pants who stumbles up with four giant cans of pineapple juice (what do these bums *do* with all that pineapple juice? I've often asked myself) so the girls come to me. Queenie puts down the jar and I take it into my fingers icy cold. Kingfish Fancy Herring Snacks in Pure Sour Cream: 49¢. Now her hands are empty, not a ring or a bracelet, bare as God made them, and I wonder where the money's coming from. Still with that prim look she lifts a folded dollar bill out of the hollow at the center of her nubbled pink top. The jar went heavy in my hand. Really, I thought that was so cute.

Still with that prim look she lifts a folded dollar bill out of the hollow at the center of her nubbled pink top. The jar went heavy in my hand. Really, I thought that was so cute.

Then everybody's luck begins to run out. Lengel comes in from haggling with a truck full of cabbages on the lot and is about to scuttle into the door

---

2 **Cape:** Cape Cod, Massachussetts

marked MANAGER behind which he hides all day when the girls touch his eye. Lengel's pretty dreary, teaches Sunday school and the rest, but he doesn't miss that much. He comes over and says, "Girls, this isn't the beach."

Queenie blushes, though maybe it's just a brush of sunburn I was noticing for the first time, now that she was so close. "My mother asked me to pick up a jar of herring snacks." Her voice kind of startled me, the way voices do when you see the people first, coming out so flat and dumb yet kind of tony, too, the way it ticked over "pick up" and "snacks." All of a sudden I slid right down her voice into her living room. Her father and the other men were standing around in ice-cream coats and bow ties and the women were in sandals picking up herring snacks on toothpicks off a big glass plate and they were all holding drinks the color of water with olives and sprigs of mint in them. When my parents have somebody over they get lemonade and if it's a real racy affair Schlitz in tall glasses with "They'll Do It Every Time" cartoons stencilled on.

"That's all right," Lengel said. "But this isn't the beach." His repeating this struck me as funny, as if it had just occurred to him, and he had been thinking all these years the A & P was a great big dune and he was the head lifeguard. He didn't like my smiling—as I say he doesn't miss much—but he concentrates on giving the girls that sad Sunday-school-superintendent stare.

Queenie's blush is no sunburn now, and the plump one in plaid, that I liked better from the back—a really sweet can—pipes up, "We weren't doing any shopping. We just came in for the one thing."

"That makes no difference," Lengel tells her, and I could see from the way his eyes went that he hadn't noticed she was wearing a two-piece before. "We want you decently dressed when you come in here."

"We *are* decent," Queenie says suddenly, her lower lip pushing, getting sore now that she remembers her place, a place from which the crowd that runs the A & P must look pretty chummy. Fancy Herring Snacks flashed in her very blue eyes.

They keep right on going, into the electric eye; the door flies open and they flicker across the lot to their car, Queenie and Plaid and Big Tall Goony-Goony (not that as raw material she was so bad), leaving me with Lengel and a kink in his eyebrow.

John Updike

"Girls, I don't want to argue with you. After this come in here with your shoulders covered. It's our policy." He turns his back. That's policy for you. Policy is what the kingpins want. What the others want is juvenile delinquency.

All this while, the customers had been showing up with their carts but, you know, sheep, seeing a scene, they had all bunched up on Stokesie, who shook open a paper bag as gently as peeling a peach, not wanting to miss a word. I could feel in the silence everybody getting nervous, most of all Lengel, who asks me, "Sammy, have you rung up their purchase?"

I thought and said "No" but it wasn't about that I was thinking. I go through the punches, 4, 9, GROC, TOT—it's more complicated than you think, and after you do it often enough, it begins to make a little song, that you hear words to, in my case "Hello (bing) there, you (gung) hap-py *pee*-pul (*splat*)!"—the *splat* being the drawer flying out. I uncrease the bill, tenderly as you may imagine, it just having come from between the two smoothest scoops of vanilla I had ever known were there, and pass a half and a penny into her narrow pink palm, and nestle the herrings in a bag and twist its neck and hand it over, all the time thinking.

The girls, and who'd blame them, are in a hurry to get out, so I say "I quit" to Lengel quick enough for them to hear, hoping they'll stop and watch me, their unsuspected hero. They keep right on going, into the electric eye; the door flies open and they flicker across the lot to their car, Queenie and Plaid and Big Tall Goony-Goony (not that as raw material she was so bad), leaving me with Lengel and a kink in his eyebrow.

"Did you say something, Sammy?"

"I said I quit."

"I thought you did."

"You didn't have to embarrass them."

"It was they who were embarrassing us."

I started to say something that came out "Fiddle-de-do." It's a saying of my grandmother's, and I know she would have been pleased.

"I don't think you know what you're saying," Lengel said.

"I know you don't," I said. "But I do." I pull the bow at the back of my apron and start shrugging it off my shoulders. A couple customers that had been heading for my slot begin to knock against each other, like scared pigs in a chute.

Lengel sighs and begins to look very patient and old and gray. He's been a friend of my parents for years. "Sammy, you don't want to do this to your

Mom and Dad," he tells me. It's true, I don't. But it seems to me that once you begin a gesture it's fatal not to go through with it. I fold the apron, "Sammy" stitched in red on the pocket, and put it on the counter, and drop the bow tie on top of it. The bow tie is theirs, if you've ever wondered. "You'll feel this for the rest of your life," Lengel says, and I know that's true, too, but remembering how he made that pretty girl blush makes me so scrunchy inside I punch the No Sale tab and the machine whirs "pee-pul" and the drawer splats out. One advantage to this scene taking place in summer, I can follow this up with a clean exit, there's no fumbling around getting your coat and galoshes, I just saunter into the electric eye in my white shirt that my mother ironed the night before, and the door heaves itself open, and outside the sunshine is skating around on the asphalt.

I look around for my girls, but they're gone, of course. There wasn't anybody but some young married[3] screaming with her children about some candy they didn't get by the door of a powder-blue Falcon station wagon. Looking back in the big windows, over the bags of peat moss and aluminum lawn furniture stacked on the pavement, I could see Lengel in my place in the slot, checking the sheep through. His face was dark gray and his back stiff, as if he'd just had an injection of iron, and my stomach kind of fell as I felt how hard the world was going to be to me hereafter.

---

3 **young married:** term for a young married woman

John Updike

Responding to the Story

1. **LITERARY LENS** Based on Sammy's narrative voice, what three words would you use to describe him? Be prepared to support your response with examples from the text.

2. Near the end of the story, Sammy says, " . . . it seems to me that once you begin a gesture it's fatal not to go through with it." Do you agree? Explain why or why not.

3. What, if anything, do you think Sammy will learn from this incident?

4. Find a passage in this story that makes you feel as if you really are in a grocery store. How does the author make the setting seem real?

5. **THE AUTHOR'S STYLE** Updike is known for his skill at depicting the tensions and frustrations of small town and suburban life in America. What tensions and frustrations does he explore in this story?

★★★

Ernest J. Gaines
1933

About the Author

Ernest J. Gaines dedicated his novel, *The Autobiography of Miss Jane Pittman*, to his handicapped aunt. She had not only inspired the book but also raised him in his birthplace of Louisiana after his parents moved to California. The author noted that although his aunt had never walked a day in her life, she taught him the importance of standing.

Gaines grew up picking cotton in plantation fields by the age of nine and attending a school where the sessions depended on the planting and harvesting seasons. African American children didn't go to school past eighth grade there, so at 15 he moved to San Francisco to join his mother and stepfather. He recalls, "I had a choice of going to three places—the library, the YMCA, and the movie house. I didn't have any money so I couldn't go to the movies. I went to the YMCA and I got beaten up by a guy who knew how to box, so I quit that and went to the library. Little old ladies can't hit that hard."

After graduating from San Francisco State University and spending two years in the army, Gaines was awarded a fellowship to Stanford University that enabled him to quit his job and devote himself to writing. One of his eight novels, *A Lesson Before Dying*, won the National Book Award in 1993.

****

The Author's Style

In his novels and stories, Gaines is concerned with the divisive and destructive effects of racial distinctions on American society—the values, priorities, and behavior of a troubled culture. Gaines' stories contain ordinary characters and everyday events set in southern Louisiana—people coming to terms with the rules and expectations that define their culture and shape their lives.

The author uses first-person narrators to make clear his characters' feelings, personalities, and social standing. Many of his narrators are men or young men, intent on understanding the nature and meaning of manhood. Using the dialect of their time and place, his African American characters describe their circumstances and explain the strategies they have developed for coping with them. Gaines reveals the effects of arbitrary racial distinctions not only through black-white interactions, as in his novel *The Autobiography of Miss Jane Pittman*, but also through interactions within African American families and communities. In the story you are about to read, "The Sky Is Gray," he gives us both.

LITERARY **LENS** Gaines uses color in significant ways in this story. As you read, watch for the use of colors and their emotional significance.

THE SKY IS GRAY

ERNEST J. GAINES

I

o'n be coming in a few minutes. Coming round that bend down there full speed. And I'm go'n get out my handkerchief and wave it down, and we go'n get on it and go.

I keep looking for it, but Mama don't look that way no more. She's looking down the road where we just come from. It's a long old road, and far's you can see you don't see nothing but gravel. You got dry weeds on both sides, and you got trees on both sides, and fences on both sides, too. And you got cows in the pastures and they standing close together. And when we was coming out here to catch the bus I seen the smoke coming out of the cows's noses.

I look at my mama and I know what she's thinking. I been with Mama so much, just me and her, I know what she's thinking all the time. Right now it's home—Auntie and them. She's thinking if they got enough wood—if she left enough there to keep them warm till we get back. She's thinking if it go'n rain and if any of them go'n have to go out in the rain. She's thinking 'bout the hog—if he go'n get out, and if Ty and Val be able to get him back in. She always worry like that when she leaves the house. She don't worry too much if she leave me there with the smaller ones, 'cause she know I'm go'n look after them and look after Auntie and everything else. I'm the oldest and she say I'm the man.

I look at my mama and I love my mama. She's wearing that black coat and that black hat and she's looking sad. I love my mama and I want put my arm round her and tell her. But I'm not supposed to do that. She say that's weakness and that's crybaby stuff, and she don't want no crybaby round her. She don't want you to be scared, either. 'Cause Ty's scared of ghosts and she's always whipping him. I'm scared of the dark, too, but I make 'tend I ain't. I make 'tend I ain't 'cause I'm the oldest, and I got to set a good sample for the rest. I can't ever be scared and I can't ever cry. And that's why I never said nothing 'bout my teeth. It's been hurting me and hurting me close to a month now, but I never said it. I didn't say it 'cause I didn't want to act like a crybaby, and 'cause we didn't have enough money to go have it pulled. But, Lord, it been hurting me. And look like it wouldn't start till at night when you was trying to get yourself little sleep. Then soon 's you shut your eyes—ummm-ummm, Lord, look like it go right down to your heartstring.

"Hurting, hanh?" Ty'd say.

I'd shake my head, but I wouldn't open my mouth for nothing. You open your mouth and let that wind in, and it almost kill you.

I'd just lay there and listen to them snore. Ty there, right 'side me, and Auntie and Val over by the fireplace. Val younger than me and Ty, and he sleeps with Auntie. Mama sleeps round the other side with Louis and Walker.

I'd just lay there and listen to them, and listen to that wind out there, and listen to that fire in the fireplace. Sometimes it'd stop long enough to let me get little rest. Sometimes it just hurt, hurt, hurt. Lord, have mercy.

II

Auntie knowed it was hurting me. I didn't tell anybody but Ty, 'cause we buddies and he ain't go'n tell nobody. But some kind of way Auntie found out. When she asked me, I told her no, nothing was wrong. But she knowed it all the time. She told me to mash up a piece of aspirin and wrap it in some cotton and jugg it down in that hole. I did it, but it didn't do no good. It stopped for a little while, and started right back again. Auntie wanted to tell Mama, but I told her, "Uh-uh." 'Cause I knowed we didn't have any money, and it just was go'n make her mad again. So Auntie told Monsieur Bayonne, and Monsieur Bayonne came over to the house and told me to kneel down 'side him on the fireplace. He put his finger in his mouth and made the Sign of the Cross[1] on my jaw. The tip of Monsieur Bayonne's finger is some hard, 'cause he's always playing on that guitar. If we sit outside at night we can always hear Monsieur Bayonne playing on his guitar. Sometimes we leave him out there playing on the guitar.

Monsieur Bayonne made the Sign of the Cross over and over on my jaw, but that didn't do no good. Even when he prayed and told me to pray some, too, that tooth still hurt me.

"How you feeling?" he say.

"Same," I say.

He kept on praying and making the Sign of the Cross and I kept on praying, too.

"Still hurting?" he say.

"Yes, sir."

Monsieur Bayonne mashed harder and harder on my jaw. He mashed so hard he almost pushed me over on Ty. But then he stopped.

"What kind of prayers you praying, boy?" he say.

"Baptist," I say.

"Well, I'll be—no wonder that tooth killing him. I'm going one way and he pulling the other. Boy, don't you know any Catholic prayers?"

"I know 'Hail Mary,'" I say.

"Then you better start saying it."

"Yes, sir."

He started mashing on my jaw again, and I could hear him praying at the same time. And, sure enough, after while it stopped hurting me.

Me and Ty went outside where Monsieur Bayonne's two hounds was and we started playing with them. "Let's go hunting," Ty say. "All right," I say; and we went on back in the pasture. Soon the hounds got on a trail, and me and Ty followed them all 'cross the pasture and then back in the woods, too. And then they cornered this little old rabbit and killed him, and me and Ty made them get back, and we picked up the rabbit and started back home. But my tooth had started hurting me again. It was hurting me plenty now, but I

---

1 **Sign of the Cross:** a Roman Catholic symbolic gesture that signifies the shape of the cross

All right, kneel down there 'side that stove," he say. "And this time make sure you pray Catholic. I don't know nothing 'bout that Baptist, and I don't want to know nothing 'bout him."

wouldn't tell Monsieur Bayonne. That night I didn't sleep a bit, and first thing in the morning Auntie told me to go back and let Monsieur Bayonne pray over me some more. Monsieur Bayonne was in his kitchen making coffee when I got there. Soon 's he seen me he knowed what was wrong.

"All right, kneel down there 'side that stove," he say. "And this time make sure you pray Catholic. I don't know nothing 'bout that Baptist, and I don't want to know nothing 'bout him."

III

Last night Mama say, "Tomorrow we going to town."

"It ain't hurting me no more," I say. "I can eat anything on it."

"Tomorrow we going to town," she say.

And after she finished eating, she got up and went to bed. She always go to bed early now. 'Fore Daddy went in the Army, she used to stay up late. All of us sitting out on the gallery or round the fire. But now, look like soon 's she finish eating she go to bed.

This morning when I woke up, her and Auntie was standing 'fore the fireplace. She say: "Enough to get there and get back. Dollar and a half to have it pulled. Twenty-five for me to go, twenty-five for him. Twenty-five for me to come back, twenty-five for him. Fifty cents left. Guess I get a little piece of salt meat with that."

"Sure can use it," Auntie say. "White beans and no salt meat ain't white beans."

"I do the best I can," Mama say.

They was quiet after that, and I made 'tend I was still sleep.

"James, hit the floor," Auntie say.

I still made 'tend I was asleep. I didn't want them to know I was listening.

"All right," Auntie say, shaking me by the shoulder. "Come on. Today's the day."

I pushed the cover down to get out, and Ty grabbed it and pulled it back.

"You, too, Ty," Auntie say.

"I ain't getting no teef pulled," Ty say.

"Don't mean it ain't time to get up." Auntie say. "Hit it, Ty."

Ty got up grumbling.

"James, you hurry up and get in your clothes and eat your food," Auntie say. "What time y'all coming back?" she said to Mama.

"That 'leven o'clock bus," Mama say. "Got to get back in that field this evening."

"Get a move on you, James," Auntie say.

I went in the kitchen and washed my face, then I ate my breakfast. I was having bread and syrup. The bread was warm and hard and tasted good. And I tried to make it last a long time.

Ty came back there grumbling and mad at me.

"Got to get up," he say. "I ain't having no teefes pulled. What I got to be getting up for?"

Ty poured some syrup in his pan and got a piece of bread. He didn't wash his hands, neither his face, and I could see that white stuff in his eyes.

"You the one getting your teef pulled," he say. "What I got to get up for. I bet if I was getting a teef pulled you wouldn't be getting up. Shucks; syrup again. I'm getting tired of this old syrup. Syrup, syrup, syrup. I'm go'n take with the sugar diabetes. I want some bacon sometime."

"Go out in the field and work and you can have your bacon," Auntie say. She stood in the middle door looking at Ty. "You better be glad you got syrup. Some people ain't got that—hard 's time is."

"Shucks," Ty say. "How can I be strong?"

"I don't know too much 'bout your strength," Auntie say; "but I know where you go'n be hot at, you keep that grumbling up. James, get a move on you; your mama waiting."

I ate my last piece of bread and went in the front room. Mama was standing 'fore the fireplace warming her hands. I put on my coat and my cap, and we left the house.

IV

I look down there again, but it still ain't coming. I almost say, "It ain't coming yet," but I keep my mouth shut. 'Cause that's something else she don't like. She don't like for you to say something just for nothing. She can see it ain't coming. I can see it ain't coming, so why say it ain't coming. I don't say it, I turn and look at the river that's back of us. It's so cold the smoke's just raising up from the water. I see a bunch of pool-doos[2] not too

---

2 **pool-doos:** slang for mud-hens, or duck-like birds

*S*he went to the corner of the fence and broke the biggest switch over there she could find. I knelt 'side the trap, crying.

far out—just on the other side of the lilies. I'm wondering if you can eat pool-doos. I ain't too sure, 'cause I ain't never ate none. But I done ate owls and blackbirds, and I done ate redbirds, too. I didn't want to kill the redbirds, but she made me kill them. They had two of them back there. One in my trap, one in Ty's trap. Me and Ty was go'n play with them and let them go, but she made me kill them 'cause we needed the food.

"I can't," I say. "I can't."

"Here," she say. "Take it."

"I can't," I say. "I can't. I can't kill him, Mama, please."

"Here," she say. "Take this fork, James."

"Please, Mama, I can't kill him," I say.

I could tell she was go'n hit me. I jerked back, but I didn't jerk back soon enough.

"Take it," she say.

I took it and reached in for him, but he kept on hopping to the back.

"I can't, Mama," I say. The water just kept on running down my face. "I can't," I say.

"Get him out of there," she say.

I reached in for him and he kept on hopping to the back. Then I reached in farther, and he pecked me on the hand.

"I can't, Mama," I say.

She slapped me again.

I reached in again, but he kept on hopping out of my way. Then he hopped to one side and I reached there. The fork got him on the leg and I heard his leg pop. I pulled my hand out 'cause I had hurt him.

"Give it here," she say, and jerked the fork out of my hand.

She reached in and got the little bird right in the neck. I heard the fork go in his neck, and I heard it go in the ground. She brought him out and helt him right in front of me.

"That's one," she say. She shook him off and gived me the fork. "Get the other one."

"I can't, Mama," I say. "I'll do anything, but don't make me do that."

She went to the corner of the fence and broke the biggest switch over there she could find. I knelt 'side the trap, crying.

Ernest J. Gaines

"Get him out of there," she say.

"I can't, Mama."

She started hitting me 'cross the back. I went down on the ground, crying.

"Get him," she say.

"Octavia?" Auntie say.

'Cause she had come out of the house and she was standing by the tree looking at us.

"Get him out of there," Mama say.

"Octavia," Auntie say, "explain to him. Explain to him. Just don't beat him. Explain to him."

But she hit me and hit me and hit me.

I'm still young—I ain't no more than eight; but I know now; I know why I had to do it. (They was so little, though. They was so little. I 'member how I picked the feathers off them and cleaned them and helt them over the fire. Then we all ate them. Ain't had but a little bitty piece each, but we all had a little bitty piece, and everybody just looked at me 'cause they was so proud.) Suppose she had to go away? That's why I had to do it. Suppose she had to go away like Daddy went away? Then who was go'n look after us? They had to be somebody left to carry on. I didn't know it then, but I know it now. Auntie and Monsieur Bayonne talked to me and made me see.

V

Time I see it I get out my handkerchief and start waving. It's still 'way down there, but I keep waving anyhow. Then it come up and stop and me and Mama get on. Mama tell me go sit in the back while she pay. I do like she say, and the people look at me. When I pass the little sign that say "White" and "Colored," I start looking for a seat. I just see one of them back there, but I don't take it, 'cause I want my mama to sit down herself. She comes in the back and sit down, and I lean on the seat. They got seats in the front, but I know I can't sit there, 'cause I have to sit back of the sign. Anyhow, I don't want sit there if my mama go'n sit back here.

They got a lady sitting 'side my mama and she looks at me and smiles little bit. I smile back, but I don't open my mouth, 'cause the wind'll get in and make that tooth ache. The lady take out a pack of gum and reach me a slice, but I shake my head. The lady just can't understand why a little boy'll turn down gum, and she reach me a slice again. This time I point to my jaw. The lady understands and smiles little bit, and I smile little bit, but I don't open my mouth, though.

They got a girl sitting 'cross from me. She got on a red overcoat and her hair's plaited in one big plait. First, I make 'tend I don't see her over there, but then I start looking at her little bit. She make 'tend she don't see me, either, but I catch her looking that way. She got a cold, and every now and then she h'ist that little handkerchief to her nose. She ought to blow it, but she don't. Must think she's too much a lady or something.

Every time she h'ist that little handkerchief, the lady side her say something in her ear. She shakes her head and lays her hands in her lap again. Then I catch her kind of looking where I'm at. I smile at her little bit. But think she'll smile back? Uh-uh. She just turn up her little old nose and turn her head. Well, I show her both of us can turn us head. I turn mine too and look out at the river.

The river is gray. The sky is gray. They have pool-doos on the water. The water is wavy, and the pool-doos go up and down. The bus go round a turn, and you got plenty trees hiding the river. Then the bus go round another turn, and I can see the river again.

I look toward the front where all the white people sitting. Then I look at that little old gal again. I don't look right at her, 'cause I don't want all them people to know I love her. I just look at her little bit, like I'm looking out that window over there. But she knows I'm looking that way, and she kind of look at me, too. The lady sitting 'side her catch her this time, and she leans over and says something in her ear.

"I don't love him nothing," that little old gal says out loud.

Everybody back there hear her mouth, and all of them look at us and laugh.

"I don't love you, either," I say. "So you don't have to turn up your nose, Miss."

"You the one looking," she say.

"I wasn't looking at you," I say. "I was looking out that window, there."

"Out that window my foot," she say. "I seen you. Everytime I turned round you was looking at me."

"You must have been looking yourself if you seen me all them times," I say.

"Shucks," she say. "I got me all kind of boyfriends."

"I got girlfriends, too," I say.

"Well, I just don't want you getting your hopes up," she say.

I don't say no more to that little old gal 'cause I don't want have to bust her in the mouth. I lean on the seat where Mama sitting, and I don't even look that way no more. When we get to Bayonne, she jugg her little old tongue out at me. I make 'tend I'm go'n hit her, and she duck down 'side her mama. And all the people laugh at us again.

VI

Me and Mama get off and start walking in town. Bayonne is a little bitty town. Baton Rouge is a hundred times bigger than Bayonne. I went to Baton Rouge once—me, Ty, Mama, and Daddy. But that was 'way back yonder, 'fore Daddy went in the Army. I wonder when we go'n see him again. I wonder when. Look like he ain't ever coming back home. . . . Even the pavement all cracked in Bayonne. Got grass shooting right out in the sidewalk. Got weeds in the ditch, too; just like they got at home.

It's some cold in Bayonne. Look like it's colder than it is home. The wind blows in my face, and I feel that stuff running down my nose. I sniff. Mama says use that handkerchief. I blow my nose and put it back.

We pass a school and see them white children playing in the yard. Big old red school, and them children just running and playing. Then we pass a café, and I see a bunch of people in there eating. I wish I was in there 'cause I'm cold. Mama tells me keep my eyes in front where they belong.

We pass stores that's got dummies, and we pass another café, and then we pass a shoe shop, and that bald-head man in there fixing on a shoe. I look at him and I butt into that white lady, and Mama jerks me in front and tells me stay there.

We come up to the courthouse, and I see the flag waving there. This flag ain't like the one we got at school. This one here ain't got but a handful of stars. One at the school got a big pile of stars—one for every state. We pass it and we turn and there it is—the dentist office. Me and Mama go in, and they got people sitting everywhere you look. They even got a little boy in there younger than me.

Me and Mama sit on that bench, and a white lady come in there and ask me what my name is. Mama tells her and the white lady goes on back. Then I hear somebody hollering in there. Soon 's that little boy hear him hollering, he starts hollering, too. His mama pats him and pats him, trying to make him hushup, but he ain't thinking 'bout his mama.

The man that was hollering in there comes out holding his jaw. He is a big old man and he's wearing overalls and a jumper.

"Got it, hanh?" another man asks him.

The man shakes his head—don't want to open his mouth.

"Man, I thought they was killing you in there," the other man says. "Hollering like a pig under a gate."

The man don't say nothing. He just heads for the door, and the other man follows him.

"John Lee," the white lady says. "John Lee Williams."

The little boy juggs his head down in his mama's lap and holler more now. His mama tells him go with the nurse, but he ain't thinking 'bout his mama. His mama tells him again, but he don't even hear her. His mama picks him up and takes him in there, and even when the white lady shuts the door I can still hear little old John Lee.

"I often wonder why the Lord let a child like that suffer," a lady says to my mama. The lady's sitting right in front of us on another bench. She's got a white dress and a black sweater. She must be a nurse or something herself, I reckon.

"Not us to question," a man says.

"Sometimes I don't know if we shouldn't," the lady says.

"I know definitely we shouldn't," the man says. The man looks like a preacher. He's big and fat and he's got on a black suit. He's got a gold chain, too.

"Why?" the lady said.

"Why anything?" the preacher says.

"Yes," the lady says. "Why anything?"

"Not us to question," the preacher says.

The lady looks at the preacher a little while and looks at Mama again.

"And look like it's the poor who suffers the most," she says. "I don't understand it."

"Best not to even try," the preacher says. "He works in mysterious ways— wonders to perform."

Right then little John Lee bust out hollering, and everybody turn their head to listen.

"He's not a good dentist," the lady says. "Dr. Robillard is much better. But more expensive. That's why most of the colored people come here. The white people go to Dr. Robillard. Y'all from Bayonne?"

SUNDAY MORNING BREAKFAST, Romare Bearden, 1967

"Down the river," my mama says. And that's all she go'n say, 'cause she don't talk much. But the lady keeps on looking at her, and so she says, "Near Morgan."

"I see," the lady says.

VII

That's the trouble with the black people in the country today," some body else says. This one here's sitting on the same side me and Mama's sitting, and he is kind of sitting in front of that preacher. He looks like a teacher or somebody that goes to college. He's got on a suit, and he's got a book that he's been reading. "We don't question is exactly our problem," he says. "We should question and question and question—question everything."

The preacher just looks at him a long time. He done put a toothpick or something in his mouth, and he just keeps turning it and turning it. You can see he don't like that boy with that book.

"Maybe you can explain to me what you mean," he says.

"I said what I meant," the boy says. "Question everything. Every stripe, every star, every word spoken. Everything."

"It 'pears to me that this young lady and I was talking 'bout God, young man," the preacher says.

"Question Him, too," the boy says.

"Wait," the preacher says. "Wait now."

"You heard me right," the boy says. "His existence as well as everything else. Everything."

The preacher just looks across the room at the boy. You can see he's getting madder and madder. But mad or no mad, the boy ain't thinking 'bout him. He looks at that preacher just 's hard 's the preacher looks at him.

"Is this what they coming to?" the preacher says. "Is this what we educating them for?"

"You're not educating me," the boy says. "I wash dishes at night so that I can go to school in the day. So even the words you spoke need questioning."

The preacher just looks at him and shakes his head.

"When I come in this room and seen you there with your book, I said to myself, 'There's an intelligent man.' How wrong a person can be."

"Show me one reason to believe in the existence of a God," the boy says.

"My heart tells me," the preacher says.

"'My heart tells me,'" the boy says. "'My heart tells me.' Sure. 'My heart tells me.' And as long as you listen to what your heart tells you, you will have only what the white man gives you and nothing more. Me, I don't listen to my heart. The purpose of the heart is to pump blood throughout the body, and nothing else."

"Who's your paw, boy?" the preacher says.

"Why?"

"Who is he?"

"He's dead."

"And your mom?"

"She's in Charity Hospital with pneumonia. Half killed herself, working for nothing."

"And 'cause he's dead and she's sick, you mad at the world?"

"I'm not mad at the world. I'm questioning it with cold logic, sir. What do words like Freedom, Liberty, God, White, Colored mean? I want to know. That's why *you* are sending us to school, to read and to ask questions. And because we ask these questions, you call us mad. No sir, it is not us who are mad."

"You keep saying 'us'?"

"'Us.' Yes—us. I'm not alone."

The preacher just shakes his head. Then he looks at everybody in the room—everybody. Some of the people look down at the floor, keep from looking at him. I think of look 'way myself, but soon 's I know he done turn his head, I look that way again.

"I'm sorry for you," he says to the boy.

"Why?" the boy says. "Why not be sorry for yourself? Why are you so much better off than I am? Why aren't you sorry for these other people in here? Why not be sorry for the lady who had to drag her child into the dentist office? Why not be sorry for the lady sitting on that bench over there? Be sorry for them. Not for me. Some way or the other I'm going to make it."

"No, I'm sorry for you," the preacher says.

"Of course, of course," the boy says, nodding his head. "You're sorry for me because I rock that pillar you're leaning on."

"You can't never rock the pillar I'm leaning on, young man. It's stronger than anything man can ever do."

You believe in God because a man told you to believe in God," the boy says. "A white man told you to believe in God. And why? To keep you ignorant so he can keep his feet on your neck."

"You believe in God because a man told you to believe in God," the boy says. "A white man told you to believe in God. And why? To keep you ignorant so he can keep his feet on your neck."

"So now we the ignorant?" the preacher says.

"Yes," the boy says. "Yes." And he opens his book again.

The preacher just looks at him sitting there. The boy done forgot all about him. Everybody else make 'tend they done forgot the squabble, too.

Then I see that preacher getting up real slow. Preacher's a great big old man and he got to brace himself to get up. He comes over where the boy is sitting. He just stands there a little while looking down at him, but the boy don't raise his head.

"Get up, boy," preacher says.

The boy looks up at him, then he shuts his book real slow and stands up. Preacher just hauls back and hit him in the face. The boy falls back 'gainst the wall, but he straightens himself up and looks right back at the preacher.

"You forgot the other cheek," he says.

The preacher hauls back and hit him again on the other side. But this time the boy braces himself and don't fall.

"That hasn't changed a thing," he says.

The preacher just looks at the boy. The preacher's breathing real hard like he just run up a big hill. The boy sits down and opens his book again.

"I feel sorry for you," the preacher says. "I never felt so sorry for a man before."

The boy makes 'tend he don't even hear that preacher. He keeps on reading his book. The preacher goes back and gets his hat off the chair.

"Excuse me," he says to us. "I'll come back some other time. Y'all, please excuse me."

And he looks at the boy and goes out the room. The boy h'ist his hand up to his mouth one time to wipe 'way some blood. All the rest of the time he keeps on reading. And nobody else in there say a word.

VIII

Little John Lee and his mama come out the dentist office, and the nurse calls somebody else in. Then little bit later they come out, and the nurse calls another name. But fast 's she calls somebody in there, somebody else comes in the place where we sitting, and the room stays full.

The people coming in now, all of them wearing big coats. One of them says something 'bout sleeting, another one says he hope not. Another one says he think it ain't nothing but rain. 'Cause, he says, rain can get awful cold this time of year.

All round the room they talking. Some of them talking to people right by them, some of them talking to people clear 'cross the room, some of them talking to anybody'll listen. It's a little bitty room, no bigger than us kitchen, and I can see everybody in there. The little old room's full of smoke, 'cause you got two old men smoking pipes over by that side door. I think I feel my tooth thumping me some, and I hold my breath and wait. I wait and wait, but it don't thump me no more. Thank God for that.

I feel like going to sleep, and I lean 'gainst the wall. But I'm scared to go to sleep. Scared 'cause the nurse might call my name and I won't hear her.

And Mama might go to sleep, too, and she'll be mad if neither one of us heard the nurse.

I look up at Mama. I love my mama. And when cotton come I'm go'n get her a new coat. And I ain't go'n get a black one, either. I think I'm go'n get her a red one.

"They got some books over there," I say. "Want read one of them?"

Mama looks at the books, but she don't answer me.

"You got yourself a little man there," the lady says.

Mama don't say nothing to the lady, but she must've smiled, 'cause I seen the lady smiling back. The lady looks at me a little while, like she's feeling sorry for me.

"You sure got that preacher out here in a hurry," she says to that boy.

The boy looks up at her and looks in his book again. When I grow up I want to be just like him. I want clothes like that and I want to keep a book with me too.

"You really don't believe in God?" the lady says.

"No," he says.

"But why?" the lady says.

"Because the wind is pink," he says.

"What?" the lady says.

The boy don't answer her no more. He just reads in his book.

"Talking 'bout the wind is pink," that old lady says. She's sitting on the same bench with the boy and she's trying to look in his face. The boy makes 'tend the old lady ain't even there. He just keeps on reading. "Wind is pink," she says again. "Eh, Lord, what children go'n be saying next?"

The lady 'cross from us bust out laughing.

"That's a good one," she says. "The wind is pink. Yes sir, that's a good one."

"Don't you believe the wind is pink?" the boy says. He keeps his head down in the book.

"Course I believe it, honey," the lady says. "Course I do." She looks at us and winks her eye. "And what color is grass, honey?"

"Grass? Grass is black."

She bust out laughing again. The boy looks at her.

"Don't you believe grass is black?" he says.

The lady quits her laughing and looks at him. Everybody else looking at him, too. The place quiet, quiet.

"Grass is green, honey," the lady says. "It was green yesterday, it's green today, and it's go'n be green tomorrow."

"How do you know it's green?"

"I know because I know."

"You don't know it's green," the boy says. "You believe it's green because someone told you it was green. If someone had told you it was black you'd believe it was black."

"It's green," the lady says. "I know green when I see green."

"Prove it's green," the boy says.

"Sure, now," the lady says. "Don't tell me it's coming to that."

"It's coming to just that," the boy says. "Words mean nothing. One means no more than the other."

"That's what it all coming to?" the old lady says. That old lady got on a turban and she got on two sweaters. She got a green sweater under a black sweater. I can see the green sweater 'cause some of the buttons on the other sweater's missing.

"Yes ma'am," he says. "Words mean nothing. Action is the only thing. Doing. That's the only thing."

"Other words, you want the Lord to come down here and show Hisself to you?" she says.

"Exactly, ma'am," he says.

"You don't mean that, I'm sure?" she says.

"I do, ma'am," he says.

"Done, Jesus," the lady says, shaking her head.

"I didn't go 'long with that preacher at first," the other lady says; "but now—I don't know. When a person says the grass is black, he's either a lunatic or something's wrong."

"Prove it to me that it's green," the boy says.

"It's green because the people say it's green."

"Those same people say we're citizens of these United States," the boy says.

"I think I'm a citizen," the lady says.

"Citizens have certain rights," the boy says. "Name me one right that you have. One right, granted by the Constitution, that you can exercise in Bayonne."

The lady don't answer him. She just looks at him like she don't know what he's talking 'bout. I know I don't.

"Things changing," she says.

"Things are changing because some black men have begun to think with their brains and not their hearts," the boy says.

"You trying to say these people don't believe in God?"

"I'm sure some of them do. Maybe most of them do. But they don't believe that God is going to touch these white people's hearts and change things tomorrow. Things change through action. By no other way."

Everybody sit quiet and look at the boy. Nobody says a thing. Then the lady 'cross the room from me and Mama just shakes her head.

"Let's hope that not all your generation feel the same way you do," she says.

"Think what you please, it doesn't matter," the boy says. "But it will be men who listen to their heads and not their hearts who will see that your children have a better chance than you had."

"Let's hope they ain't all like you, though," the old lady says. "Done forgot the heart absolutely."

"Yes ma'am, I hope they aren't all like me," the boys says. "Unfortunately, I was born too late to believe in your God. Let's hope that the ones who come after will have your faith—if not in your God, then in something else, something definitely that they can lean on. I haven't anything. For me, the wind is pink, the grass is black."

IX

The nurse comes in the room where we are all sitting and waiting and says the doctor won't take no more patients till one o'clock this evening. My mama jumps up off the bench and goes up to the white lady.

"Nurse, I have to go back in the field this evening," she says.

"The doctor is treating his last patient now," the nurse says. "One o'clock this evening."

"Can I at least speak to the doctor?" my mama asks.

"I'm his nurse," the lady says.

"My little boy's sick," my mama says. "Right now his tooth almost killing him."

The nurse looks at me. She's trying to make up her mind if to let me come in. I look at her real pitiful. The tooth ain't hurting me at all, but Mama say it is, so I make 'tend for her sake.

"This evening," the nurse says, and goes on back in the office.

"Don't feel 'jected, honey," the lady says to Mama. "I been round them a long time—they take you when they want to. If you was white, that's something else; but we the wrong color."

Mama don't say nothing to the lady, and me and her go outside and stand 'gainst the wall. It's cold out there. I can feel that wind going through my coat. Some of the other people come out of the room and go up the street. Me and Mama stand there a little while and we start walking. I don't know where we going. When we come to the other street we just stand there.

"You don't have to make water, do you?" Mama says. "No, ma'am," I say.

We go up on the street. Walking real slow. I can tell Mama don't know where she's going. When we come to a store we stand there and look at the dummies. I look at a little boy wearing a brown overcoat. He's got on brown shoes, too. I look at my old shoes and look at his'n again. You wait till summer, I say.

Me and Mama walk away. We come up to another store and we stop and look at them dummies, too. Then we go on again. We pass a café where the white people in there eating. Mama tells me keep my eyes in front where they belong, but I can't help from seeing them people eat. My stomach starts to growling 'cause I'm hungry. When I see people eating, I get hungry; when I see a coat, I get cold.

A man whistles at my mama when we go by a filling station. She makes 'tend she don't even see him. I look back and I feel like hitting him in the mouth. If I was bigger, I say; if I was bigger, you'd see.

We keep on going. I'm getting colder and colder, but I don't say nothing. I feel that stuff running down my nose and I sniff.

"That rag," Mama says.

I get it out and wipe my nose. I'm getting cold all over now—my face, my hands, my feet, everything. We pass another little café, but this'n for white people, too, and we can't go in there, either. So we just walk. I'm so cold now I'm 'bout ready to say it. If I knowed where we was going I wouldn't be so cold, but I don't know where we going. We go, we go, we go. We walk clean out of Bayonne. Then we cross the street and we come back. Same thing I seen when I got off the bus this morning. Same old trees, same old walks, same old weeds, same old cracked pave—same old everything.

I sniff again.

"That rag," Mama says.

I wipe my nose real fast and jugg that handkerchief back in my pocket 'fore my hands gets too cold. I raise my head and I can see David's hardware store. When we come up to it, we go in. I don't know why, but I'm glad.

It's warm in there. It's so warm in there you don't ever want to leave. I look for the heater, and I see it over by them barrels. Three white men standing round the heater talking in Creole. One of them comes over to see what my mama want.

"Got any axe handles?" she says.

Me, Mama and the white man start to the back, but Mama stops me when we come up to the heater. She and the white man go on. I hold my hands over the heater and look at them. They go all the way to the back, and I see the white man pointing to the axe handles 'gainst the wall.

Mama takes one of them and shakes it like she's trying to figure how much it weighs. Then she rubs her hand over it from one end to the other end. She turns it over and looks at the other side, then she shakes it again, and shakes her head and puts it back. She gets another one and she does it just like she did the first one, then she shakes her head. Then she gets a brown one and do it that, too. But she don't like this one, either. Then she gets another one, but 'fore she shakes it or anything, she looks at me. Look like she's trying to say something to me, but I don't know what it is. All I know is I done got warm now and I'm feeling right smart better. Mama shakes this axe handle just like she did the others, and shakes her head and says something to the white man. The white man just looks at his pile of axe handles, and when Mama pass him to come to the front, the white man just scratch his head and follows her. She tells me to come on and we go on out and start walking again.

We walk and walk, and no time at all I'm cold again. Look like I'm colder now 'cause I can still remember how good it was back there. My stomach growls and I suck it in to keep Mama from hearing it. She's walking right 'side me, and it growls so loud you can hear it a mile. But Mama don't say a word.

X

When we come to the courthouse, I look at the clock. It's got quarter to twelve. Mean we got another hour and a quarter to be out here in the cold. We go and stand 'side a building. Something hits my cap and I look up at the sky. Sleet's falling.

I look at Mama standing there. I want stand close 'side her, but she don't like that. She say that's crybaby stuff. She say you got to stand for yourself, by yourself.

"Let's go back to that office," she says.

We cross the street. When we get to the dentist office I try to open the door, but I can't. I twist and twist, but I can't. Mama pushes me to the side and she twist the knob, but she can't open the door, either. She turns 'way from the door. I look at her, but I don't move and I don't say nothing. I done seen her like this before and I'm scared of her.

"You hungry?" she says. She says it like she's mad at me, like I'm the cause of everything.

"No, ma'am," I say.

"You want eat and walk back, or you rather don't eat and ride?"

"I ain't hungry," I say.

I ain't just hungry, but I'm cold, too. I'm so hungry and cold I want to cry. And look like I'm getting colder and colder. My feet done got numb. I try to work my toes, but I don't even feel them. Look like I'm go'n die. Look like I'm go'n stand right here and freeze to death. I think 'bout home. I think 'bout Val and Auntie and Ty and Louis and Walker. It's 'bout twelve o'clock and I know they eating dinner now. I can hear Ty making jokes. He done forgot 'bout getting up early this morning and right now he's probably making jokes. Always trying to make somebody laugh. I wish I was right there listening to him. Give anything in the world if I was home round the fire.

"Come on," Mama says.

We start walking again. My feet so numb I can't hardly feel them. We turn the corner and go on back up the street. The clock in the courthouse starting hitting for twelve.

The sleet's coming down plenty now. They hit the pave and bounce like rice. Oh, Lord; oh, Lord, I pray. Don't let me die, don't let me die, don't let me die, Lord.

XI

Now I know where we going. We going back of town where the colored people eat. I don't care if I don't eat. I been hungry before. I can stand it. But I can't stand the cold.

I can see we go'n have a long walk. It's 'bout a mile down there. But I don't mind. I know when I get there I'm go'n warm myself. I think I can hold out. My hands numb in my pockets and my feet numb, too, but if I keep moving I can hold out. Just don't stop no more, that's all.

The sky's gray. The sleet keeps on falling. Falling like rain now—plenty,

plenty. You can hear it hitting the pave. You can see it bouncing. Sometimes it bounces two times 'fore it settles.

We keep on going. We don't say nothing. We just keep on going, keep on going.

I wonder what Mama's thinking. I hope she ain't mad at me. When summer come I'm go'n pick plenty cotton and get her a coat. I'm go'n get her a red one.

I hope they'd make it summer all the time. I'd be glad if it was summer all the time—but it ain't. We got to have winter, too. Lord, I hate the winter. I guess everybody hate the winter.

I don't sniff this time, I get out my handkerchief and wipe my nose. My hands's so cold I can hardly hold the handkerchief.

I think we getting close, but we ain't there yet. I wonder where everybody is. Can't see a soul but us. Look like we the only two people moving round today. Must be too cold for the rest of the people to move round in.

I can hear my teeth. I hope they don't knock together too hard and make that bad one hurt. Lord, that's all I need, for that bad one to start off.

I hear a church bell somewhere. But today ain't Sunday. They must be ringing for a funeral or something.

I wonder what they doing at home. They must be eating. Monsieur Bayonne might be there with his guitar. One day Ty played with Monsieur Bayonne's guitar and broke one of the strings. Monsieur Bayonne was some mad with Ty. He say Ty wasn't go'n ever 'mount to nothing. Ty can go just like Monsieur Bayonne when he ain't there. Ty can make everybody laugh when he starts to mocking Monsieur Bayonne.

I used to like to be with Mama and Daddy. We used to be happy. But they took him in the Army. Now, nobody happy no more. . . . I be glad when Daddy comes home.

Monsieur Bayonne say it wasn't fair for them to take Daddy and give Mama nothing and give us nothing. Auntie say, "Shhh, Etienne. Don't let them hear you talk like that." Monsieur Bayonne say, "It's God truth. What they giving his children? They have to walk three and a half miles to school hot or cold. That's anything to give for a paw? She's got to work in the field rain or shine just to make ends meet. That's anything to give for a husband?" Auntie say, "Shhh, Etienne, shhh." "Yes, you right," Monsieur Bayonne say. "Best don't say it in front of them now. But one day they go'n find out. One day." "Yes, I suppose so," Auntie say. "Then what, Rose Mary?" Monsieur

Bayonne say. "I don't know, Etienne," Auntie say. "All we can do is us job, and leave everything else in His hand . . ."

We getting closer, now. We getting closer. I can even see the railroad tracks.

We cross the tracks, and now I see the café. Just to get in there, I say. Just to get in there. Already I'm starting to feel little better.

XII

We go in. Ahh, it's good. I look for the heater; there 'gainst the wall. One of them little brown ones. I just stand there and hold my hands over it. I can't open my hands too wide 'cause they almost froze.

Mama's standing right 'side me. She done unbuttoned her coat. Smoke rises out of the coat, and the coat smells like a wet dog.

I move to the side so Mama can have room. She opens out her hands and rubs them together. I rub mine together, too, 'cause this keep them from hurting. If you let them warm too fast, they hurt you sure. But if you let them warm just little bit at a time, and you keep rubbing them, they be all right every time.

They got just two more people in the café. A lady back of the counter, and a man on this side of the counter. They been watching us ever since we come in.

Mama gets out the handkerchief and count up the money. Both of us know how much money she's got there. Three dollars. No, she ain't got three dollars, 'cause she had to pay us way up here. She ain't got but two dollars and a half left. Dollar and half to get my tooth pulled, and fifty cents for us to go back on, and fifty cents worth of salt meat.

She stirs the money round with her finger. Most of the money is change 'cause I can hear it rubbing together. She stirs it and stirs it. Then she looks at the door. It's still sleeting. I can hear it hitting 'gainst the wall like rice.

"I ain't hungry, Mama," I say.

"Got to pay them something for they heat," she says.

She takes a quarter out the handkerchief and ties the handkerchief up again. She looks over her shoulder at the people, but she still don't move. I

You see, one day, I'm go'n make all this up. I want say it now; I want tell her how I feel right now; but Mama don't like us to talk like that.

hope she don't spend the money. I don't want her spending it on me. I'm hungry, I'm almost starving I'm so hungry, but I don't want her spending the money on me.

She flips the quarter over like she's thinking. She's must be thinking 'bout us walking back home. Lord, I sure don't want walk home. If I thought it'd do any good to say something, I'd say it. But Mama makes up her own mind 'bout things.

She turns 'way from the heater right fast, like she better hurry up and spend the quarter 'fore she change her mind. I watch her go toward the counter. The man and the lady look at her, too. She tells the lady something and the lady walks away. The man keeps on looking at her. Her back's turned to the man, and she don't even know he's standing there.

The lady puts some cakes and a glass of milk on the counter. Then she pours up a cup of coffee and set it 'side the other stuff. She's looking real sad. I say to myself, I'm go'n make all this up one day. You see, one day, I'm go'n make all this up. I want say it now; I want tell her how I feel right now; but Mama don't like us to talk like that.

"I can't eat all this," I say.

They ain't got but just three little old cakes there. I'm so hungry right now, the Lord knows I can eat a hundred times three, but I want my mama to have one.

Mama don't even look my way. She knows I'm hungry, she knows I want it. I let it stay there a little while, then I get it and eat it. I eat just on my front teeth, though, 'cause if cake touch that back tooth I know what'll happen. Thank God it ain't hurt me at all today.

After I finish eating I see the man go to the juke box. He drops a nickel in it, then he just stand there a little while looking at the record. Mama tells me keep my eyes in front where they belong. I turn my head like she say, but then I hear the man coming toward us.

"Dance, pretty?" he says.

Mama gets up to dance with him. But 'fore you know it, she done grabbed the little man in the collar and done heaved him 'side the wall. He hit the wall so hard he stop the juke box from playing.

"Some pimp," the lady back of the counter says. "Some pimp."

The little man jumps up off the floor and starts toward my mama. 'Fore you know it, Mama done sprung open her knife and she's waiting for him.

"Come on," she says. "Come on. I'll gut you from your neighbo to your throat. Come on."

The Sky Is Gray

I got up to the little man to hit him, but Mama makes me come and stand 'side her. The little man looks at me and Mama and goes on back to the counter.

"Some pimp," the lady back of the counter says. "Some pimp." She starts laughing and pointing at the little man. "Yes sir, you a pimp, all right. Yes sir-ree."

XIII

Fasten that coat, let's go," Mama says.

"You don't have to leave," the lady says.

Mama don't answer the lady, and we right out in the cold again. I'm warm right now—my hands, my ears, my feet—but I know this ain't go'n last too long. It done sleet so much now you got ice everywhere you look.

We cross the railroad tracks, and soon's we do, I get cold. That wind goes through this little old coat like it ain't even there. I got on a shirt and a sweater under the coat, but that wind don't pay them no mind. I look up and I can see we got a long way to go. I wonder if we go'n make it 'fore I get too cold.

We cross over to walk on the sidewalk. They got just one sidewalk back here, and it's over there.

After we go just a little piece, I smell bread cooking. I look, then I see a baker shop. When we get closer, I can smell it more better, I shut my eyes and make 'tend I'm eating. But I keep them shut too long and I butt up 'gainst a telephone post. Mama grabs me and see if I'm hurt. I ain't bleeding or nothing and she turns me loose.

I can feel I'm getting colder and colder, and I look up to see how far we still got to go. Uptown is 'way up yonder. A half mile more, I reckon. I try to think of something. They say think and you won't get cold. I think of that poem, "Annabel Lee." I ain't been to school in so long—this bad weather—I reckon they done passed "Annabel Lee" by now. But passed it or not, I'm sure Miss Walker go'n make me recite it when I get there. That woman don't never forget nothing. I ain't never seen nobody like that in my life.

I'm still getting cold. "Annabel Lee" or no "Annabel Lee," I'm still getting cold. But I can see we getting closer. We getting there gradually.

Soon's we turn the corner, I see a little old white lady up in front of us. She's the only lady on the street. She's all in black and she's got a long black rag over her head.

"Stop," she says.

Me and Mama stop and look at her. She must be crazy to be out in all this bad weather. Ain't got but a few other people out there, and all of them's men.

"Y'all done ate?" she says.

"Just finish," Mama says.

"Y'all must be cold then?" she says.

"We headed for the dentist," Mama says. "We'll warm up when we get there."

"What dentist?" the old lady says. "Mr. Bassett?"

"Yes, Ma'am," Mama says.

"Come on in," the old lady says. "I'll telephone him and tell him y'all coming."

Me and Mama follow the old lady in the store. It's a little bitty store, and it don't have much in there. The old lady takes off her head rag and folds it up.

"Helena?" somebody calls from the back.

"Yes, Alnest?" the old lady says.

"Did you see them?"

"They're here. Standing beside me."

"Good. Now you can stay inside."

The old lady looks at Mama. Mama's waiting to hear what she brought us in here for. I'm waiting for that, too.

"I saw y'all each time you went by," she says. "I came out to catch you, but you were gone."

"We went back of town," Mama says.

"Did you eat?"

"Yes, ma'am."

The old lady looks at Mama a long time, like she's thinking Mama might be just saying that. Mama looks right back at her. The old lady looks at me to see what I have to say. I don't say nothing. I sure ain't going 'gainst my Mama.

"There's food in the kitchen," she says to Mama. "I've been keeping it warm."

Mama turns right around and starts for the door.

"Just a minute," the old lady says. Mama stops. "The boy'll have to work for it. It isn't free."

"We don't take no handout," Mama says.

"I'm not handing out anything," the old lady says. "I need my garbage moved to the front. Ernest has a bad cold and can't go out there."

"James'll move it for you," Mama says.

"Not unless you eat," the old lady says. "I'm old, but I have my pride, too, you know."

Mama can see she ain't go'n beat this old lady down, so she just shakes her head.

"All right," the old lady says. "Come into the kitchen."

She leads the way with that rag in her hand. The kitchen is a little bitty little old thing, too. The table and the stove just 'bout fill it up. They got a little room to the side. Somebody in there laying 'cross the bed—'cause I can see one of his feet. Must be the person she was talking to: Ernest or Alnest—something like that.

"Sit down," the old lady says to Mama. "Not you," she says to me. "You have to move the cans."

"Helena?" the man says in the other room.

"Yes, Alnest?" the old lady says.

"Are you going out there again?"

"I must show the boy where the garbage is Alnest," the old lady says.

"Keep that shawl over your head," the old man says.

"You don't have to remind me, Alnest. Come, boy," the old lady says.

We go out in the yard. Little old back yard ain't no bigger than the store or the kitchen. But it can sleet here just like it can sleet in any big back yard. And 'fore you know it, I'm trembling.

"There," the old lady says, pointing to the cans. I pick up one of the cans and set it right back down. The can's so light, I'm go'n see what's inside of it.

"Here," the old lady says. "Leave that can alone."

I look back at her standing there in that door. She's got that black rag wrapped around her shoulders, and she's pointing one of her little old fingers at me.

"Pick it up and carry it to the front," she says. I go by her with the can, and she's looking at me all the time. I'm sure the can's empty. I'm sure she could've carried it herself—maybe both of them at the same time. "Set it on the sidewalk by the door and come back for the other one," she says.

I go and come back, and Mama looks at me when I pass her. I get the other can and take it to the front. It don't feel a bit heavier than the first one. I tell myself I ain't go'n be nobody's fool, and I'm go'n look inside this can to see just what I been hauling. First, I look up the street, then down the street. Nobody coming. Then I look over my shoulder toward the door. That little old lady done slipped up there quiet's mouse, watching me again. Look like she knowed what I was go'n do.

"Ehh, Lord," she says. "Children, children. Come in here, boy, and go wash your hands."

I follow her in the kitchen. She point toward the bathroom, and I go in there and wash up. Little bitty old bathroom, but it's clean, clean. I don't use any of her towels; I wipe my hands on my pants leg.

When I come back in the kitchen, the old lady done dished up the food. Rice, gravy, meat—and she even got some lettuce and tomato in a saucer. She even got a glass of milk and a piece of cake there, too. It looks so good, I almost start eating 'fore I say my blessing.

"Helena?" the old man says.

"Yes, Alnest?"

"Are they eating?"

"Yes," she says.

"Good," he says. "Now you'll stay inside."

The old lady goes in there where he is and I can hear them talking. I look at Mama. She's eating slow like she's thinking. I wonder what's the matter now. I reckon she's thinking 'bout home.

The old lady comes back in the kitchen.

"I talked to Dr. Bassett's nurse," she says. "Dr. Bassett will take you as soon as you get there."

"Thank you, ma'am," Mama says.

"Perfectly all right," the old lady says. "Which one is it?"

Mama nods toward me. The old lady looks at me real sad. I look sad, too.

"You're not afraid, are you?" she says.

"No ma'am," I say.

"That's a good boy," the old lady says. "Nothing to be afraid of. Dr. Bassett will not hurt you."

When me and Mama get through eating, we thank the old lady again.

"Helena, are they leaving?" the old man says.

"Yes, Alnest."

"Tell them I say good-bye."

"They can hear you, Alnest."

"Good-bye both mother and son," the old man says. "And may God be with you."

Me and Mama tell the old man good-bye, and we follow the old lady in the front room. Mama opens the door to go out, but she stops and comes back in the store.

"You sell salt meat?" she says.

"Yes."

"Give me two bits worth."

"That isn't very much salt meat," the old lady says.

"That's all I have," Mama says.

The old lady goes back of the counter and cuts a big piece off the chunk. Then she wraps it up and put it in a paper bag.

"Two bits," she says.

"That looks like awful lot of meat for a quarter," Mama says.

"Two bits," the old lady says. "I've been selling salt meat behind this counter twenty-five years. I think I know what I'm doing."

"You got a scale there," Mama says.

"What?" the old lady says.

"Weigh it," Mama says.

"What?" the old lady says. "Are you telling me how to run my business?"

"Thanks very much for the food," Mama says.

"Just a minute," the old lady says.

"James," Mama says to me. I move toward the door.

"Just one minute, I said," the old lady says.

Me and Mama stop again and look at her. The old lady takes the meat out of the bag and unwraps it and cuts 'bout half of it off. Then she wraps it up again and juggs it back in the bag and gives the bag to Mama. Mama lays the quarter on the counter.

"Your kindness will never be forgotten," she says. "James," she says to me.

We go out, and the old lady comes to the door to look at us. After we go a little piece I look back, and she's still there watching us.

The sleet's coming down heavy, heavy now, and I turn up my coat collar to keep my neck warm. My Mama tells me turn it right back down.

"You not a bum," she says. "You a man."

Responding to the Story

1. **LITERARY LENS** Besides gray, what other colors appear in the story and what emotional significance does each color carry?

2. Every stop along the way in this trip to the dentist offers a lesson for James, the protagonist. What are some of these lessons?

3. By some standards, the mother's treatment of the boy appears harsh, even cruel. What is your opinion of the mother's treatment of the boy? Use specific examples to support your position.

4. Both "The Black Ball" in the previous unit and this story concern African American parents dealing with the effects of racial discrimination on their children. Use a chart like the one below to identify similarities and differences between the two stories. Consider such topics as issues addressed in the story, tone, final outcome of the plot, and main theme or message of the story.

Issue or Concept	The Sky Is Gray	The Black Ball
Narrative Point of View	*The story is told by the boy.*	*The story is told by the father.*

5. The passage in the dentist's waiting room (page 277–285) explores the relationship between faith and reason. Summarize the two positions in the argument. Given the ending of the story, which position do you think the boy will adopt in life?

6. **THE AUTHOR'S STYLE** Tone is an important element of this story. Describe the tone; then analyze how the author achieves it.

Harry Mark Petrakis
1923

About the Author

Contracting tuberculosis at the age of 12 turned out to be a blessing in disguise for Harry Mark Petrakis. Because of it, he spent several months in bed, at first wistfully listening to his friends play in the alley below the apartment his family lived in as part of Chicago's Greek community. Then his parents brought him books to while away the long hours in bed, starting a love of reading that eventually led to writing.

The months of self-education put Petrakis ahead of his peers in school. Bored, he dropped out to work at various jobs, which included steelworking and speechwriting, always writing his own fiction on the side. His work began to be published when he turned to the world he knew so well—the long rows of apartments like the one he shared with his nine family members, the elderly Greek women dancing in black shawls, the church rituals, and dusty corner markets.

Petrakis doesn't like being labeled an ethnic writer. Instead, he considers himself a writer who writes about what he knows—Greek life in America—but with the universal themes and emotions of loneliness, death, and joy. His novels include *Days of Vengeance*, *Lion At My Heart* and *A Dream of Kings*, his favorite novel and one he adapted for the screen himself.

****

The Author's Style

Petrakis' novels and stories concern the urban lives of Greek Americans, with a focus on the fundamental human problems that emerge from everyday incidents and relationships. At the heart of his stories is the exuberant vitality in the lives of immigrants and the immigrant community. His characters are earnest and unapologetic in expressing their needs and emotions.

Petrakis sees the possibility of passion, humor, and even heroic behavior in ordinary life; among the conflicts of his stories are those between traditional Greek culture and the less ethnically self-conscious approach to life that some would associate with being "generically American." His narrative style is simple and direct. He creates character and setting through concrete details. He also conveys a sense of the way fate and human limitations inevitably conflict with people's dreams and wishes.

The tone of a Petrakis story is one of sympathy and quiet acceptance; Petrakis prefers to create a mood of understanding humor rather than one of unforgiving judgment of his characters.

LITERARY LENS Conflict is at the heart of the plot of short stories. Trace the conflicts in this short story as you read.

★★

THE WOOING OF ARIADNE

HARRY MARK PETRAKIS

knew from the beginning she must accept my love—put aside foolish female protestations. It is the distinction of the male to be the aggressor and the cloak of the female to lend grace to the pursuit. Aha! I am wise to these wiles.

I first saw Ariadne at a dance given by the Spartan brotherhood[1] in the Legion Hall on Laramie Street. The usual assemblage of prune-faced and banana-bodied women smelling of virtuous **anemia**. They were an outrage to a man such as myself.

Then I saw her! A tall stately woman, perhaps in her early thirties. She had firm and slender arms bare to the shoulder and a graceful neck. Her hair was black and thick and piled in a great bun at the

anemia:
weakness of the blood; lack of vitality

---

1 **Spartan brotherhood:** an organized group of Greek men

aberration:
abnormality;
monstrosity

back of her head. That grand abundance of hair attracted me at once. This modern **aberration** women have of chopping their hair close to the scalp and leaving it in fantastic disarray I find revolting.

I went at once to my friend Vasili, the baker, and asked him who she was.

"Ariadne Langos," he said. "Her father is Janco Langos, the grocer."

"Is she engaged or married?"

"No," he said slyly. "They say she frightens off the young men. They say she is very spirited."

"Excellent," I said and marveled at my good fortune in finding her unpledged. "Introduce me at once."

"Marko," Vasili said with some apprehension. "Do not commit anything rash."

I pushed the little man forward. "Do not worry, little friend," I said. "I am a man suddenly possessed by a vision. I must meet her at once."

We walked together across the dance floor to where my beloved stood. The closer we came the more impressive was the majestic swell of her breasts and the fine great sweep of her thighs. She towered over the insignificant apple-core women around her. Her eyes, dark and thoughtful, seemed to be restlessly searching the room.

Be patient, my dove! Marko is coming.

"Miss Ariadne," Vasili said. "This is Mr. Marko Palamas. He desires to have the honor of your acquaintance."

> *S*he doubled up her fist and struck me in the eye. A stout blow for a woman that brought a haze to my vision, but I shook my head and moved a step closer.

She looked at me for a long and piercing moment. I imagined her gauging my mighty strength by the width of my shoulders and the circumference of my arms. I felt the tips of my mustache bristle with pleasure. Finally she nodded with the barest minimum of courtesy. I was not discouraged.

"Miss Ariadne," I said, "may I have the pleasure of this dance?"

She stared at me again with her fiery eyes. I could imagine more timid men shriveling before her fierce gaze. My heart flamed at the passion her rigid exterior concealed.

"I think not," she said.

"Don't you dance?"

Vasili gasped beside me. An old prune-face standing nearby clucked her toothless gums.

"Yes, I dance," Ariadne said coolly. "I do not wish to dance with you."

"Why?" I asked courteously.

"I do not think you heard me," she said. "I do not wish to dance with you."

Oh, the sly and lovely darling. Her **subterfuge** so apparent. Trying to conceal her pleasure at my interest.

subterfuge: deceptive strategy

"Why?" I asked again.

"I am not sure," she said. "It could be your appearance, which bears considerable resemblance to a gorilla, or your manner, which would suggest closer alliance to a pig."

"Now that you have met my family," I said engagingly, "let us dance."

"Not now," she said, and her voice rose. "Not this dance or the one after. Not tonight or tomorrow night or next month or next year. Is that clear?"

Sweet, sweet Ariadne. Ancient and eternal game of retreat and pursuit. My pulse beat more quickly.

Vasili pulled at my sleeve. He was my friend, but without the courage of a goat. I shook him off and spoke to Ariadne.

"There is a joy like fire that consumes a man's heart when he first sets eyes on his beloved," I said. "This I felt when I first saw you." My voice trembled under a mighty passion. "I swear before God from this moment that I love you."

She stared shocked out of her deep dark eyes and, beside her, old prune-face staggered as if she had been kicked. Then my beloved did something which proved indisputably that her passion was as intense as mine.

She doubled up her fist and struck me in the eye. A stout blow for a woman that brought a haze to my vision, but I shook my head and moved a step closer.

"I would not care," I said, "if you struck out both my eyes. I would cherish the memory of your beauty forever."

By this time the music had stopped, and the dancers formed a circle of idiot faces about us. I paid them no attention and ignored Vasili, who kept whining and pulling at my sleeve.

"You are crazy!" she said. "You must be mad! Remove yourself from my presence or I will tear out both your eyes and your tongue besides!"

You see! Another woman would have cried, or been frightened into silence. But my Ariadne, worthy and venerable, hurled her spirit into my teeth.

"I would like to call on your father tomorrow," I said. From the assembled dancers who watched there rose a few **vagrant** whispers and some rude laughter. I stared at them carefully and they hushed at once. My temper and strength of arm were well known.

vagrant:
fleeting; random

Ariadne did not speak again, but in a magnificent spirit stamped from the floor. The music began, and men and women began again to dance. I permitted Vasili to pull me to a corner.

"You are insane!" he said. He wrung his withered fingers in anguish. "You assaulted her like a Turk![2] Her relatives will cut out your heart!"

THE PAINTER OF TBILISI
1989
Timothy Harney

---

2 **like a Turk:** like someone from Turkey; the longstanding hostilities between the Turks and the Greeks give the phrase a strong negative slant.

"My intentions were honorable," I said. "I saw her and loved her and told her so." At this point I struck my fist against my chest. Poor Vasili jumped.

"But you do not court a woman that way," he said.

"You don't, my anemic friend," I said. "Nor do the rest of these sheep. But I court a woman that way!"

He looked to heaven and helplessly shook his head. I waved good-by and started for my hat and coat.

"Where are you going?" he asked.

"To prepare for tomorrow," I said. "In the morning I will speak to her father."

I went to my rooms above my tavern. I could not sleep. All night I tossed in restless frenzy. I touched my eye that she had struck with her spirited hand.

I left the hall and in the street felt the night wind cold on my flushed cheeks. My blood was inflamed. The memory of her loveliness fed fuel to the fire. For the first time I understood with a terrible clarity the driven heroes of the past performing mighty deeds in love. Paris stealing Helen in passion, and Menelaus[3] pursuing with a great fleet. In that moment if I knew the whole world would be plunged into conflict I would have followed Ariadne to Hades.[4]

I went to my rooms above my tavern. I could not sleep. All night I tossed in restless frenzy. I touched my eye that she had struck with her spirited hand.

Ariadne! Ariadne! my soul cried out.

In the morning I bathed and dressed carefully. I confirmed the address of Langos, the grocer, and started to his store. It was a bright cold November morning, but I walked with spring in my step.

When I opened the door of the Langos grocery, a tiny bell rang shrilly. I stepped into the store piled with fruits and vegetables and smelling of cabbage and greens.

A stooped little old man with white bushy hair and owlish eyes came

---

3 **Paris . . . Helen . . . Menelaus:** characters from Greek mythology. Helen, the wife of Menelaus, was kidnapped by Paris, an event which began the Trojan War.

4 **Hades:** the underworld of dead and departed souls in Greek mythology

toward me. He looked as if his veins contained vegetable juice instead of blood, and if he were, in truth, the father of my beloved I marveled at how he could have produced such a **paragon** of women.

paragon:
perfect model

"Are you Mr. Langos?"

"I am," he said and came closer. "I am."

"I met your daughter last night," I said. "Did she mention I was going to call?"

He shook his head somberly.

"My daughter mentioned you," he said. "In thirty years I have never seen her in such a state of agitation. She was possessed."

"The effect on me was the same," I said. "We met for the first time last night, and I fell passionately in love."

"Incredible," the old man said.

"You wish to know something about me," I said. "My name is Marko Palamas. I am a Spartan emigrated to this country eleven years ago. I am forty-one years old. I have been a wrestler and a sailor and fought with the resistance movement[5] in Greece in the war. For this service I was decorated by the king. I own a small but profitable tavern on Dart Street. I attend church regularly. I love your daughter."

As I finished he stepped back and bumped a rack of fruit. An orange rolled off to the floor. I bent and retrieved it to hand it to him, and he cringed as if he thought I might bounce it off his old head.

"She is a bad-tempered girl," he said. "Stubborn, impatient and spoiled. She has been the cause of considerable concern to me. All the **eligible** young men have been driven away by her temper and **disposition**."

eligible:
worthy; suitable

disposition:
temperament;
character

"Poor girl," I said. " Subjected to the courting of calves and goats."

The old man blinked his owlish eyes. The front door opened and a battleship of a woman sailed in.

"Three pounds of tomatoes, Mr. Langos," she said. "I am in a hurry. Please to give me good ones. Last week two spoiled before I had a chance to put them into Demetri's salad."

"I am very sorry," Mr. Langos said. He turned to me. "Excuse me, Mr. Poulmas."

"Palamas," I said. "Marko Palamas."

---

5 **resistance movement:** Greece's effort to remain neutral during World War II

Harry Mark Petrakis

He nodded nervously. He went to wait on the battleship, and I spent a moment examining the store. Neat and small. I would not imagine he did more than hold his own. In the rear of the store there were stairs leading to what appeared to be an apartment above. My heart beat faster.

When he had bagged the tomatoes and given change, he returned to me and said, "She is also a terrible cook. She cannot fry an egg without burning it." His voice shook with woe. "She cannot make pilaf[6] and lamb with squash." He paused. "You like pilaf and lamb with squash?"

"Certainly."

"You see?" he said in triumph. "She is useless in the kitchen. She is thirty years old, and I am resigned she will remain an old maid. In a way I am glad because I know she would drive some poor man to drink."

"Do not deride her to discourage me," I said. "You need have no fear that I will mistreat her or cause her unhappiness. When she is married to me she will cease being a problem to you." I paused. "It is true that I am not pretty by the **foppish** standards that prevail today. But I am a man. I wrestled Zahundos and pinned him two straight times in Baltimore. A giant of a man. Afterward he conceded he had met his master. This from Zahundos was a mighty compliment."

foppish:
pretentious; foolish

"I am sure," the old man said without enthusiasm. "I am sure."

He looked toward the front door as if hoping for another customer.

"Is your daughter upstairs?"

He looked startled and tugged at his apron. "Yes," he said. "I don't know. Maybe she has gone out."

"May I speak to her? Would you kindly tell her I wish to speak to her."

She is also a terrible cook. She cannot fry an egg without burning it." His voice shook with woe.

"You are making a mistake," the old man said. "A terrible mistake."

"No mistake," I said firmly.

The old man shuffled toward the stairs. He climbed them slowly. At the top he paused and turned the knob of the door. He rattled it again.

"It is locked," he called down. "It has never been locked before. She has locked the door."

---

6 **pilaf:** seasoned rice often combined with meat

"Knock," I said. "Knock to let her know I am here."

"I think she knows," the old man said. "I think she knows."

He knocked gently.

"Knock harder," I suggested. "Perhaps she does not hear."

"I think she hears," the old man said. "I think she hears."

"Knock again," I said. "Shall I come up and knock for you?"

"No, no," the old man said quickly. He gave the door a sound kick. Then he groaned as if he might have hurt his foot.

"She does not answer," he said in a quavering voice. "I am very sorry she does not answer."

"The coy darling," I said and laughed. "If that is her game." I started for the front door of the store.

I went out and stood on the sidewalk before the store. Above the grocery were the front windows of their apartment. I cupped my hands about my mouth.

"Ariadne!" I shouted. "Ariadne!"

The old man came out the door running disjointedly. He looked frantically down the street.

"Are you mad?" he asked shrilly. "You will cause a riot. The police will come. You must be mad!"

"Ariadne!" I shouted. "Beloved!"

A window slammed open, and the face of Ariadne appeared above me. Her dark hair tumbled about her ears.

"Go away!" she shrieked. "Will you go away!"

"Ariadne," I said loudly. "I have come as I promised. I have spoken to your father. I wish to call on you."

"Go away!" she shrieked. "Madman! Imbecile! Go away!"

By this time a small group of people had assembled around the store and were watching curiously. The old man stood wringing his hands and uttering what sounded like small groans.

I went to my tavern for a while and set up the glasses for the evening trade. I made arrangements for Pavlakis to tend bar in my place. Afterward I sat alone in my apartment and read a little piece of majestic Pindar to ease the agitation of my heart.

"Ariadne," I said. "I wish to call on you. Stop this nonsense and let me in."

She pushed farther out the window and showed me her teeth.

"Be careful, beloved," I said. "You might fall."

She drew her head in quickly, and I turned then to the assembled crowd.

"A misunderstanding," I said. "Please move on."

Suddenly old Mr. Langos shrieked. A moment later something broke on the sidewalk a foot from where I stood. A vase or a plate. I looked up, and Ariadne was preparing to hurl what appeared to be a water pitcher.

"Ariadne!" I shouted. "Stop that!"

The water pitcher landed closer than the vase, the fragments of glass struck my shoes. The crowd scattered, and the old man raised his hands and wailed to heaven.

Ariadne slammed down the window.

The crowd moved in again a little closer, and somewhere among them I heard laughter. I fixed them with a cold stare and waited for some one of them to say something offensive. I would have tossed him around like sardines, but they slowly dispersed and moved on. In another moment the old man and I were alone.

I followed him into the store. He walked an awkward dance of agitation. He shut the door and peered out through the glass.

"A disgrace," he wailed. "A disgrace. The whole street will know by nightfall. A disgrace."

"A girl of heroic spirit," I said. "Will you speak to her for me? Assure her of the sincerity of my feelings. Tell her I pledge eternal love and devotion."

The old man sat down on an orange crate and weakly made his cross.

"I had hoped to see her myself," I said. "But if you promise to speak to her, I will return this evening."

"That soon?" the old man said.

"If I stayed now," I said, "it would be sooner."

"This evening," the old man said and shook his head in resignation. "This evening."

I went to my tavern for a while and set up the glasses for the evening trade. I made arrangements for Pavlakis to tend bar in my place. Afterward I sat alone in my apartment and read a little piece of majestic Pindar[7] to ease the agitation of my heart.

---

7 **Pindar:** (518–438 B.C.) Greek poet who often wrote glowingly about war and the military

Once in the mountains of Greece when I fought with the guerrillas in the last year of the great war, I suffered a wound from which it seemed I would die. For days high fever raged in my body. My friends brought a priest at night secretly from one of the captive villages to read the last rites. I accepted the coming of death and was grateful for many things. For the gentleness and wisdom of my old grandfather, the loyalty of my companions in war, the years I sailed between the wild ports of the seven seas, and the strength that flowed to me from the Spartan earth. For one thing only did I weep when it seemed I would leave life, that I have never set ablaze the world with burning song of passion for one woman. Women I had known, pockets of pleasure that I tumbled for quick joy, but I had been denied the mighty love for one woman. For that I wept.

In Ariadne I swore before God I had found my woman. I knew by the storm-lashed hurricane that swept within my body. A woman whose majesty was in harmony with the earth, who would be faithful and beloved to me as Penelope had been to Ulysses.[8]

That evening near seven I returned to the grocery. Deep twilight had fallen across the street, and the lights in the window of the store had been dimmed. The apples and oranges and pears had been covered with brown paper for the night.

I tried the door and found it locked. I knocked on the glass, and a moment later the old man came shuffling out of the shadows and let me in.

"Good evening, Mr. Langos."

He muttered some greeting in answer. "Ariadne is not here," he said. "She is at the church. Father Marlas wishes to speak with you."

"A fine young priest," I said. "Let us go at once."

I waited on the sidewalk while the old man locked the store. We started the short walk to the church.

"A clear and ringing night," I said. "Does it not make you feel the wonder and glory of being alive?"

The old man uttered what sounded like a groan, but a truck passed on the street at that moment and I could not be sure.

At the church we entered by a side door leading to the office of Father Marlas. I knocked on the door, and when he called to us to enter we walked in.

---

8 **Penelope . . . Ulysses:** famous characters in Greek mythology. While Ulysses led troops in the Trojan War, his wife Penelope resisted a series of suitors.

Young Father Marlas was sitting at his desk in his black cassock and with his black goatee trim and imposing beneath his clean-shaven cheeks. Beside the desk, in a dark blue dress sat Ariadne, looking somber and beautiful. A bald-headed, big-nosed old man with flint and fire in his eyes sat in a chair beside her.

"Good evening, Marko," Father Marlas said and smiled.

"Good evening, Father," I said.

"Mr. Langos and his daughter you have met," he said and he cleared his throat. "This is Uncle Paul Langos."

"Good evening, Uncle Paul," I said. He glared at me and did not answer. I smiled warmly at Ariadne in greeting, but she was watching the priest.

"Sit down," Father Marlas said.

I sat down across from Ariadne, and old Mr. Langos took a chair beside Uncle Paul. In this way we were arrayed in battle order as if we were opposing armies.

A long silence prevailed during which Father Marlas cleared his throat several times. I observed Ariadne closely. There were grace and poise even in the way her slim-fingered hands rested in her lap. She was a dark and lovely flower, and my pulse beat more quickly at her nearness.

"Marko," Father Marlas said finally. "Marko, I have known you well for the three years since I assumed duties in this parish. You are most regular in your devotions and very generous at the time of the Christmas and Easter offerings. Therefore, I find it hard to believe this complaint against you."

"My family are not liars!" Uncle Paul said, and he had a voice like a hunk of dry hard cheese being grated.

"Of course not," Father Marlas said quickly. He smiled benevolently at Ariadne. "I only mean to say—"

"Tell him to stay away from my niece," Uncle Paul burst out.

"Excuse me, Uncle Paul," I said very politely. "Will you kindly keep out of what is not your business."

Uncle Paul looked shocked. "Not my business?" He looked from Ariadne to Father Marlas and then to his brother. "Not my business?"

"This matter concerns Ariadne and me," I said. "With outside interference it becomes more difficult."

"Not my business!" Uncle Paul said. He couldn't seem to get that through his head.

"Marko," Father Marlas said, and his composure was slightly shaken. "The family feels you are forcing your attention upon this girl. They are concerned."

"I understand, Father," I said. "It is natural for them to be concerned. I respect their concern. It is also natural for me to speak of love to a woman I have chosen for my wife."

"Not my business!" Uncle Paul said again, and shook his head violently.

"My daughter does not wish to become your wife," Mr. Langos said in a squeaky voice.

"That is for your daughter to say," I said courteously.

Ariadne made a sound in her throat, and we all looked at her. Her eyes were deep and cold, and she spoke slowly and carefully as if weighing each word on a scale in her father's grocery.

"I would not marry this madman if he were one of the Twelve Apostles,"[9] she said.

> Suddenly a great bitterness assailed me, and anger at myself, and a terrible sadness that flowed like night through my body because I could not make them understand.

"See!" Mr. Langos said in triumph.

"Not my business!" Uncle Paul snarled.

"Marko," Father Marlas said. "Try to understand."

"We will call the police!" Uncle Paul raised his voice.

"Put this hoodlum under a bond!"[10]

"Please!" Father Marlas said. "Please!"

"Today he stood on the street outside the store," Mr. Langos said excitedly. "He made me a laughingstock."

"If I were a younger man," Uncle Paul growled, "I would settle this without the police. Zi-ip!" He drew a callused finger violently across his throat.

"Please," Father Marlas said.

"A disgrace!" Mr. Langos said.

"An outrage!" Uncle Paul said.

"He must leave Ariadne alone!" Mr. Langos said.

"We will call the police!" Uncle Paul said.

"Silence!" Father Marlas said loudly.

With everyone suddenly quiet he turned to me. His tone softened.

---

9 **Twelve Apostles:** in the Bible, men who followed Jesus and were charged with spreading God's word

10 **bond:** a type of legal restraint

Harry Mark Petrakis

"Marko," he said and he seemed to be pleading a little. "Marko, you must understand."

Suddenly a great bitterness assailed me, and anger at myself, and a terrible sadness that flowed like night through my body because I could not make them understand.

"Father," I said quietly, "I am not a fool. I am Marko Palamas and once I pinned the mighty Zahundos in Baltimore. But this battle, more important to me by far, I have lost. That which has not the grace of God is better far in silence."

I turned to leave and it would have ended there.

"Hoodlum!" Uncle Paul said. "It is time you were silent!"

I swear in that moment if he had been a younger man I would have flung him to the dome of the church. Instead I turned and spoke to them all in fire and fury.

"Listen," I said. "I feel no shame for the violence of my feelings. I am a man bred of the Spartan earth and my emotions are violent. Let those who squeak of life feel shame. Nor do I feel shame because I saw this flower and loved her. Or because I spoke at once of my love."

No one moved or made a sound.

"We live in a dark age," I said. "An age where men say one thing and mean another. A time of dwarfs afraid of life. The days are gone when mighty Pindar sang his radiant blossoms of song. When the noble passions of men set ablaze cities, and the heroic deeds of men rang like thunder to every corner of the earth."

I spoke my final words to Ariadne. "I saw you and loved you," I said gently. "I told you of my love. This is my way—the only way I know. If this way has proved offensive to you I apologize to you alone. But understand clearly that for none of this do I feel shame."

I turned then and started to the door. I felt my heart weeping as if waves were breaking within my body.

"Marko Palamas," Ariadne said. I turned slowly. I looked at her. For the first time the warmth I was sure dwelt in her body radiated within the circles of her face. For the first time she did not look at me with her eyes like glaciers.

"Marko Palamas," she said and there was strange moving softness in the way she spoke my name. "You may call on me tomorrow."

Uncle Paul shot out of his chair. "She is mad too!" he shouted. "He has bewitched her!"

"A disgrace!" Mr. Langos said.

"Call the police!" Uncle Paul shouted. "I'll show him if it's my business!"

"My poor daughter!" Mr. Langos wailed.

"Turk!" Uncle Paul shouted. "Robber!"

"Please!" Father Marlas said. "Please!"

I ignored them all. In that winged and zestful moment I had eyes only for my beloved, for Ariadne, blossom of my heart and black-eyed flower of my soul!

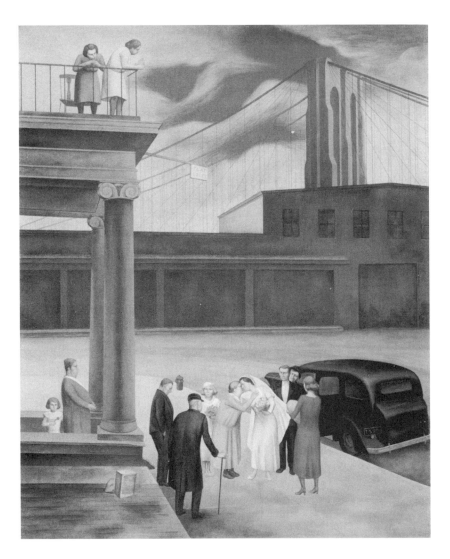

WEDDING IN
SOUTH STREET
1936
O. Louis Guglielmi
The Museum of Modern Art

Responding to the Story

1. LITERARY LENS Conflict in literature usually involves a struggle between the protagonist and at least one of the following: nature, another character, society, or some internal force. How would you characterize Marko's conflicts?

2. Why do you think Ariadne eventually accepts Marko's suit?

3. Is there a passage that you found humorous? If so, what made it funny?

4. Marko makes allusions to Greek mythology on pages 303 and 308. Why do you think the author includes these allusions?

5. Although much of this author's work is set in the Greek American community, Petrakis' work enjoys a wide readership beyond ethnic boundaries. Critics refer to such works as *concrete universal.* That is, works of art that address universal human concerns through a concrete or local setting. In what way is "The Wooing of Ariadne" an example of the concrete universal?

6. THE AUTHOR'S STYLE Consider the quotation below by Kurt Vonnegut on the topic of larger-than-life characters. What makes the characters in "The Wooing of Ariadne" larger than life?

Larger Than Life

I've often thought what a wonderful basketball team could be formed from Petrakis' characters. Every one of them is at least fourteen feet tall.

— Kurt Vonnegut

Experiencing

1. An integral part of the conflict of a story is its resolution, or the manner in which the main conflict is worked out. In some stories the conflict is resolved completely; in others, the author leaves an ambiguous ending, forcing readers to draw their own conclusions. Consider your experience reading the stories in this unit. In your opinion, which story has the most satisfying resolution? Explain your choice.

2. Some stories yield most of their pleasure on first reading. Others, like people, are harder to get to know but are well worth knowing. Which story in this unit did you like best on first reading, and which grew on you the most after examining it more closely? Explain.

Interpreting

3. "Everything That Rises Must Converge" and "The Sky Is Gray" both deal with interactions between races. What is the message of the interactions in each story?

4. Compare and contrast the attitudes the children in "The Veldt" and "Barn Burning" have toward their parents. What were the end results of these attitudes?

5. "Barn Burning," "Angel Levine," and "Everything That Rises Must Converge" all contain images or references to wings or flight. Select two of these stories and compare and contrast the images of flight. In what ways do the authors use these images?

Evaluating

6. Harrison in "Harrison Bergeron" and Marko in "The Wooing of Ariadne" are two larger-than-life protagonists in this unit. Other characters, such as Sammy in "A & P" or Manischevitz in "Angel Levine" share qualities of the antihero. Of the two types of protagonists—larger-than-life or antihero—which do you think best represents the human condition? Use references to any of the stories you have read in this unit to support your evaluation.

7. Upon accepting the Nobel Prize in 1950, William Faulkner said, "It is the writer's privilege to help man endure by lifting his heart." Based on your response to the stories in this unit, do you think a story has to be upbeat or have a happy ending to lift your heart? Explain why or why not.

WRITING ABOUT THE LITERATURE

Comparing Styles

William Faulkner's style is often characterized as difficult and obscure. John Updike's style in "A & P," on the other hand, is very accessible, or easy to understand. Write a short essay in which you compare and contrast the styles of these two authors. What do you think are the strengths and weaknesses of each?

Universality

One of the hallmarks of good literature is that while it has a unique setting and compelling characters, it also deals with universal themes—emotions and problems that affect everyone. Pick your favorite story from this unit. Write an essay evaluating what elements make it both unique and universal.

WRITING WITH STYLE

A Setting of Your Own

The setting of a story often influences its tone. For example, Gaines' description of the setting in "The Sky Is Gray" creates an almost oppressive tone, whereas Bradbury's description of the nursery in "The Veldt" creates an ominous tone. Select a location you know well, such as a store or a location in your school. Describe it in the tone of one of the short stories in this unit. Feel free to exaggerate the tone of your selected author. See if your classmates can guess the source of your "influence."

IN YOUR OWN STYLE

In "The Veldt," "Barn Burning," and "Everything That Rises Must Converge," parents and children have difficulty communicating. In your own style, write a scene that shows a parent and son or daughter struggling to understand each other. You will want to make choices about setting the scene, using dialogue, and showing nonverbal communication.

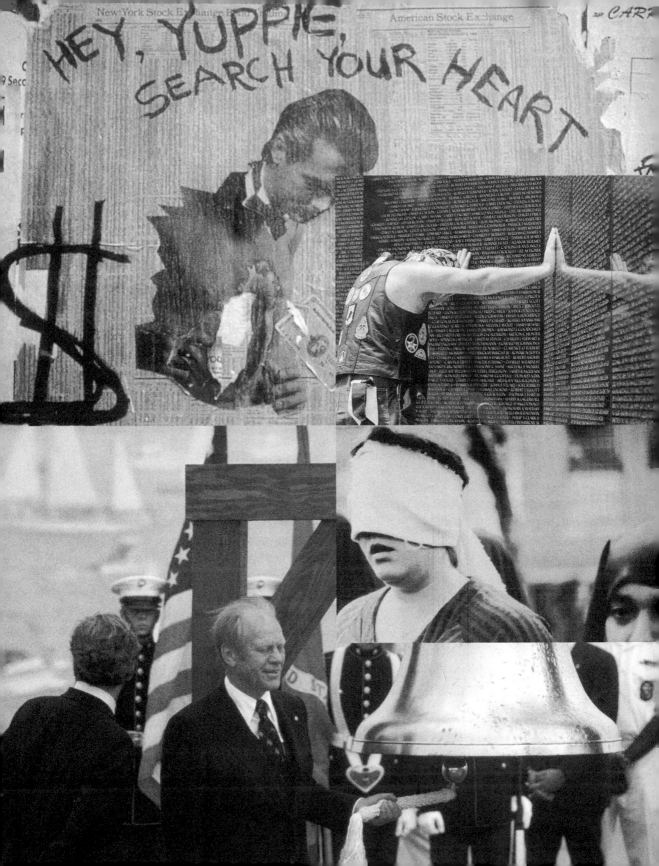

UNIT THREE

Literature from the 1970s and 1980s

Literature from the 1970s and 1980s

top to bottom: A graffiti-like collage illustrates the gulf between the haves, or yuppies, (young urban professionals) and the have-nots of the 1980s.
★ A veteran grieves for fallen comrades at the Vietnam War Memorial in Washington, DC. ★ Pop icon Madonna begins her rise to rock stardom.

Many observers believe that the seventies and eighties in the United States were a time of disillusionment, an era in which Americans mourned the loss of their national innocence and idealism in the wake of the Vietnam War. During this period, many traditions came into question. Parents feuded with teenage sons over the length of their hair. Sandra Day O'Connor became the first woman to serve on the Supreme Court. The personal computer came into its own, causing some to predict that within ten years, society would be paperless. Literature was swept along on these currents of change. Experimentation thrived, taking advantage of the momentum toward innovation that had come about in the preceding decade.

Following the lead of popular entertainment and professional sports, American politics and social life became increasingly diverse. It was an ideal time for writers to mine the imaginative potential of fiction. In the seventies, the modern women's movement emerged, flourishing on the ideas and energy of the Civil Rights era. Writing by and about women took on energy of its own. Stories of girls and women from across American society appeared in the novels and stories of Alice Walker, Bobbie Ann Mason, and Amy Tan. These authors testified to the intensity, impact, and scope of the change in female lives.

At the same time, Raymond Carver, E. L. Doctorow, and Russell Banks gave voice to working-class people made desperate by economic necessity as well as their own human needs and limitations. Many writers continued to address the search for individual identity and explore the dynamics of family relationships in a period of rapid social change.

With heartbreaking candor, Tim O'Brien and other Vietnam veterans began to tell the rest of the country—still torn in strife over whether the war was right or wrong—what it meant to serve in Vietnam.

Stylistic experimentation continued, producing extremely short stories called "snap" fiction and the "minimalist" stories of writers such as Carver, whose tone was deliberately unemotional and flat. Even Carver's titles had a conversational tone and rhythm: "Will You Please Be Quiet, Please?" And "What We Talk About When We Talk About Love." Bobbie Ann Mason and Garrison Keillor honored ordinary people by writing about their daily concerns in styles that were plain and easy to understand.

Some writers drew on sources that were outside the American mainstream. For example, Louise Erdrich explored the Native American tradition of reverence for nature, creating a fictional world in contrast to an overall American culture that often focused on television, celebrity, and consumerism. The traditions of Jewish mysticism were a wellspring for Isaac Bashevis Singer, who peopled his urban myths with angels and demons. Like many of their peers, Erdrich and Singer set the particular concerns of an ethnic or racial group against a backdrop of the universal joys and tragedies of the human condition.

Writers working out of diverse traditions took different kinds of creative risks. Along with the direct and unadorned prose style of writers such as Mason and Banks, there were stories that read like fables as well as edgy and fantastic stories from surprising points of view. For the American short story, it was an invigorating time.

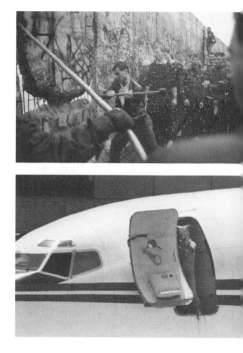

top to bottom: 1976: President Gerald Ford rings in America's bicentennial celebration ★ 1979: Fifty-two Americans are taken hostage after Iranian students seize the American Embassy in Tehran. The hostages remained in captivity for 444 days. ★ 1989: Germans tear down the wall that separated East and West Berlin. The destruction of the wall marked the beginning of the end for the Soviet Union's Communist system. ★ 1985: TWA flight 847 was hijacked to Beirut by Shiite Muslims. One hundred fifty-three people aboard were held hostage for several days. Serviceman Robert Stethem was executed by the terrorists and his body tossed to the tarmac.

Isaac Bashevis Singer
1904–1991

About the Author

Born in Poland to a Jewish family, Isaac Bashevis Singer wrote in Yiddish all of his life, often supervising the translation of his work into English after he left his homeland for the United States. The son of a rabbi, he received a traditional rabbinical education in Poland, but chose the life of a writer instead, moving to New York in 1935.

As a writer for *The Jewish Daily Forward*, Singer brought forth an astonishing number of stories under various psuedonyms. During his lifetime, he published 55 volumes of short stories, novels, plays, children's stories, and memoirs; five more volumes were published after his death. Among his best-known works are his novel, *The Family Moskat*, and a collection of short stories titled *Gimpel the Fool*.

Singer believed that the first job of literature is to entertain. He said many times that "A good writer is basically a story-teller, not a scholar or a redeemer of mankind."

****

The Author's Style

Singer's fiction reflects his roots; he grew up learning the tradition of the Yiddish folktale in his native Poland. His stories are allegories in which the fantastic and supernatural often come into play in the lives of people who find themselves in extreme situations. His style is to link lives of sad and earthly everyday reality with a world of mystery and superstition. Here demons, specters, and dreams have a real and permanent impact on human lives. Whether ordinary or fantastic, events in Singer's stories are described in simple, direct, matter-of-fact prose.

Singer's characters are often colorful and compelling exaggerations; they are overly stubborn, perhaps, or compulsive or gullible. They are often victimized by the deceptiveness and unkindness of others, their own imaginations, and the general unfairness of life. At times Singer draws a contrast between the cruel and disorienting modern world and an alternative life of mystical possibilities, peopled with both angels and demons.

Many of Singer's stories were written specifically for children, but because of the folk origins and fable-like appeal, his writing has always had a wide-ranging audience.

LITERARY LENS In literature, an *epiphany* refers to an event, sometimes mystical in nature, in which a character changes in profound ways due to the revelation of a simple yet powerful truth. Watch for such an event in this story.

THE
KEY

ISAAC BASHEVIS SINGER

At about three o'clock in the afternoon, Bessie Popkin began to prepare to go down to the street. Going out was connected with many difficulties, especially on a hot summer day: first, forcing her fat body into a corset, squeezing her swollen feet into shoes, and combing her hair, which Bessie dyed at home and which grew wild and was streaked in all colors—yellow, black, gray, red; then making sure that while she was out her neighbors would not break into her apartment and steal linen, clothes, documents, or just disarrange things and make them disappear.

Besides human tormentors, Bessie suffered from demons, imps, Evil Powers. She hid her eyeglasses in the night table and found them in a slipper. She placed her bottle of hair dye in the medicine chest; days later she discovered it under the pillow. Once, she left a pot of borscht[1] in the refrigerator, but the Unseen took it from there and after long searching Bessie came upon it in her clothes closet. On its surface was a thick layer of fat that gave off the smell of rancid tallow.[2]

What she went through, how many tricks were played on her and how much she had to wrangle in order not to perish or fall into insanity, only God knew. She had given up the telephone because racketeers and degenerates called her day and night, trying to get secrets out of her. The Puerto Rican milkman once tried to rape her. The errand boy from the grocery store attempted to burn her belongings with a cigarette. To evict her from the rent-controlled apartment where she had lived for thirty-five years, the company and the superintendent infested her rooms with rats, mice, cockroaches.

> *H*er chin sprouted a little white beard. She wore a faded dress in a flowered print, a misshapen straw hat trimmed with wooden cherries and grapes, and shabby shoes.

Bessie had long ago realized that no means were adequate against those determined to be spiteful—not the metal door, the special lock, her letters to the police, the mayor, the FBI, and even the president in Washington. But while one breathed one had to eat. It all took time: checking the windows, the gas vents, securing the drawers. Her paper money she kept in volumes of the encyclopedia, in back copies of the *National Geographic*, and in Sam Popkin's old ledgers. Her stocks and bonds Bessie had hidden among the logs in the fireplace, which was never used, as well as under the seats of the easy chairs. Her jewels she had sewn into the mattress. There was a time when Bessie had safe-deposit boxes at the bank, but she long ago convinced herself that the guards there had passkeys.

At about five o'clock, Bessie was ready to go out. She gave a last look at herself in the mirror—small, broad, with a narrow forehead, a flat nose, and eyes slanting and half-closed, like a Chinaman's. Her chin sprouted a little white beard. She wore a faded dress in a flowered print, a misshapen straw hat trimmed with wooden cherries and grapes, and shabby shoes. Before she left, she made a final inspection of the three rooms and the kitchen.

---

1 **borscht:** hot or cold beet soup served with sour cream

2 **tallow:** white fat from cattle or sheep used in soap and candles

322   Isaac Bashevis Singer

Everywhere there were clothes, shoes, and piles of letters that Bessie had not opened. Her husband, Sam Popkin, who had died almost twenty years ago, had liquidated his real-estate business before his death, because he was about to retire to Florida. He left her stocks, bonds, and a number of passbooks from savings banks, as well as some mortgages. To this day, firms wrote to Bessie, sent her reports, checks. The Internal Revenue Service claimed taxes from her. Every few weeks she received announcements from a funeral company that sold plots in an "airy cemetery." In former years, Bessie used to answer letters, deposit her checks, keep track of her income and expenses. Lately she had neglected it all. She even stopped buying the newspaper and reading the financial section.

In the corridor, Bessie tucked cards with signs on them that only she could recognize between the door and the door frame. The keyhole she stuffed with putty. What else could she do—a widow without children, relatives, or friends? There was a time when the neighbors used to open their doors, look out, and laugh at her exaggerated care; others teased her. That had long passed. Bessie spoke to no one. She didn't see well, either. The glasses she had worn for years were of no use. To go to an eye doctor and be fitted for new ones was too much of an effort. Everything was difficult—even entering and leaving the elevator, whose door always closed with a slam.

Bessie seldom went farther than two blocks from her building. The street between Broadway and Riverside Drive became noisier and filthier from day to day. Hordes of urchins ran around half-naked. Dark men with curly hair and wild eyes quarreled in Spanish with little women whose bellies were always swollen in pregnancy. They talked back in rattling voices. Dogs barked, cats meowed. Fires broke out and fire engines, ambulances, and police cars drove up. On Broadway, the old groceries had been replaced by supermarkets, where food must be picked out and put in a wagon and one had to stand in line before the cashier.

God in heaven, since Sam died, New York, America—perhaps the whole world—was falling apart. All the decent people had left the neighborhood and it was overrun by a mob of thieves, robbers, whores. Three times Bessie's pocketbook had been stolen. When she reported it to the police, they just laughed. Every time one crossed the street, one risked one's life. Bessie took a step and stopped. Someone had advised her to use a cane, but she was far from considering herself an old woman or a cripple. Every few weeks she painted her nails red. At times, when the rheumatism left her in peace, she took clothes she used to wear from the closets, tried them on, and studied herself in the mirror.

Opening the door of the supermarket was impossible. She had to wait till someone held it for her. The supermarket itself was a place that only the Devil could have invented. The lamps burned with a glaring light. People pushing wagons were likely to knock down anyone in their path. The shelves were either too high or too low. The noise was deafening, and the contrast between the heat outside and the freezing temperature inside! It was a miracle that she didn't get pneumonia. More than anything else, Bessie was tortured by indecision. She picked up each item with a trembling hand and read the label. This was not the greed of youth but the uncertainty of age. According to Bessie's figuring, today's shopping should not have taken longer than three-quarters of an hour, but two hours passed and Bessie was still not finished. When she finally brought the wagon to the cashier, it occurred to her that she had forgotten the box of oatmeal. She went back and a woman took her place in line. Later, when she paid, there was new trouble. Bessie had put the bill in the right side of her bag, but it was not there. After long rummaging, she found it in a small change purse on the opposite side. Yes, who could believe that such things were possible? If she told someone, he would think she was ready for the madhouse.

When Bessie went into the supermarket, the day was still bright; now it was drawing to a close. The sun, yellow and golden, was sinking toward the Hudson, to the hazy hills of New Jersey. The buildings on Broadway radiated the heat they had absorbed. From under gratings where the subway trains rumbled, evil-smelling fumes arose. Bessie held the heavy bag of food in one hand, and in the other she grasped her pocketbook tightly. Never had Broadway seemed to her so wild, so dirty. It stank of softened asphalt, gasoline, rotten fruit, the excrement of dogs. On the sidewalk, among torn newspapers and the butts of cigarettes, pigeons hopped about. It was difficult to understand how these creatures avoided being stepped on in the crush of passers-by. From the blazing sky a golden dust was falling. Before a storefront hung with artificial grass, men in sweated shirts poured papaya juice and pineapple juice into themselves with haste, as if trying to extinguish a fire that consumed their insides. Above their heads hung coconuts carved in the shapes of Indians. On a side street, black and white children had opened a hydrant and were splashing naked in the gutter. In the midst of that heat wave, a truck with microphones drove around blaring out shrill songs and deafening blasts about a candidate for political office. From the rear of a truck, a girl with hair that stood up like wires threw out leaflets.

It was all beyond Bessie's strength—crossing the street, waiting for the elevator, and then getting out on the fifth floor before the door slammed. Bessie put the groceries down at the threshold and searched for her keys. She used her nail file to dig the putty out of the keyhole. She put in the key and turned it. But woe, the key broke. Only the handle remained in her hand. Bessie fully grasped the catastrophe. The other people in the building had copies of their keys hanging in the superintendent's apartment, but she trusted no one—some time ago, she had ordered a new combination lock, which she was sure no master key could open. She had a duplicate key somewhere in a drawer, but with her she carried only this one. "Well, this is the end," Bessie said aloud.

There was nobody to turn to for help. The neighbors were her blood enemies. The super only waited for her downfall. Bessie's throat was so constricted that she could not even cry. She looked around, expecting to see the fiend who had delivered this latest blow. Bessie had long since made peace with death, but to die on the steps or in the streets was too harsh. And who knows how long such agony could last? She began to ponder. Was there still open somewhere a store where they fitted keys? Even if there were, what could the locksmith copy from? He would have to come up here with his tools. For that, one needed a mechanic associated with the firm which produced these special locks. If at least she had money with her. But she never carried more than she needed to spend. The cashier in the supermarket had given her back only some twenty-odd cents. "O dear Momma, I don't want to live anymore!" Bessie spoke Yiddish, amazed that she suddenly reverted to that half-forgotten tongue.

After many hesitations, Bessie decided to go back down to the street. Perhaps a hardware store or one of those tiny shops that specialize in keys was still open. She remembered that there used to be such a key stand in the neighborhood. After all, other people's keys must get broken. But what should she do with the food? It was too heavy to carry with her. There was no choice. She would have to leave the bag at the door. "They steal anyhow," Bessie said to herself. Who knows, perhaps the neighbors intentionally

The elevator went down and the man opened the door for her. She wanted to thank him, but remained silent. Why thank her enemies? These were all sly tricks.

manipulated her lock so that she would not be able to enter the apartment while they robbed her or vandalized her belongings.

Before Bessie went down to the street, she put her ear to the door.

She heard nothing except a murmur that never stopped, the cause and origin of which Bessie could not figure out. Sometimes it ticked like a clock; other times it buzzed, or groaned—an entity imprisoned in the walls or the water pipes. In her mind Bessie said good-bye to the food, which should have been in the refrigerator, not standing here in the heat. The butter would melt, the milk would turn sour. "It's a punishment! I am cursed, cursed," Bessie muttered. A neighbor was about to go down in the elevator and Bessie signaled to him to hold the door for her. Perhaps he was one of the thieves. He might try to hold her up, assault her. The elevator went down and the man opened the door for her. She wanted to thank him, but remained silent. Why thank her enemies? These were all sly tricks.

When Bessie stepped out into the street, night had fallen. The gutter was flooded with water. The streetlamps were reflected in the black pool as in a lake. Again there was a fire in the neighborhood. She heard the wailing of a siren, the clang of fire engines. Her shoes were wet. She came out on Broadway, and the heat slapped her like a sheet of tin. She had difficulty seeing in daytime; at night she was almost blind. There was light in the stores, but what they displayed Bessie could not make out. Passers-by bumped into her, and Bessie regretted that she didn't have a cane. Nevertheless, she began to walk along, close to the windows. She passed a drugstore, a bakery, a shop of rugs, a funeral parlor, but nowhere was there a sign of a hardware store. Bessie continued on her way. Her strength was ebbing, but she was determined not to give up. What should a person do when her key was broken off—die? Perhaps apply to the police. There might be some institution that took care of such cases. But where?

There must have been an accident. The sidewalk was crowded with spectators. Police cars and an ambulance blocked the street. Someone sprayed the asphalt with a hose, probably cleaning away the blood. It occurred to Bessie that the eyes of the onlookers gleamed with an uncanny satisfaction. They enjoy other people's misfortunes, she thought. It is their only comfort in this miserable city. No, she wouldn't find anybody to help her.

She had come to a church. A few steps led to the closed door, which was protected by an overhang and darkened by shadows. Bessie was barely able to sit down. Her knees wobbled. Her shoes had begun to pinch in the toes and above the heels. A bone in her corset broke and cut into her flesh. "Well, all the Powers of Evil are upon me tonight." Hunger mixed with nausea gnawed at her. An acid fluid came up to her mouth. "Father in Heaven, it's my end." She remembered the Yiddish proverb "If one lives without a reckoning, one dies without confession." She had even neglected to write her will.

Bessie must have dozed off, because when she opened her eyes there was a late-night stillness, the street half-empty and darkened. Store windows were no longer lit. The heat had evaporated and she felt chilly under her dress. For a moment she thought that her pocketbook had been stolen, but it lay on a step below her, where it had probably slipped. Bessie tried to stretch out her hand for it; her arm was numb. Her head, which rested against the wall, felt as heavy as a stone. Her legs had become wooden. Her ears seemed to be filled with water. She lifted one of her eyelids and saw the moon. It hovered low in the sky over a flat roof, and near it twinkled a greenish star. Bessie gaped. She had almost forgotten that there was a sky, a moon, stars. Years had passed and she never looked up—always down. Her windows were hung with draperies so that the spies across the street could not see her. Well, if there was a sky, perhaps there was also a God, angels, Paradise. Where else did the souls of her parents rest? And where was Sam now? She, Bessie, had abandoned all her duties. She never visited Sam's grave in the cemetery. She didn't even light a candle on the anniversary of his death. She was so steeped in wrangling with the lower powers that she did not remember the higher ones. For the first time in years, Bessie felt the need to recite a prayer. The Almighty would have mercy on her even though she did not deserve it. Father and Mother might intercede for her on high. Some Hebrew words hung on the tip of her tongue, but she could not recall them. Then she remembered. "Hear, O Israel."[3] But what followed? "God forgive me," Bessie said. "I deserve everything that falls on me."

It became even quieter and cooler. Traffic lights changed from red to green, but a car rarely passed. From somewhere a Negro appeared. He staggered. He stopped not far from Bessie and turned his eyes to her. Then he walked

---

3 **"Hear, O Israel.":** the beginning of a common Jewish prayer

on. Bessie knew that her bag was full of important documents, but for the first time she did not care about her property. Sam had left a fortune; it all had gone for naught. She continued to save for her old age as if she were still young. "How old am I?" Bessie asked herself. "What have I accomplished in all these years? Why didn't I go somewhere, enjoy my money, help somebody?" Something in her laughed. "I was possessed, completely not myself. How else can it be explained?" Bessie was astounded. She felt as if she had awakened from a long sleep. The broken key had opened a door in her brain that had shut when Sam died.

The moon had shifted to the other side of the roof—unusually large, red, its face **obliterated**. It was almost cold now. Bessie shivered. She realized that she could easily get pneumonia, but the fear of death was gone, along with her fear of being homeless. Fresh breezes drifted from the Hudson River. New stars appeared in the sky. A black cat approached from the other side of the street. For a while, it stood on the edge of the sidewalk and its green eyes looked straight at Bessie. Then slowly and cautiously it drew near. For years Bessie had hated all animals—dogs, cats, pigeons, even sparrows. They carried sicknesses. They made everything filthy. Bessie believed that there was a demon in every cat. She especially dreaded an encounter with a black cat, which was always an **omen** of evil. But now Bessie felt love for this creature that had no home, no possessions, no doors or keys, and lived on God's bounty. Before the cat neared Bessie, it smelled her bag. Then it began to rub its back on her leg, lifting up its tail and meowing. The poor thing is hungry. I wish I could give her something. How can one hate a creature like this, Bessie wondered. O Mother of mine, I was bewitched, bewitched. I'll begin a new life. A treacherous thought ran through her mind: perhaps remarry?

The night did not pass without adventure. Once, Bessie saw a white butterfly in the air. It hovered for a while over a parked car and then took off. Bessie knew it was a soul of a newborn baby, since real butterflies do not fly after dark. Another time, she wakened to see a ball of fire, a kind of lit-up soap bubble, soar from one roof to another and sink behind it. She was aware that what she saw was the spirit of someone who had just died.

Bessie had fallen asleep. She woke up with a start. It was daybreak. From the side of Central Park the sun rose. Bessie could not see it from here, but on Broadway the sky became pink and reddish. On the building to the left, flames kindled in the windows; the panes ran and blinked like the portholes of a ship. A pigeon landed nearby. It hopped on its

obliterated:
wiped away;
destroyed

omen:
sign or symbol
of future events

Isaac Bashevis Singer

little red feet and pecked into something that might have been a dirty piece of stale bread or dried mud. Bessie was baffled. How do these birds live? Where do they sleep at night? And how can they survive the rains, the cold, the snow? I will go home, Bessie decided. People will not leave me in the streets.

Getting up was a torment. Her body seemed glued to the step on which she sat. Her back ached and her legs tingled. Nevertheless, she began to walk slowly toward home. She inhaled the moist morning air. It smelled of grass and coffee. She was no longer alone. From the side streets men and women emerged. They were going to work. They bought newspapers at the stand and went down into the subway. They were silent and strangely peaceful, as if they, too, had gone through a night of soul-searching and come out of it cleansed. When do they get up if they are already on their way to work now, Bessie marveled. No, not all in this neighborhood were gangsters and murderers. One young man even nodded good morning to Bessie. She tried to smile at him, realizing she had forgotten that feminine gesture she knew so well in her youth; it was almost the first lesson her mother had taught her.

She reached her building, and outside stood the Irish super, her deadly enemy. He was talking to the garbage collectors. He was a giant of a man, with a short nose, a long upper lip, sunken cheeks, and a pointed chin. His yellow hair covered a bald spot. He gave Bessie a startled look. "What's the matter, Grandma?"

Stuttering, Bessie told him what had happened to her. She showed him the handle of the key she had clutched in her hand all night.

"Mother of God!" he called out.

"What shall I do?" Bessie asked.

"I will open your door."

"But you don't have a passkey."

"We have to be able to open all doors in case of fire."

The super disappeared into his own apartment for a few minutes, then he came out with some tools and a bunch of keys on a large ring. He went up in the elevator with Bessie. The bag of food still stood on the threshold, but it looked depleted. The super busied himself at the lock. He asked, "What are these cards?"

Bessie did not answer.

"Why didn't you come to me and tell me what happened? To be roaming around all night at your age—my God!" As he poked with his tools, a door opened and a little woman in a housecoat and slippers, her hair bleached and done up in curlers, came out. She said, "What happened to you? Every time I opened the door, I saw this bag. I took out your butter and milk and put them in my refrigerator."

Bessie could barely restrain her tears. "O my good people," she said. "I didn't know that . . ."

The super pulled out the other half of Bessie's key. He worked a little longer. He turned a key and the door opened. The cards fell down. He entered the hallway with Bessie and she sensed the musty odor of an apartment that has not been lived in for a long time. The super said, "Next time, if something like this happens call me. That's what I'm here for."

Bessie wanted to give him a tip, but her hands were too weak to open her bag. The neighbor woman brought in the milk and butter. Bessie went into her bedroom and lay down on the bed. There was a pressure on her breast and she felt like vomiting. Something heavy vibrated up from her feet to her chest. Bessie listened to it without alarm, only curious about the whims of the body; the super and the neighbor talked, and Bessie could not make out what they were saying. The same thing had happened to her over thirty years ago when she had been given anesthesia in the hospital before an operation—the doctor and the nurse were talking but their voices seemed to come from far away and in a strange language.

Soon there was silence, and Sam appeared. It was neither day nor night—a strange twilight. In her dream, Bessie knew that Sam was dead but that in some **clandestine** way he had managed to get away from the grave and visit her. He was feeble and embarrassed. He could not speak. They wandered through a space without a sky, without earth, a tunnel full of debris—the wreckage of a nameless structure—a corridor dark and winding, yet somehow familiar. They came to a region where two mountains met, and the passage between shone like sunset or sunrise. They stood there hesitating and even a little ashamed. It was like that night of their honeymoon when they went to Ellenville in the Catskills and were let by the hotel owner into their bridal suite. She heard the same words he had said to them then, in the same voice and intonation: "You don't need no key here. Just enter—and *mazel tov.*"[4]

clandestine:
secretive

---

4 *mazel tov:* a Hebrew expression for "best wishes" or "congratulations"

Responding to the Story

1. **LITERARY LENS** Use a chart like the one below to describe the
   epiphany that Bessie experiences. First describe Bessie before
   the epiphany, then describe the revelation she experiences,
   and finally describe her after the event.

Before	Epiphany	After

2. Singer describes Bessie in detail in the first paragraph of the story.
   From this description, what can you conclude about Bessie's
   relationship to the outside world?

3. Critics often say Singer's work explores the weaknesses in human
   nature. What human weaknesses does Singer expose in this short
   story?

4. The key takes on symbolic significance in this story. What do you
   think the key symbolizes?

5. **THE AUTHOR'S STYLE** In this story, Singer shows the power of
   naming: what we choose to name something affects what we believe
   about it. For example, in the beginning of the story, when Bessie is
   fearful and paranoid, she refers to "Evil Powers." Briefly trace the
   manner in which Bessie's language changes along with her view
   of the world.

Alice Walker
1944

About the Author

Born in Eatonton, Georgia, as the eighth child of sharecroppers, Alice Walker grew up poor in material goods but rich in values. After a long, hard day of labor in the fields, her mother worked in the family's backyard garden. Seeing this convinced the author that beauty is worth searching for, laboring for, and celebrating. She began to read and write poetry at the age of eight.

Valedictorian of her high school class, Walker attended Sarah Lawrence College in New York, from which she traveled to Africa as an exchange student. After graduation, she moved to Jackson, Mississippi, and married a Jewish Civil Rights lawyer whom she later divorced. They were said to have been the first married interracial couple in that city in 1967.

Known for using her writing as a vehicle for commentary on issues such as Civil Rights, human rights, and nuclear war, Walker has also worked to rediscover and honor African American authors who went before her. Perhaps her best known work is her novel *The Color Purple*, for which she won the Pulitzer Prize in 1983; it was made into a film in 1985.

✶✶✶✶✶✶✶✶✶✶✶

The Author's Style

Walker's fiction reflects her awareness that racism and its appalling social impact take a particular toll on females. Walker addresses this issue in numerous stories in *You Can't Keep a Good Woman Down* and *In Love and Trouble*, in her acclaimed novel *The Color Purple* (written in the form of letters in black English vernacular), and in the essays in *In Search of Our Mothers' Gardens*. She refers to herself as a black feminist, or "womanist," and her stories involve girls and women who face injustice and struggle for change. The focus in "The Flowers," the story you are about to read, is on a single female figure. This approach follows the example of Zora Neale Hurston, an earlier African American woman writer whose life and work Walker finds inspirational.

Several of Walker's stories use objects or artifacts to illustrate her themes, the most familiar of which is a family quilt in the story "Everyday Use." Her use of key metaphors and striking imagery is also consistent with her work as a poet. Walker's tone is often one of irony shaded with sarcasm. Frequently, this is because her central character has begun to realize that she has been mistreated, and that early signs of that were everywhere.

LITERARY LENS Watch for the subtle use of foreshadowing in this story.

THE
FLOWERS

ALICE WALKER

t seemed to Myop as she skipped lightly from hen house to pigpen to smokehouse that the days had never been as beautiful as these. The air held a keenness that made her nose twitch. The harvesting of the corn and cotton, peanuts and squash, made each day a golden surprise that caused excited little tremors to run up her jaws.

Myop carried a short, knobby stick. She struck out at random at chickens she liked, and worked out the beat of a song on the fence around the pigpen. She felt light and good in the warm sun. She was ten, and nothing existed for her but her song, the stick clutched in her dark brown hand, and the tat-de-ta-ta-ta of accompaniment.

Turning her back on the rusty boards of her family's sharecropper cabin, Myop walked along the fence till it ran into the stream made by the spring. Around the spring, where the family got drinking water, silver ferns and wild-flowers grew. Along the shallow banks pigs rooted. Myop watched the tiny white bubbles disrupt the thin black scale of soil and the water that silently rose and slid away down the stream.

She had explored the woods behind the house many times. Often, in late autumn, her mother took her to gather nuts among the fallen leaves. Today she made her own path, bouncing this way and that way, vaguely keeping an eye out for snakes. She found, in addition to various common but pretty ferns and leaves, an armful of strange blue flowers with velvety ridges and a sweetsuds bush full of the brown, fragrant buds.

laden:
loaded; burdened

By twelve o'clock, her arms **laden** with sprigs of her findings, she was a mile or more from home. She had often been as far before, but the strange-ness of the land made it not as pleasant as her usual haunts. It seemed gloomy in the little cove in which she found herself. The air was damp, the silence close and deep.

Myop began to circle back to the house, back to the peacefulness of the morning. It was then she stepped smack into his eyes. Her heel became lodged in the broken ridge between brow and nose, and she reached down quickly, unafraid, to free herself. It was only when she saw his naked grin that she gave a little yelp of surprise.

He had been a tall man. From feet to neck covered a long space. His head lay beside him. When she pushed back the leaves and layers of earth and debris Myop saw that he'd had large white teeth, all of them cracked or bro-ken, long fingers, and very big bones. All his clothes had rotted away except some threads of blue denim from his overalls. The buckles of the overalls had turned green.

Myop gazed around the spot with interest. Very near where she'd stepped into the head was a wild pink rose. As she picked it to add to her bundle she noticed a raised mound, a ring, around the rose's root. It was the rotted remains of a noose, a bit of shredding plowline, now blending benignly into the soil. Around an overhanging limb of a great spreading oak clung anoth-er piece. Frayed, rotted, bleached, and frazzled—barely there—but spinning restlessly in the breeze. Myop laid down her flowers.

And the summer was over.

Responding to the Story

1. **LITERARY LENS** What foreshadowing of the ending did you encounter?

2. Readers experience a very abrupt break in this story. Identify where the break comes, describe what it does to the tone of the story, and explain how you responded to it.

3. Why do you think Myop lays down her flowers?

4. How do you interpret the last line of the story: "And the summer was over"?

5. Walker has written, "Black women are called, in the folklore that so aptly identifies one's status in society, the 'mules of the world' because we have been handed the burdens that everyone else—*everyone* else—refused to carry." Based on what you can glean about Myop, what burdens do you think she will have to carry in life?

6. **THE AUTHOR'S STYLE** The work of Walker, who is a poet as well as a prose writer, is known for its rich Imagery. Pick the image from "The Flowers" that you think is the most memorable and tell how it contributes to the overall success of the story.

Tim O'Brien
1946

About the Author

It has been said that in the Vietnam era, those in the White House and Pentagon who sent troops to Vietnam were concerned about the possibility of anti-war protests, but couldn't have imagined the power of literature written after the war. Tim O'Brien, who grew up in Minnesota, is an important contributor to that literature.

O'Brien admits his contributions stem from cowardice. In 1968, he graduated from Macalester College, where he had written anti-war editorials for the college newspaper and knocked on doors seeking support for the presidential candidacy of Eugene McCarthy, who opposed the war. After graduation he received his draft notice and intended to flee to Canada but stopped just yards short of the border. He told a reporter, "My conscience told me to run, but I was ashamed of my conscience, ashamed to be doing the right thing. I was a coward. I went to Vietnam."

Upon his return to the United States, O'Brien attended Harvard University, where he worked on his graduate degree as one of the few student veterans there at the time. Since then, O'Brien has published many books and articles, including the novel *Going After Cacciato,* which won the National Book Award.

****

The Author's Style

O'Brien's experiences in the Vietnam War have inspired some of his best writing, including the novels *Going After Cacciato* and *The Things They Carried.* Both are composed of linked stories. The fear, confusion, and panic of combat make O'Brien's characters wish for safety and peace, and they often find themselves absorbed in nightmares and fantasies. These mental states are far from irresponsible attempts to escape reality and duty; instead, they are often shown to be unconscious or unavoidable strategies for survival.

O'Brien makes his soldiers human by showing their vulnerability to the irrational brutality of war. He also shows us their survival strategies, including intentional and unintentional mental tricks for making it through the day. The plight of combat soldiers is at times so bleak that it seems like a bad joke. The soldiers often respond with irony and black humor of their own.

O'Brien's writing is often simple and direct, conveying the facts and ironic truths of the soldiers' lives. Frequently it develops through calculated repetition and simple figures of speech. At times his prose is reminiscent of Hemingway's.

LITERARY LENS
The choice of similes and metaphors does much to establish the tone and the meaning of a story. Watch for them in this story.

WHERE HAVE YOU GONE, CHARMING BILLY?

TIM O'BRIEN

The platoon of twenty-six soldiers moved slowly in the dark, single file, not talking.

One by one, like sheep in a dream, they passed through the hedgerow,[1] crossed quietly over a meadow and came down to the rice paddy.[2] There they stopped. Their leader knelt down, motioning with his hand, and one by one the other soldiers squatted in the shadows, vanishing in the primitive stealth of warfare. For a long time they did not move. Except for the sounds of their breathing, . . . the twenty-six men were very quiet: some of them excited by the adventure, some of them afraid, some of them exhausted from the long night march, some of them looking forward to reaching the sea where they would be safe. At the rear of

---

1 **hedgerow:** a thick hedge separating sections of land

2 **rice paddy:** a water-logged field where rice is grown

the column, Private First Class Paul Berlin lay quietly with his forehead resting on the black plastic stock of his rifle, his eyes closed. He was pretending he was not in the war, pretending he had not watched Billy Boy Watkins die of a heart attack that afternoon. He was pretending he was a boy again, camping with his father in the midnight summer along the Des Moines River. In the dark, with his eyes pinched shut, he pretended. He pretended that when he opened his eyes, his father would be there by the campfire and they would talk softly about whatever came to mind and then roll into their sleeping bags, and that later they'd wake up and it would be morning and there would not be a war, and that Billy Boy Watkins had not died of a heart attack that afternoon. He pretended he was not a soldier.

In the morning, when they reached the sea, it would be better. The hot afternoon would be over, he would bathe in the sea and he would forget how frightened he had been on his first day at the war. The second day would not be so bad. He would learn.

There was a sound beside him, a movement and then a breathed: "Hey!"

He opened his eyes, shivering as if emerging from a deep nightmare.

"Hey!" a shadow whispered. "We're *moving*. . . . Get up."

"Okay."

"You sleepin', or something?"

"No." He could not make out the soldier's face. With clumsy, concrete hands he clawed for his rifle, found it, found his helmet.

The soldier-shadow grunted. "You got a lot to learn, buddy. I'd shoot you if I thought you was sleepin'. Let's go."

Private First Class Paul Berlin blinked.

Ahead of him, silhouetted against the sky, he saw the string of soldiers wading into the flat paddy, the black outline of their shoulders and packs and weapons. He was comfortable. He did not want to move. But he was afraid, for it was his first night at the war, so he hurried to catch up, stumbling once, scraping his knee, groping as though blind; his boots sank into the thick paddy water and he smelled it all around him. He would tell his mother how it smelled: mud and algae and cattle manure and chlorophyll,[3] decay, breeding mosquitoes and leeches as big as mice, the **fecund** warmth of the paddy waters rising up to his cut knee. But he would not tell how frightened he had been.

Once they reached the sea, things would be better. They would have their rear guarded by three thousand miles of ocean, and they would swim and

fecund:
fertile

---

3 **chlorophyll:** the green pigment found in plants

COME A LITTLE CLOSER, Michael Brostowitz, 1997, The National Vietnam Veterans Art Museum

dive into the breakers and hunt crayfish and smell the salt, and they would be safe.

He followed the shadow of the man in front of him. It was a clear night. Already the Southern Cross[4] was out. And other stars he could not yet name—soon, he thought, he would learn their names. And puffy night

4 **Southern Cross:** a cross-shaped constellation of stars

clouds. There was not yet a moon. Wading through the paddy, his boots made sleepy, sloshing sounds, like a lullaby, and he tried not to think. Though he was afraid, he now knew that fear came in many degrees and types and peculiar categories, and he knew that his fear now was not so bad as it had been in the hot afternoon, when poor Billy Boy Watkins got killed by a heart attack. His fear now was **diffuse** and unformed: ghosts in the tree line, nighttime fears of a child, a boogieman in the closet that his father would open to show empty, saying "See? Nothing there, champ. Now you can sleep." In the afternoon it had been worse; the fear had been bundled and tight and he'd been on his hands and knees, crawling like an insect, an ant escaping a giant's footsteps and thinking nothing, brain flopping like wet cement in a mixer, not thinking at all, watching while Billy Boy Watkins died.

diffuse: broad; nonspecific

> *Though he was afraid, he now knew that fear came in many degrees and types and peculiar categories, and he knew that his fear now was not so bad as it had been in the hot afternoon, when poor Billy Boy Watkins got killed by a heart attack.*

Now as he stepped out of the paddy onto a narrow dirt path, now the fear was mostly the fear of being so terribly afraid again.

He tried not to think.

There were tricks he'd learned to keep from thinking. Counting: He counted his steps, concentrating on the numbers, pretending that the steps were dollar bills and that each step through the night made him richer and richer, so that soon he would become a wealthy man, and he kept counting and considered the ways he might spend the money after the war and what he would do. He would look his father in the eye and shrug and say, "It was pretty bad at first, but I learned a lot and I got used to it." Then he would tell his father the story of Billy Boy Watkins. But he would never let on how frightened he had been. "Not so bad," he would say instead, making his father feel proud.

Songs, another trick to stop from thinking: *Where have you gone, Billy Boy, Billy Boy, Oh, where have you gone, charming Billy? I have gone to seek a wife, she's the joy of my life, but she's a young thing and cannot leave her mother,* and other songs that he sang in his thoughts as he walked toward the sea. And when he reached the sea he would dig a deep hole in the sand and he would sleep like the high clouds, and he would not be afraid any more.

The moon came out. Pale and shrunken to the size of a dime. The helmet was heavy on his head. In the morning he would adjust the leather binding. He would clean his rifle, too. Even though he had been frightened to shoot it during the hot afternoon, he would carefully clean the breech and the muzzle and the ammunition so that next time he would be ready and not so afraid. In the morning, when they reached the sea, he would begin to make friends with some of the other soldiers. He would learn their names and laugh at their jokes. Then when the war was over he would have war buddies, and he would write to them once in a while and exchange memories.

Walking, sleeping in his walking, he felt better. He watched the moon come higher.

Once they skirted a sleeping village. The smells again—straw, cattle, mildew. The men were quiet. On the far side of the village, buried in the dark smells, a dog barked. The graveyard had a perfumy smell. A nice place to spend the night, he thought. The mounds would make fine battlements, and the smell was nice and the place was quiet. But they went on, passing through a hedgerow and across another paddy and east toward the sea.

He walked carefully. He remembered what he'd been taught: Stay off the center of the path, for that was where the land mines and booby traps were planted, where stupid and lazy soldiers like to walk. Stay alert, he'd been taught. Better alert than **inert**. Ag-ile, mo-bile, hos-tile.[5] He wished he'd paid better attention to the training. He could not remember what they'd said about how to stop being afraid; they hadn't given any lessons in courage— not that he could remember—and they hadn't mentioned how Billy Boy Watkins would die of a heart attack, his face turning pale and the veins popping out.

Private First Class Paul Berlin walked carefully.

Stretching ahead of him like dark beads on an invisible chain, the string of shadow-soldiers whose names he did not yet know moved with the silence and slow grace of smoke. Now and again moonlight was reflected off a machine gun or a wrist watch. But mostly the soldiers were quiet and hidden and far-away-seeming in a peaceful night, strangers on a long street, and he felt quite separate from them, as if trailing behind like the caboose on a night train, pulled along by inertia, sleepwalking, an afterthought to the war.

Inert: unable to move

---

5 **Ag-ile, mo-bile, hos-tile:** a chant reminding soldiers to be light on their feet, ready to move, and aggressive

So he walked carefully, counting his steps. When he had counted to three thousand, four hundred and eighty-five, the column stopped.

One by one the soldiers knelt or squatted down.

The grass along the path was wet. Private First Class Paul Berlin lay back and turned his head so that he could lick at the dew with his eyes closed, another trick to forget the war. He might have slept. "I *wasn't* afraid," he was screaming or dreaming, facing his father's stern eyes. "I wasn't afraid," he was saying. When he opened his eyes, a soldier was sitting beside him, quietly chewing a stick of Doublemint gum.

"You sleepin' again?" the soldier whispered.

"No," said Private First Class Paul Berlin. . . .

The soldier grunted, chewing his gum. Then he twisted the cap off his canteen, took a swallow and handed it through the dark.

"Take some," he whispered.

"Thanks."

"You're the new guy?"

"Yes." He did not want to admit it, being new to the war.

The soldier grunted and handed him a stick of gum. "Chew it quiet—okay? Don't blow no bubbles or nothing."

"Thanks. I won't." He could not make out the man's face in the shadows.

They sat still and Private First Class Paul Berlin chewed the gum until all the sugars were gone; then the soldier said, "Bad day today, buddy."

Private First Class Paul Berlin nodded wisely, but he did not speak.

"Don't think it's always so bad," the soldier whispered. "I don't wanna scare you. You'll get used to it soon enough. . . . They been fighting wars a long time, and you get used to it."

"Yeah."

"You will."

They were quiet awhile. And the night was quiet, no crickets or birds, and it was hard to imagine it was truly a war. He searched for the soldier's face but could not find it. It did not matter much. Even if he saw the fellow's face, he would not know the name; and even if he knew the name, it would not matter much.

"Haven't got the time?" the soldier whispered.

"No."

"Rats. . . . Don't matter, really. Goes faster if you don't know the time, anyhow."

"Sure."

"What's your name, buddy?"

"Paul."

"Nice to meet ya," he said, and in the dark beside the path they shook hands. "Mine's Toby. Everybody calls me Buffalo, though." The soldier's hand was strangely warm and soft. But it was a very big hand. "Sometimes they just call me Buff," he said.

And again they were quiet. They lay in the grass and waited. The moon was very high now and very bright, and they were waiting for cloud cover.

The soldier suddenly snorted.

"What is it?"

"Nothin'," he said, but then he snorted again. "A bloody *heart attack!*" the soldier said. "Can't get over it—old Billy Boy croaking from a lousy heart attack. . . . A heart attack—can you believe it?"

The idea of it made Private First Class Paul Berlin smile. He couldn't help it.

"Ever hear of such a thing?"

"Not till now," said Private First Class Paul Berlin, still smiling.

"Me neither," said the soldier in the dark. ". . . Dying of a heart attack. Didn't know him, did you?"

"No."

"Tough as nails."

"Yeah."

"And what happens? A heart attack. Can you imagine it?"

"Yes," said Private First Class Paul Berlin. He wanted to laugh. "I can imagine it." And he imagined it clearly. He giggled—he couldn't help it. He imagined Billy's father opening the telegram: SORRY TO INFORM YOU THAT YOUR SON BILLY BOY WAS YESTERDAY SCARED TO DEATH IN ACTION IN THE REPUBLIC OF VIETNAM, **VALIANTLY SUCCUMBING** TO A HEART ATTACK SUFFERED WHILE UNDER ENORMOUS STRESS, AND IT IS WITH GREATEST SYMPATHY THAT . . . He giggled again. He rolled onto his belly and pressed his face into his arms. His body was shaking with giggles.

valiantly: courageously

succumbing: giving in

The big soldier hissed at him to shut up, but he could not stop giggling and remembering the hot afternoon, and poor Billy Boy, and how they'd been drinking Coca-Cola from bright-red aluminum cans, and how they'd started on the day's march, and how a little while later poor Billy Boy stepped on the mine, and how it made a tiny little sound—*poof*—and how

Billy Boy stood there with his mouth wide-open, looking down at where his foot had been blown off, and how finally Billy Boy sat down very casually, not saying a word, with his foot lying behind him, most of it still in the boot.

He giggled louder—he could not stop. He bit his arm, trying to stifle it, but remembering: "War's over, Billy," the men had said in **consolation**, but Billy Boy got scared and started crying and said he was about to die. "Nonsense," the medic said, Doc Peret, but Billy Boy kept bawling, tightening up, his face going pale and transparent and his veins popping out. Scared stiff. Even when Doc Peret stuck him with morphine,[6] Billy Boy kept crying.

"Shut up!" the big soldier hissed, but Private First Class Paul Berlin could not stop. Giggling and remembering, he covered his mouth. His eyes stung, remembering how it was when Billy Boy died of fright.

"Shut up!"

But he could not stop giggling, the same way Billy Boy could not stop bawling that afternoon.

Afterward Doc Peret had explained: "You see, Billy Boy really died of a heart attack. He was scared he was gonna die—so scared, he had himself a heart attack—and that's what really killed him. I seen it before."

So they wrapped Billy in a plastic poncho, his eyes still wide-open and scared stiff, and they carried him over the meadow to a rice paddy, and then when the Medevac helicopter[7] arrived they carried him through the paddy and put him aboard, and the mortar rounds[8] were falling everywhere, and the helicopter pulled up and Billy Boy came tumbling out, falling slowly and then faster, and the paddy water sprayed up as if Billy Boy had just **executed** a long and dangerous dive, as if trying to escape Graves Registration, where he would be tagged and sent home under a flag, dead of a heart attack.

"Shut up, . . . !" the soldier hissed, but Paul Berlin could not stop giggling, remembering: scared to death.

Later they waded in after him, probing for Billy Boy with their rifle butts, elegantly and delicately probing for Billy Boy in the stinking paddy, singing—some of them—*Where have you gone, Billy Boy, Billy Boy, Oh, where have you gone, charming Billy?* Then they found him. Green and covered with algae, his eyes still wide-open and sacred stiff, dead of a heart attack suffered while—

consolation: sympathy; encouragement

executed: completed

---

6 **morphine:** a drug used to soothe pain and induce calm

7 **Medevac helicopter:** Short for "medical evacuation," this helicopter was used to transport injured soldiers by air to medical facilities.

8 **mortar rounds:** shells fired from small cannons

ON THE ROAD TO CON THIEN, Charlie Shobe, 1980, The National Vietnam Veterans Art Museum

"Shut up, . . . !" the soldier said loudly, shaking him.

But Private First Class Paul Berlin could not stop. The giggles were caught in his throat, drowning him in his own laughter: scared to death like Billy Boy.

Giggling, lying on his back, he saw the moon move, or the clouds moving across the moon. Wounded in action, dead of fright. A fine war story. He would tell it to his father, how Billy Boy had been scared to death, never letting on . . . He could not stop.

The soldier smothered him. He tried to fight back, but he was weak from the giggles.

The moon was under the clouds and the column was moving. The soldier helped him up. "You okay now, buddy?"

"Sure."

"What was so bloody funny?"

"Nothing."

"You can get killed, laughing that way."

"I know. I know that."

"You got to stay calm, buddy." The soldier handed him his rifle. "Half the battle, just staying calm. You'll get better at it," he said. "Come on, now."

He turned away and Private First Class Paul Berlin hurried after him. He was still shivering.

He would do better once he reached the sea, he thought, still smiling a little. A funny war story that he would tell to his father, how Billy Boy Watkins was scared to death. A good joke. But even when he smelled salt and heard the sea, he could not stop being afraid.

Responding to the Story

1. **LITERARY LENS** This story contains numerous similes such as "his boots made sleepy, sloshing sounds, like a lullaby." Find another simile in this story. What do these comparisons add to the tone and meaning?

2. Private Berlin's thoughts race wildly back and forth among scenarios of the past, present, and future. Using a chart like the one below, find an example of each. What do you think are some reasons for the way his mind works in this story?

Time	Example
Past	*Remembers going camping with his father*
Present	
Future	

3. Reread the imaginary telegram on page 343. Why do you think it makes Private Berlin laugh?

4. Both a chant ("Ag-ile, mo-bile, hos-tile") and the lyrics of the title song are used in this story. What do they add to the story?

5. **THE AUTHOR'S STYLE** Repetition is a striking feature of this story. For example, the name Private First Class Paul Berlin is repeated several times. And in the second paragraph, a form of the word "pretend" appears six times. Find other examples in the story. What is the overall effect of the use of repetition?

****

Raymond Carver
1938–1988

About the Author

Raymond Carver was born in Oregon in 1938 during the postwar era that was a prosperous time for many Americans. For the Carver family, though, life was a tumultuous struggle with problems that included alcoholism, domestic abuse, mental illness, and unemployment. Married at age nineteen, Carver worked at various minimum-wage jobs, including one as a deliveryman. On a delivery one day, he was given a copy of *Poetry* magazine. This gave him a taste for literature, and Carver enrolled at Chico State College in California, where he took a creative writing course and met his mentor, the late author John Gardner. Under Gardner's guidance, Carver founded a college literary magazine and published his first story.

He later studied for a time at the University of Iowa Writers' Workshop, but could not afford to finish his master's degree there. Instead he worked as a custodian and filed for bankruptcy several times, but eventually began publishing stories such as "Will You Please Be Quiet, Please?" included in the 1967 edition of *The Best American Short Stories*. Personal troubles accompanied his professional success, however, including alcoholism, which he overcame in 1977. His short story collections include *What We Talk About When We Talk About Love*, *Cathedral*, and *Where I'm Calling From*. A heavy smoker, he died of lung cancer at the age of 50.

****

The Author's Style

Many of Carver's "minimalist" stories are unusually short with simple plots. In reading these stories it is good to look at what's left out—especially when the narrator is a main character. Carver's characters are often working-class people who have trouble expressing their feelings. Even so, Carver develops them with empathy and respect, writing stories about what happens when something in their lives is broken beyond repair. His characters' situations are often pathetic, and because he wants us to see how things got that way, he frequently has them attempt to tell their own stories.

Carver's use of concrete words and very short declarative sentences make for an unemotional style many have compared to that of Hemingway. Typically, Carver's characters make simple observations that suggest there are unanswered questions and an inclination to cut off any discussion that might lead to unwelcome explanations. It is also typical of Carver to give us endings that are neither clear nor particularly happy—not necessarily "the end" of the characters' stories at all. Instead, he gives us a sense of their lives at a brief, crucial moment when everything else that has happened becomes clear.

LITERARY LENS Watch for two narrators in this story: the narrator who tells the story overall (the frame narrator), and the narrator of the story-within-the-story.

Everything Stuck to Him

RAYMOND CARVER

he's in Milan for Christmas and wants to know what it was like when she was a kid.

Tell me, she says. Tell me what it was like when I was a kid. She sips Strega, waits, eyes him closely.

She is a cool, slim, attractive girl, a survivor from top to bottom.

That was a long time ago. That was twenty years ago, he says.

You can remember, she says. Go on.

What do you want to hear? he says. What else can I tell you? I could tell you about something that happened when you were a baby. It involves you, he says. But only in a minor way.

Tell me, she says. But first fix us another so you won't have to stop in the middle.

The baby came along in late November during a cold spell that just happened to coincide with the peak of the waterfowl season. The boy loved to hunt, you see. That's part of it.

He comes back from the kitchen with drinks, settles into his chair, begins.

They were kids themselves, but they were crazy in love, this eighteen-year-old boy and this seventeen-year-old girl when they married. Not all that long afterwards they had a daughter.

The baby came along in late November during a cold spell that just happened to coincide with the peak of the waterfowl season. The boy loved to hunt, you see. That's part of it.

The boy and girl, husband and wife, father and mother, they lived in a little apartment under a dentist's office. Each night they cleaned the dentist's place upstairs in exchange for rent and utilities. In summer they were expected to maintain the lawn and the flowers. In winter the boy shoveled snow and spread rock salt on the walks. Are you still with me? Are you getting the picture?

I am, she says.

That's good, he says. So one day the dentist finds out they were using his letterhead for their personal correspondence. But that's another story.

He gets up from his chair and looks out the window. He sees the tile rooftops and the snow that is falling steadily on them.

Tell the story, she says.

The two kids were very much in love. On top of this they had great ambitions. They were always talking about the things they were going to do and the places they were going to go.

Now the boy and girl slept in the bedroom, and the baby slept in the living room. Let's say the baby was about three months old and had only just begun to sleep through the night.

On this one Saturday night after finishing his work upstairs, the boy stayed in the dentist's office and called an old hunting friend of his father's.

Carl, he said when the man picked up the receiver, believe it or not, I'm a father.

Congratulations, Carl said. How is the wife?

She's fine, Carl. Everybody's fine.

That's good, Carl said, I'm glad to hear it. But if you called about going hunting, I'll tell you something. The geese are flying to beat the band. I don't think I've ever seen so many. Got five today. Going back in the morning, so come along if you want to.

I want to, the boy said.

The boy hung up the telephone and went downstairs to tell the girl. She watched while he laid out his things. Hunting coat, shell bag, boots, socks, hunting cap, long underwear, pump gun.

What time will you be back? the girl said.

Probably around noon, the boy said. But maybe as late as six o'clock. Would that be too late?

The boy was a little in love with Sally, just as he was a little in love with Betsy, who was another sister the girl had.

It's fine, she said. The baby and I will get along fine. You go and have some fun. When you get back, we'll dress the baby up and go visit Sally.

The boy said, Sounds like a good idea.

Sally was the girl's sister. She was striking. I don't know if you've seen pictures of her. The boy was a little in love with Sally, just as he was a little in love with Betsy, who was another sister the girl had. The boy used to say to the girl, If we weren't married, I could go for Sally.

What about Betsy? the girl used to say. I hate to admit it, but I truly feel she's better looking than Sally and me. What about Betsy?

Betsy too, the boy used to say.

After dinner he turned up the furnace and helped her bathe the baby. He marveled again at the infant who had half his features and half the girl's. He powdered the tiny body. He powdered between fingers and toes.

He emptied the bath into the sink and went upstairs to check the air. It was overcast and cold. The grass, what there was of it, looked like canvas, stiff and gray under the street light.

Snow lay in piles beside the walk. A car went by. He heard sand under the tires. He let himself imagine what it might be like tomorrow, geese beating the air over his head, shotgun plunging against his shoulder.

Then he locked the door and went downstairs.

In bed they tried to read. But both of them fell asleep, she first, letting the magazine sink to the quilt.

It was the baby's cries that woke him up.

The light was on out there, and the girl was standing next to the crib rocking the baby in her arms. She put the baby down, turned out the light, and came back to the bed.

He heard the baby cry. This time the girl stayed where she was. The baby cried fitfully and stopped. The boy listened, then dozed. But the baby's cries woke him again. The living room light was burning. He sat up and turned on the lamp.

I don't know what's wrong, the girl said, walking back and forth with the baby. I've changed her and fed her, but she keeps on crying. I'm so tired I'm afraid I might drop her.

You come back to bed, the boy said. I'll hold her for a while.

He got up and took the baby, and the girl went to lie down again.

Just rock her for a few minutes, the girl said from the bedroom. Maybe she'll go back to sleep.

The boy sat on the sofa and held the baby. He jiggled it in his lap until he got its eyes to close, his own eyes closing right along. He rose carefully and put the baby back in the crib.

It was a quarter to four, which gave him forty-five minutes. He crawled into bed and dropped off. But a few minutes later the baby was crying again, and this time they both got up.

The boy did a terrible thing. He swore.

For God's sake, what's the matter with you? The girl said to the boy. Maybe she's sick or something. Maybe we shouldn't have given her the bath.

The boy picked up the baby. The baby kicked its feet and smiled.

Look, the boy said, I really don't think there's anything wrong with her.

How do you know that? the girl said. Here, let me have her. I know I ought to give her something, but I don't know what it's supposed to be.

The girl put the baby down again. The boy and the girl looked at the baby, and the baby began to cry.

The girl took the baby. Baby, baby, the girl said with tears in her eyes.

Probably it's something on her stomach, the boy said.

The girl didn't answer. She went on rocking the baby, paying no attention to the boy.

The boy waited. He went to the kitchen and put on water for coffee. He drew his woolen underwear on over his shorts and T-shirt, buttoned up, then got into his clothes.

What are you doing? the girl said.

Going hunting, the boy said.

I don't think you should, she said. I don't want to be left alone with her like this.

Carl's planning on me going, the boy said. We've planned it.

I don't care about what you and Carl planned, she said. And I don't care about Carl, either. I don't even know Carl.

You've met Carl before. You know him, the boy said. What do you mean you don't know him?

That's not the point and you know it, the girl said.

What is the point? the boy said. The point is we planned it.

The girl said, I'm your wife. This is your baby. She's sick or something. Look at her. Why else is she crying?

I know you're my wife, the boy said.

The girl began to cry. She put the baby back in the crib. But the baby started up again. The girl dried her eyes on the sleeve of her nightgown and picked the baby up.

The boy laced up his boots. He put on his shirt, his sweater, his coat. The kettle whistled on the stove in the kitchen.

You're going to have to choose, the girl said. Carl or us. I mean it.

What do you mean? the boy said.

You heard what I said, the girl said. If you want a family, you're going to have to choose.

They stared at each other. Then the boy took up his hunting gear and went outside. He started the car. He went around to the car windows and, making a job of it, scraped away the ice.

He turned off the motor and sat awhile. And then he got out and went back inside.

The living-room light was on. The girl was asleep on the bed. The baby was asleep beside her.

The boy took off his boots. Then he took off everything else. In his socks and his long underwear, he sat on the sofa and read the Sunday paper.

The girl and the baby slept on. After a while, the boy went to the kitchen and started frying bacon.

The girl came out in her robe and put her arms around the boy.

Hey, the boy said.

I'm sorry, the girl said.

It's all right, the boy said.

I didn't mean to snap like that.

It was my fault, he said.

You sit down, the girl said. How does a waffle sound with bacon?

Sounds great, the boy said.

She took the bacon out of the pan and made waffle batter. He sat at the table and watched her move around the kitchen.

She put a plate in front of him with bacon, a waffle. He spread butter and poured syrup. But when he started to cut, he turned the plate into his lap.

I don't believe it, he said, jumping up from the table.

If you could see yourself, the girl said.

The boy looked down at himself, at everything stuck to his underwear.

I was starved, he said, shaking his head.

You were starved, she said, laughing.

He peeled off the woolen underwear and threw it at the bathroom door. Then he opened his arms and the girl moved into them.

We won't fight anymore, she said.

The boy said, We won't.

He gets up from his chair and refills their glasses.

That's it, he says. End of story. I admit it's not much of a story.

I was interested, she says.

He shrugs and carries his drink over to the window. It's dark now but still snowing.

Things change, he says. I don't know how they do. But they do without your realizing it or wanting them to.

Yes, that's true, only— But she does not finish what she started.

She drops the subject. In the window's reflection he sees her study her nails. Then she raises her head. Speaking brightly, she asks if he is going to show her the city, after all.

He says, Put your boots on and let's go.

But he stays by the window, remembering. They had laughed. They had leaned on each other and laughed until the tears had come, while everything else—the cold, and where he'd go in it—was outside, for a while anyway.

Responding to the Story

1. **LITERARY LENS** Use a chart like the one below to compare the two narrators of this story.

Points of Comparison	Frame narrator	Story-within-the-story narrator
Narrative point of view		
Attitude toward story		
Use of dialogue		
Description of setting		
Description of character's inner thoughts and feelings		-

How would you describe these two narrators?

2. What layers of meaning do you think the title might have?

3. After he tells the story, the father says, "It's not much of a story." Do you agree? Explain.

4. Near the end of the story, the father says, "Things change . . . I don't know how they do. But they do without your realizing it or wanting them to." What changes do you think he is referring to?

5. **THE AUTHOR'S STYLE** Carver and other minimalist writers were influenced by Hemingway's terse style. Consider the Hemingway quotation below. What do you think makes up some of the seven-eighths of "Everything Stuck to Him" that is hidden?

Hemingway's Principle of the Iceberg

I always try to write on the principle of the iceberg. There is seven-eighths of it underwater for every part that shows.

—Ernest Hemingway, *Paris Review*

★★

Bobbie Ann Mason
1940

About the Author

Bobbie Ann Mason grew up in rural Kentucky on a dairy farm doing chores before sunrise and more after school, but always finding time for her favorite Nancy Drew and Bobbsey Twins books. A shy "homebody," as she describes herself, she learned that it was her journeys away from home that most affected her appreciation of it.

After graduating from the University of Kentucky, Mason moved to New York City and made a living writing for movie magazines. She later received her Ph.D. in literature and moved to the woodlands of northern Pennsylvania with her husband, author Roger Rawlings.

Known particularly as a short story writer, among Mason's best-known works are her short story collection *Shiloh and Other Stories* and her novel *In Country*. In an interview in the book *Passion and Craft*, Mason agreed that she writes about people and places that do not seem very literary, adding "I have my material, what's been allotted to me. And along with that comes a Southern defensive posture and a desire to reclaim a measure of pride and identity for my people."

****

The Author's Style

Many of Mason's stories deal sympathetically with the changing lives of people from rural Kentucky. Mason frequently writes from the viewpoints of women or girls who are undergoing changes that are confusing but often exhilarating. Her female characters try to understand both family relationships and the changing nature of their own expectations. Often her country people learn from confronting city life or "the mystery of travel."

Mason's prose style is simple and direct. Her characters experience and talk rather than ponder and write. She uses relatively short, declarative sentences that provide efficient descriptions of people and places and allow characters to reveal themselves without her interpretation or judgment.

Her stories reveal cultural differences and fascinating discoveries that her characters need to adjust to and understand. From adolescence on, Mason has followed American popular culture closely, and references to it often appear in her stories. Sometimes characters are inspired by learning how the acceptable way of doing things varies from place to place; sometimes they are confused or defeated. In "Detroit Skyline, 1949," which is both serious and comical, we see not only where people live and how they interact, but also how the adult world can create wonder and confusion for a child.

LITERARY **L**ENS Notice the regional flavor of the dialogue in this story.

Detroit Skyline, 1949

Bobbie Ann Mason

When I was nine, my mother took me on a long journey up North, because she wanted me to have a chance to see the tall buildings of Detroit. We lived on a farm in western Kentucky, not far from the U.S. highway that took so many Southerners northward to work in the auto industry just after World War II. We went to visit Aunt Mozelle, Mama's sister, and Uncle Boone Cashon, who had headed north soon after Boone's discharge from the service. They lived in a suburb of Detroit, and my mother had visited them once before. She couldn't get the skyscrapers she had seen out of her mind.

The Brooks bus took all day and all night to get there. On our trip, my mother threw up and a black baby cried all the way. I couldn't sleep for thinking about Detroit. Mama had tried in vain to show me how high the buildings were, pointing at the straight horizon beyond the cornfields. I had the impression that they towered halfway to the moon.

"Don't let the Polacks get you," my father had warned when we left. He had to stay home to milk the cows. My two-year-old brother, Johnny, stayed behind with him.

My aunt and uncle met us in a taxi at the bus station, and before I got a good look at them, they had engulfed me in their arms.

"I wouldn't have knowed you, Peggy Jo," my uncle said. "You was just a little squirt the last time I saw you."

"Don't this beat all?" said Aunt Mozelle. "Boone here could have built us a car by now—and us coming in a taxi."

"We've still got that old plug, but it gets us to town," said Mama.

"How could I build a car?" said Uncle Boone. "All I know is bumpers."

"That's what he does," my aunt said to me. "He puts on bumpers."

"We'll get a car someday soon," Uncle Boone said to his wife.

> *My uncle was a thin, delicate man with a receding hairline. His speckled skin made me think of the fragile shells of sparrow eggs. My aunt, on the other hand, was stout and tanned, with thick, dark hair draped like wings over her ears.*

My uncle was a thin, delicate man with a receding hairline. His speckled skin made me think of the fragile shells of sparrow eggs. My aunt, on the other hand, was stout and tanned, with thick, dark hair draped like wings over her ears. I gazed at my aunt and uncle, trying to match them up with the photograph my mother had shown me.

"Peggy's all worked up over seeing the tall buildings," said Mama as we climbed into the taxi. "The cat's got her tongue."

"It has *not!*"

"I'm afraid we've got bad news," said Aunt Mozelle. "The city buses is on strike and there's no way to get into Detroit."

"Don't say it!" cried Mama. "After we come all this way."

"It's trouble with the unions," said Boone. "But they might start up before y'all go back." He patted my knee and said, "Don't worry, littlun."

"The unions is full of reds," Aunt Mozelle whispered to my mother.

"Would it be safe to go?" Mama asked.

"We needn't worry," said Aunt Mozelle.

From the window of the squat yellow taxi, driven by a froglike man who grunted, I scrutinized the strange and vast neighborhoods we were passing through. I had never seen so many houses, all laid out in neat rows. The houses were new, and their pastel colors seemed peaceful and alluring. The skyscrapers were still as remote to me as the castles in fairy tales, but these houses were real, and they were nestled next to each other in a thrilling intimacy. I knew at once where I wanted to live when I grew up—in a place like this, with neighbors.

My relatives' house, on a treeless new street, had venetian blinds and glossy hardwood floors. The living room carpet had giant pink roses that made me think you could play hopscotch on them. The guest room had knotty-pine paneling and a sweet-smelling cedar closet. Aunt Mozelle had put His and Her towels in our room. They had dogs on them and were pleasurably soft. At home, all of our washrags came out of detergent boxes, and our towels were faded and thin. The house was grand. And I had never seen my mother sparkling so. When she saw the kitchen, she whirled around happily, like a young girl, forgetting her dizziness on the bus. Aunt Mozelle had a toaster, a Mixmaster, an electric stove, and a large electric clock shaped like a rooster. On the wall, copper-bottomed pans gleamed in a row like golden-eyed cats lined up on a fence.

"Ain't it the berries?" my mother said to me. "Didn't I tell you?"

"Sometimes I have to pinch myself," said my aunt.

Just then, the front door slammed and a tall girl with a ponytail bounded into the house, saying "Hey!" in an offhand manner.

"Corn!" I said timidly, which seemed to perplex her, for she stared at me as though I were some odd sort of pet allowed into the house. This was my cousin Betsy Lou, in bluejeans rolled up halfway to her knees.

"Our kinfolks is here," Aunt Mozelle announced.

"Law, you've growed into a beanpole," said Mama to Betsy Lou.

"Welcome to our fair city, and I hope you don't get polio," Betsy Lou said to me.

"Watch what you're saying!" cried her mother. "You'll scare Peggy Jo."

"I imagine it'll be worse this summer than last," said Mama, looking worried.

"If we're stuck here without a car, you won't be any place to catch polio," Aunt Mozelle said, smiling at me.

"Polio spreads at swimming pools," Betsy Lou said.

"Then I'm not going to any swimming pool," I announced flatly.

Aunt Mozelle fussed around in her splendid kitchen, making dinner. I sat at the table, listening to Mama and her sister talk, in a gentle, flowing way, exchanging news, each stopping now and then to smile at the other in disbelief, or to look at me with pride. I couldn't take my eyes off my aunt, because she looked so much like my mother. She was older and heavier, but they had the same wide smile, the same unaffected laughter. They had similar sharp tips on their upper lips, which they filled in with bright red lipstick.

Mama said, "Boone sure is lucky. He's still young and ain't crippled and has a good job."

"Knock on wood," said Aunt Mozelle, rapping the door facing.

> *S*uddenly I found myself watching a chubby girl in a lilac piqué playsuit zoom up and down the sidewalk on roller skates.

They had arranged for me to have a playmate, a girl my age who lived in the neighborhood. At home, in the summertime, I did not play with anyone, for the girls I knew at school lived too far away. Suddenly I found myself watching a chubby girl in a lilac **piqué** playsuit zoom up and down the sidewalk on roller skates.

piqué: durable, ribbed fabric

"Come on," she said, "It's not hard."

"I'm coming." Betsy Lou had let me have her old skates, but I had trouble fastening them on my Weather-Bird sandals. I had never been on skates. At home there was no sidewalk. I decided to try skating on one foot, like a kid on a scooter, but the skate came loose.

"Put both of them on," said the girl, laughing at me.

Her name was Sharon Belletieri. She had to spell it for me. She said my name over and over until it sounded absurd. "Peggy Peggy Peggy Peggy Peggy." She made my name sound like "piggy."

"Don't you have a permanent?" she asked.

"No," I said, touching my pigtails. "My hair's in plaits[1] 'cause it's summer."

"Har? Oh, you mean *hair*? Like air?" She waved at the air. She was standing there, perfectly balanced on her skates. She pronounced "hair" with two syllables. *Hayer*. I said something like a cross between *herr* and *harr*.

---

[1] **plaits:** braids

Sharon turned and whizzed down the sidewalk, then skidded to a stop at the corner, twisted around, and faced me.

"Are you going to skate or not?" she asked.

My uncle smoked Old Golds, and he seemed to have excess nervous energy. He was always jumping up from his chair to get something, or to look outside at the thermometer. He had found his name in a newspaper ad recently and had won a free pint of Cunningham's ice cream. My aunt declared that that made him somewhat famous. When I came back that day with the skates, he was sitting on the porch fanning himself with a newspaper. There was a heat wave, he said.

"What did you think of Sharon Belletieri?" he asked.

"She talks funny," I said, sitting down beside him.

"Folks up here all talk funny, I've noticed that too."

Uncle Boone had been a clerk in the war. He told me about the time he had spent in the Pacific theater, sailing around on a battleship, looking for Japs.

"Me and some buddies went to a Pacific island where there was a tribe of people with little tails," he said.

"Don't believe a word he says," said my aunt, who had been listening.

"It's true," said Uncle Boone. "Cross my heart and hope to die." He solemnly crossed his hands on his chest, then looked at his watch and said abruptly to me, "What do you think of Gorgeous George?"[2]

"I don't know."

"How about Howdy Doody?"[3]

"Who's Howdy Doody?"

"This child don't know nothing," he said to my aunt. "She's been raised with a bunch of country hicks."

"He's fooling," said Aunt Mozelle. "Go ahead and show her, Boone, for gosh sakes. Don't keep it a secret."

He was talking about television. I hadn't noticed the set in the living room because it had a sliding cover over the screen. It was a ten-inch table model with an upholstered sound box in a rosewood cabinet.

---

2 **Gorgeous George:** George Wagner (1915–1963), professional wrestler known for his theatrical performances and outrageous fashion sense

3 **Howdy Doody:** a cowboy puppet who starred in the television show *Howdy Doody*

AMERICAN LANDSCAPE, Charles Sheeler, 1930, The Museum of Modern Art

"We've never seen a television," my mother said.

"This will ruin her," said my aunt. "It's ruined Boone."

Uncle Boone turned on the television set. A wrestling match appeared on the screen, and I could see Gorgeous George flexing his muscles and tossing his curls. The television set resembled our radio. For a long time I was confused, thinking that I would now be able to see all my favorite radio programs.

"It's one of those sets you can look at in normal light and not go blind," my aunt said, to reassure us. "It's called Daylight TV."

"Wait till you see Howdy Doody," said Uncle Boone.

The picture on the television set was not clear. The reception required some imagination, and the pictures frequently dissolved, but I could see Gorgeous George moving across the screen, his curls bouncing. I could see him catch hold of his opponent and wrestle him to the floor, holding him so tight I thought he would choke.

That night, I lay in the cedar-perfumed room, too excited to sleep. I did not know what to expect next. The streetlamps glowed like moons through the venetian blinds, and as I lay there, my guardian angel slowly crept into my mind. In *Uncle Arthur's Bedtime Stories*, there was a picture of a child with his guardian angel hovering over him. It was a man angel, and gigantic, with immense white feathery bird's wings. Probably the boy could never see him because the angel stayed in what drivers of automobiles call a blind spot. I had a feeling that my own guardian angel had accompanied the bus to Michigan and was in the house with me. I imagined him floating above the bus. I knew that my guardian angel was supposed to keep me from harm, but I did not want anyone to know about him. I was very afraid of him. It was a long time before I fell asleep.

In the North, they drank coffee. Aunt Mozelle made a large pot of coffee in the mornings, and she kept it in a Thermos so she could drink coffee throughout the day.

Mama began drinking coffee. "Whew! I'm higher than a kite!" she would say. "I'll be up prowling half the night."

"Little girls shouldn't ought to drink coffee," Uncle Boone said to me more than once. "It turns them black."

"I don't even want any!" I protested. But I did like the enticing smell, which awoke me early in the mornings.

My aunt made waffles with oleomargarine. She kneaded a capsule of yellow dye into the pale margarine.

"It's a law," she told me one morning.

"They don't have that law down home anymore," said Mama. "People's turning to oleo and it's getting so we can't sell butter."

"I guess everybody forgot how it tasted," said Aunt Mozelle.

"I wouldn't be surprised if that business about the dye was a Communist idea," said my uncle. "A buddy of mine at the plant thinks so.

He says they want to make it look like butter. The big companies, they're full of reds now."

"That makes sense to me," said Mama. "Anything to hurt the farmer."

It didn't make sense to me. When they talked about reds, all I could imagine was a bunch of little devils in red suits, carrying pitchforks. I wondered if they were what my uncle had seen in the Pacific, since devils had tails. Everything about the North was confusing. Lunetta Jones, for instance, bewildered me. She came for coffee every morning, after my uncle had left in a car pool. Lunetta, a seventh-grade teacher, was from Kentucky, and her parents were old friends of my aunt's, so Mozelle and Boone took a special interest in her welfare. Lunetta's life was tragic, my aunt said. Her sailor-boy husband had died in the war. Lunetta never spoke to me, so I often stared at her unself-consciously. She resembled one of the Toni twins, except for her horsey teeth. She wore her hair curled tight at the bottom, with a fluffy topknot, and she put hard, precise *g*'s on the ends of words like "talking" and "going," the way both Sharon Belletieri and Betsy Lou did. And she wore elaborate dresses—rayon marquisette[4] dresses with Paris pockets, dresses with tiered tucks, others of tissue chambray,[5] with what she called "taffeta understudies." Sometimes I thought her dresses could carry her away on a frantic ride through the sky, they were so billowy and thin.

> *W*hen they talked about reds, all I could imagine was a bunch of little devils in red suits, carrying pitchforks. I wondered if they were what my uncle had seen in the Pacific, since devils had tails.

"Lunetta's man-crazy," my aunt explained to me. "She's always dressed up in one of them Sunday-go-to-meetin' outfits in case she might come across a man to marry."

Uncle Boone called her thick lipstick "man bait."

The buses remained on strike, and I spent the days in the house. I avoided Sharon Belletieri, preferring to be alone, or to sit entranced before the television set. Sometimes the fading outlines of the characters on the screen were like ghosts. I watched Milton Berle, Morey Amsterdam, *Believe It Or Not*, *Wax Wackies*, and even *Blind Date*. Judy

---

4 **marquisette:** a shear meshed fabric

5 **chambray:** a lightweight fabric

Splinters, a ventriloquist's dummy with pigtails like mine, was one of my favorites, and I liked the magician Foodini on *Lucky Pup* better than Howdy Doody. Betsy Lou teased me, saying I was too old for those baby shows. She was away most of the time, out on "jelly dates." A jelly date was a Coke date. She had jelly dates with Bob and Jim and Sam all on the same day. She was fond of singing "Let's Take an Old-Fashioned Walk," although one of her boyfriends had a car and she liked to go riding in it more than anything else. Why couldn't he take us to Detroit? I wondered, but I was afraid to ask. I had a sick feeling that we were never going to get to see the buildings of the city.

In the mornings, when there was nothing but snow on television, and the women were gossiping over their coffee in the kitchen, I sat on the enclosed porch and watched the people and the cars pass. During the heat wave, it was breezy there. I sat on the rattan chaise lounge and read Aunt Mozelle's scrapbooks, which I had found on a shelf above the television set. They were filled with brittle newspaper clippings mounted in overlapping rows. The clippings included household hints and cradle notes, but most of the stories were about bizarre occurrences around the world—diseases and kidnappings and disasters. One headline that fascinated me read: TIBETAN STOMACH STOVE DECLARED CANCER CAUSE. The story said that people in Tibet who carry little hot stoves against their abdomens in winter frequently develop cancer from the irritation. I was thankful that I didn't live in a cold climate. Another story was about a boa constrictor that swallowed a horse blanket. And there were a number of strange stories about blue babies. When my aunt found me reading the scrapbooks, she said to me, "Life is amazing. I keep these to remind me of just how strange everything is. And how there are always people worse off." I nodded agreement. The porch was my favorite place. I felt secure there, as I read about these faraway wonders and afflictions. I would look up now and then and imagine I could see the tall buildings of Detroit in the distance.

T his is a two-tone gabardine spectator dress[6] with a low-slung belt in the back," said Lunetta one morning as she turned to model her new dress for us. Lunetta always had official descriptions for her extravagant costumes.

My mother said in a wistful voice, "Law me, that's beautiful. But what would I look like, feeding chickens in that getup?"

---

6 **gabardine spectator dress:** a dress of two contrasting colors in a twilled, durable fabric

When my uncle came home from work, I greeted him at the door and asked him bluntly, "Are you going to get fired because of the reds?"

"Just look at them shoes," Aunt Mozelle said.

Lunetta's shoes had butterfly bows and sling heels and open toes. She sat down and tapped her toes as Aunt Mozelle poured coffee for her. She said then, "Is Boone worried about his job now that they caught that red?"

"Well, he is, but he don't let on," said Aunt Mozelle, frowning.

Lunetta seized yesterday's newspaper and spread it out on the table. She pointed at the headlines. I remember the way the adults had murmured over the newspaper the day before. Aunt Mozelle had said, "Don't worry, Boone. You don't work for that company." He had replied, "But the plant is full of sympathizers." Now Lunetta said, "Just think. That man they caught could have given Russia all the plans for the power plant. Nothing's safe. You never know who might turn out to be a spy."

My mother was disturbed. "Everything you all have worked so hard for—and the reds could just come in and take it." She waved her hand at the kitchen. In my mind a strange scene appeared: a band of little red devils marching in with their pitchforks and taking the entire Kelvinator kitchen to hell. Later, it occurred to me that they would take the television set first.

When my uncle came home from work, I greeted him at the door and asked him bluntly, "Are you going to get fired because of the reds?"

He only laughed and twitched my plaits. "No, sugar," he said.

"That don't concern younguns," Aunt Mozelle told me. She said to her husband, "Lunetta was here, spreading ideas."

"Leave it to Lunetta," said Uncle Boone wearily.

That evening they were eager to watch the news on the television set. When the supervisor who had been fired was shown, my uncle said, "I hope they give him what-for."

"He was going to tell Russia about the power plant," I said.

"Hush, Peggy," said Mama.

That evening, I could hear their anxious voices on the porch, as I watched Arthur Godfrey,[7] wrestling, and the barbershop quartets. It seemed odd to me that my uncle did not want to watch the wrestling. He had told me wrestling was his favorite program.

---

7 **Arthur Godfrey:** (1903–1983), radio and television personality

Sharon Belletieri had a birthday party. Aunt Mozelle took Mama and me to a nearby Woolworth's, where I selected a coloring book for a present. The store was twice the size of ours at home. I also bought a souvenir of my trip—a pair of china dogs, with a label that read "Made in Japan." And my mother bought me a playsuit like Sharon's.

"It's Sanforized.[8] That's good," she said with an air of satisfaction, as she examined seams and labels.

My mother looked pale and tired. At breakfast she had suddenly thrown up, the way she had during our bus trip. "I can't keep anything down this early," she had said. My aunt urged her to drink more coffee, saying it would settle her stomach.

Sharon Belletieri lived with her parents in a famous kind of sanitary house where you couldn't get TB or rheumatic fever because it had no drafts. "You won't have to worry about polio," Betsy Lou had told me. The house had venetian blinds like my aunt's, and there was also a television set, an immense one, on legs. Howdy Doody was on, but no one was watching. I did not know what to say to the children. They all knew each other, and their screams and giggles had a natural continuity, something like the way my mother talked with her sister, and like the splendid houses of the neighborhood, all set so close together.

For her birthday, Sharon's parents gave her a Toni doll that took my breath away. It had a bolero sundress, lace-edged panties and slip, and white shoes and socks—an outfit as fine as any of Lunetta's. It came with a Play Wave, including plastic spin curlers and Toni Creme Rinse. The doll's magic nylon hair was supposed to grow softer in texture the more you gave it permanent waves. Feeling self-conscious in my new playsuit, I sat quietly at the party, longing to give that doll a permanent.

Eventually, even though I had hardly opened my mouth, someone laughed at my accent. I had said the unfortunate word "hair" again, in reference to the doll.

Sharon said, "*She*'s from Kentucky."

Growing bold and inspired, I said, "Well, we don't have any reds in Kentucky."

Some of the children laughed, and Sharon took me aside and told me a secret, making me cross my heart and hope to die. "I know who's a red," she told me in a whisper. "My father knows him."

---

8 **Sanforized:** refers to fabric that has been preshrunk

"Who?"

"One of the men your uncle rides with to work. The one who drives the car on Thursdays. He's a red and I can prove it."

Before I could find out more, it was my turn to pin the tail on the donkey. Sharon's mother blindfolded me and spun me around. The children were squealing, and I could feel them shrinking from me. When I took the blindfold off, I was dizzy. I had pinned the donkey's tail on the wallpaper, in the center of a large yellow flower.

That evening Betsy Lou went out with a boy named Sam, the one with the car, and Lunetta came to play canasta[9] with the adults. During *Cavalcade of Stars*,[10] I could hear them in the kitchen, accusing each other of hiding reds, when they meant hearts and diamonds. They laughed so loudly I sometimes missed some of Jack Carter's[11] jokes. The wrestling came on afterward, but my uncle did not notice, so I turned off the television and looked at a magazine. I spent a long time trying to write the last line to a Fab jingle so that I could win a television set and five hundred dollars a month for life. I knew that life in Kentucky would be unbearable without a television.

Between hands, Uncle Boone and Lunetta got into an argument. My uncle claimed there were more reds teaching school than making cars, and Lunetta said it was just the opposite.

"They're firing schoolteachers too," he said to Lunetta.

"Don't look at *me*," she said. "I signed the loyalty oath."

"Hush your mouth, Boone," said Aunt Mozelle.

"I know who a red is," I said suddenly, coming to the table.

They all looked at me and I explained what Sharon had told me. Too late, I remembered my promise not to tell.

"Don't let anybody hear you say that," said Lunetta. "Your uncle would lose his job. If they even *think* you know somebody that knows somebody, you can get in trouble."

"You better not say anything, hon," said Uncle Boone.

"Peggy, it's past your bedtime," my mother said.

"What did *I* do?"

"Talk gets around," said Lunetta. "There's sympathizers even in the woodwork."

---

9 **canasta:** a form of the card game rummy

10 **Cavalcade of Stars:** a comedic showcase featuring skits, singing, and dancing that aired from 1949 to 1952

11 **Jack Carter:** the first emcee of *Cavalcade of Stars*

The next day, after a disturbing night in which my guardian angel did nothing to protect me from my terrible secret, I was glum and cranky, and for the first time I refused Aunt Mozelle's waffles.

"Are you burnt out on them?" she asked me.

"No, I just ain't hungry."

"She played too hard at the birthday party," Mama said knowingly to my aunt.

When Lunetta arrived and Mama told her I had played too hard at the birthday party, I burst into tears.

The next day, after a disturbing night in which my guardian angel did nothing to protect me from my terrible secret, I was glum and cranky, and for the first time I refused Aunt Mozelle's waffles.

"It's nobody's business if I played too hard," I cried. "Besides," I shrieked at Mama, "you don't feel good at breakfast either. You always say you can't keep anything down."

"Don't be ugly," my mother said sharply. To the others, she said apologetically, "I reckon sooner or later she was bound to show out."

It was Sunday, and the heat wave continued. We all sat on the porch, looking at the Sunday papers. Betsy Lou was reading *Pleasant Valley* by Louis Bromfield. Uncle Boone read the Sunday comics aloud to himself. Actually, he was trying to get my attention, for I sat in a corner, determined to ignore everyone. Uncle Boone read "Abbie an' Slats," "The Gumps," and "Little Orphan Annie." He pretended he was Milton Berle as he read them, but I wouldn't laugh.

Lunetta and Uncle Boone seemed to have forgotten their argument. Lunetta had dressed up for church, but the man she planned to go with had gone to visit his mother's grave instead.

"That man sure did love his mother," she said.

"Why don't you go to church anyway?" asked Betsy Lou. "You're all dressed up."

"I just don't have it in me," said Lunetta. She was wearing a shell-tucked summer shantung[12] dress and raffia[13] T-strap sandals.

"Ain't you hot in that outfit?" asked my aunt. "We're burning up."

"I guess so." Lunetta seemed gloomy and distracted. I almost forgave her

---

12 **shantung:** a woven fabric with a slightly uneven surface

13 **raffia:** a durable fiber usually used in baskets and hats

for upsetting me about the sympathizers, but then she launched into a complicated story about a babysitter who got double-crossed. "This woman baby-sat for her best friend, who was divorced and had two little babies. And come to find out, the friend was going out on dates with the woman's own husband!"

"If that don't beat all," said Mama, her eyes wide. She was drinking her second cup of coffee.

"No telling how long that could have kept up," said my aunt.

"It made a big divorce case," Lunetta said.

"I never saw so many divorce cases," said Mama.

"Would you divorce somebody if you found out they were a Communist?" Lunetta asked.

"I don't know as I would," said Aunt Mozelle. "Depends."

"*I* would," said Mama.

"I probably would," said Lunetta. "How about you, Boone?"

"If I found out Mozelle was a red?" Boone asked, grinning. "I'd probably string her up and tickle her feet till she hollered uncle."

"Oh, Boone," Lunetta said with a laugh. "I know you'd stick up for Mozelle, no matter what."

> *M*ama was too much in pain to speak. Her face was distorted, her sharp-pointed lips stretched out like a slingshot. My aunt helped her to the bathroom, and a short while later, my aunt and uncle flew away with her in a taxi.

They sat around that morning talking like this, good-naturedly. In the light of day, the reds were only jokes after all, like the comics. I had decided to eat a bowl of Pep cereal, and "Some Enchanted Evening" was playing on the radio. Suddenly everything changed, as if a black storm had appeared to break the heat wave. My mother gave out a loud whoop and clutched her stomach in pain.

"Where does it hurt?" my aunt cried, grabbing at Mama.

Mama was too much in pain to speak. Her face was distorted, her sharp-pointed lips stretched out like a slingshot. My aunt helped her to the bathroom, and a short while later, my aunt and uncle flew away with her in a taxi. Mama had straightened up enough to say that the pain had subsided, but she looked scared, and the blood had drained from her face. I said nothing to her, not even good-bye.

Betsy Lou, left alone with me, said, "I hope she hasn't got polio."

"Only children get polio," I said, trembling. "She don't have polio."

The telephone rang, and Betsy Lou chattered excitedly, telling one of her boyfriends what had happened. Alone and frightened, I sat on the porch, hugging a fat pile of newspapers and gazing at the street. I could see Sharon Belletieri, skating a block away with two other girls. She was wearing a blue playsuit. She and her friends reminded me of those privileged children in the Peanut Gallery on *Howdy Doody*.

To keep from thinking, I began searching the newspaper for something to put in Aunt Mozelle's scrapbook, but at first nothing seemed so horrible as what had just happened. Some babies had turned blue from a diaper dye, but that story didn't impress me. Then I found an item about a haunted house, and my heart began to race. A priest claimed that mysterious disturbances in a house in Wisconsin were the work of an angelic spirit watching over an eight-year-old boy. Cryptic messages were found on bits of paper in the boy's room. The spirit manifestation had occurred fifteen times. I found my aunt's scissors and cut out the story.

Within two hours, my aunt and uncle returned, with broad smiles on their faces, but I knew they were pretending.

"She's just fine," said Aunt Mozelle. "We'll take you to see her afterwhile, but right now they gave her something to make her sleep and take away the pain."

"She'll get to come home in the morning," said my uncle.

He had brought ice cream, and while he went to the kitchen to dish it out, I showed my aunt the clipping I had found. I helped her put it in her scrapbook.

"Life sure is strange," I said.

"Didn't I tell you?" she said. "Now, don't you worry about your mama, hon. She's going to be all right."

L ater that day, my aunt and uncle stood in the corridor of the hospital while I visited my mother. The hospital was large and gray and steaming with the heat. Mama lay against a mound of pillows, smiling weakly.

"*I'm* the one that showed out," she said, looking ashamed. She took my hand and made me sit on the bed next to her. "You *were* going to have a little brother or sister," she said. "But I was mistaken."

"What happened to it?"

"I lost it. That happens sometimes."

When I looked at her blankly, she tried to explain that there wasn't *really* a baby, as there was when she had Johnny two years before.

She said, "You know how sometimes one or two of the chicken eggs don't hatch? The baby chick just won't take hold. That's what happened."

It occurred to me to ask what the baby's name would have been.

"I don't know," she said. "I'm trying to tell you there wasn't really a baby. I didn't know about it, anyway."

"You didn't even know there was a baby?"

"No. I didn't know about it till I lost it."

She tried to laugh, but she was weak, and she seemed as confused as I was. She squeezed my hand and closed her eyes for a moment. Then she said, "Boone says the buses will start up this week. You could go with your aunt to Detroit and see the big buildings."

"Without you?"

"The doctor said I should rest up before we go back. But you go ahead. Mozelle will take you." She smiled at me sleepily. "I wanted to go so bad— just to see those big fancy store windows. And I wanted to see your face when you saw the city."

That evening, *Toast of the Town* was on television, and then Fred Waring, and *Garroway at Large*.[14] I was lost among the screen phantoms—the magic acts, puppets, jokes, clowns, dancers, singers, wisecracking announcers. My aunt and uncle laughed uproariously. Uncle Boone was drinking beer, something I had not seen him do, and the room stank with the smoke of his Old Golds. Now and then I was aware of all of us sitting there together, laughing in the dim light from the television, while my mother was in the hospital. Even Betsy Lou was watching with us. Later, I went to the guest room and sat on the large bed, trying to concentrate on finishing the Fab jingle.

> Here's to a fabulous life with Fab
> There's no soap scum to make wash drab
> Your clothes get cleaner—whiter, too—

---

14 ***Garroway at Large:*** a musical variety show hosted by Dave Garroway that aired from 1949 to 1954

I heard my aunt calling to me excitedly. I was missing something on the television screen. I had left because the news was on.

"Pictures of Detroit!" she cried. "Come quick. You can see the big buildings."

I raced into the living room in time to see some faint, dark shapes, hiding behind the snow, like a forest in winter, and then the image faded into the snow.

"Mozelle can take you into Detroit in a day or two," my uncle said. "The buses is starting up again."

"I don't want to go," I said.

"You don't want to miss the chance," said my aunt.

"Yes, I do."

The reds had stolen the baby. They took things. They were after my aunt's copper-bottomed pans. They stole the butter.

That night, alone in the pine-and-cedar room, I saw everything clearly, like the sharpened images that floated on the television screen. My mother had said an egg didn't hatch, but I knew better. The reds had stolen the baby. They took things. They were after my aunt's copper-bottomed pans. They stole the butter. They wanted my uncle's job. They were invisible, like the guardian angel, although they might wear disguises. You didn't know who might be a red. You never knew when you might lose a baby that you didn't know you had. I understood it all. I hadn't trusted my guardian angel, and so he had failed to protect me. During the night, I hit upon a last line to the Fab jingle, but when I awoke I saw how silly and inappropriate it was. It was going over and over in my mind: *Red soap makes the world go round.*

On the bus home a few days later, I slept with my head in my mother's lap, and she dozed with her head propped against my seat back. She was no longer sick, but we were both tired and we swayed, unresisting, with the rhythm of the bus. When the bus stopped in Fort Wayne, Indiana, at midnight, I suddenly woke up, and at the sight of an unfamiliar place, I felt—with a new surge of clarity—the mystery of travel, the vastness of the world, the strangeness of life. My own life was a curiosity, an item for a scrapbook. I wondered what my mother would tell my father about the baby she had lost. She had been holding me tightly against her stomach as though she feared she might lose me too.

I had refused to let them take me into Detroit. At the bus station, Aunt Mozelle had hugged me and said, "Maybe next time you come we can go to Detroit."

"If there *is* a next time," Mama said. "This may be her only chance, but she had to be contrary."

"I didn't want to miss *Wax Wackies* and *Judy Splinters*," I said, protesting.

"We'll have a car next time you come," said my uncle. "If they don't fire everybody," he added with a laugh.

"If that happens, y'all can always come back to Kentucky and help us get a crop out," Mama told him.

The next afternoon, we got off the bus on the highway at the intersection with our road. Our house was half a mile away. The bus driver got our suitcases out of the bus for us, and then drove on down the highway. My father was supposed to meet us, but he was not there.

"I better not carry this suitcase," said Mama. "My insides might drop."

We left our suitcases in a ditch and started walking, expecting to meet Daddy on the way.

My mother said, "You don't remember this, but when you was two years old I went to Jackson, Tennessee, for two weeks to see Mozelle and Boone—came back before Boone was called overseas?—and when I come back the bus driver let me off here and I come walking down the road to the house carrying my suitcase. You was playing in the yard and you saw me walk up and you didn't recognize me. For the longest time, you didn't know who I was. I never *will* forget how funny you looked."

"They won't recognize us," I said solemnly. "Daddy and Johnny."

As we got to the top of the hill, we could see that our little white house was still there. The tin roof of the barn was barely visible through the tall oak trees.

Responding to the Story

1. LITERARY LENS Find an especially colorful exchange of dialogue in "Detroit Skyline, 1949." What does it tell you about the time, place, and characters?

2. Mason allows the characters in the story to reveal themselves without providing much interpretation or judgment. Pick one character from the story. What do you know about him or her by the end?

3. Coming from a small town, Peggy isn't used to city life. What are some of the culture shocks she encounters?

4. Find three references to "the reds." What do these references tell you about the characters and the times they live in?

5. Why do you think Peggy declines to see the Detroit skyline that is so prominent in the title and the story, saying at the end, "I understood it all"?

6. At the end of the story, Peggy is certain her father and brother won't recognize her and her mother. Why do you think she feels that way?

7. THE AUTHOR'S STYLE Consider the quotation from Mason below. In it, she comments on her interest in the impact of rapid changes on the lives of working-class people. How do social forces affect the characters in this story?

My Version of Rock-and-Roll

Writing is my version of rock-and-roll . . . . I identify with Bruce Springsteen's songs, and of course I'm not alone in this. I like the way his songs are stories with characters. He writes about the disintegration of lives due to social forces. But his people keep striving, hoping.

—Bobbie Ann Mason, *Passion and Craft*

Louise Erdrich
1954

About the Author

Louise Erdrich grew up in North Dakota, one of eight children of a German American father and an Ojibwa (Chippewa) Indian mother. Both her parents were teachers at a Bureau of Indian Affairs Boarding School. They encouraged her talents. Her grandfather, a tribal chair for the Turtle Mountain Reservation, used to give Erdrich a nickel for every story she wrote.

She went east to attend Dartmouth College and Johns Hopkins University, and married the late writer Michael Dorris, who collaborated with her on several works until his suicide.

Among her best-known works is her first novel, the award-winning *Love Medicine,* published in 1984. Erdrich followed the three families of characters that appeared in *Love Medicine* in her later novels *The Beet Queen, Tracks,* and *The Bingo Palace.*

In an interview with the *Chicago Tribune* in 1986, she commented, "My fondest hope is that people will be reading me in 10 or 20 years from now as someone who has written about the American experience in all of its diversity."

****

The Author's Style

Erdrich explores the mysteries of religion, culture, and family ties in her stories and novels. Often they are set in the flat, open spaces of North Dakota. Her heritage is part Ojibwa (Chippewa) and her stories focus on the impact on Indians of various aspects of the non-Indian world—for example, alcohol, Christianity, and the government. The Native Americans of Erdrich's stories struggle constantly for the survival of their cultural identity, always aware of betrayal and mistreatment in the past. An example is when Indian children were removed from their homes and sent to government-run "Indian schools" earlier in the 20th century.

Erdrich develops precise descriptions of bleak landscapes and reservation life. She is adept at characterization, conveying the personalities and relationships of her characters through alternating points of view. Her characters are aware of the ways language works in their lives, both for and against them. The use of dreams, visions, and miracles in Erdrich's fiction is one measure of the passionate intensity of her characters. It is also a constant reminder of her closeness to Native American culture. Erdrich also writes poetry, and the poet's eye for powerful images and complex metaphors can be found throughout her fiction.

LITERARY LENS Watch for the conflict between Native American and non-Indian cultures in this story.

AMERICAN HORSE

LOUISE ERDRICH

The woman sleeping on the cot in the woodshed was Albertine American Horse. The name was left over from her mother's short marriage. The boy was the son of the man she had loved and let go. Buddy was on the cot too, sitting on the edge because he'd been awake three hours watching out for his mother and besides, she took up the whole cot. Her feet hung over the edge, limp and brown as two trout. Her long arms reached out and slapped at things she saw in her dreams.

Buddy had been knocked awake out of hiding in a washing machine while herds of policemen with dogs searched through a large building with many tiny rooms. When the arm came down, Buddy screamed because it had a blue cuff and sharp silver buttons. "Tss," his mother mumbled, half awake, "wasn't nothing." But Buddy sat up after her breathing went deep again, and he watched.

There was something coming and he knew it.

It was coming from very far off but he had a picture of it in his mind. It was a large thing made of metal with many barbed hooks, points, and drag chains on it, something like a giant potato peeler that rolled out of the sky, scraping clouds down with it and jabbing or crushing everything that lay in its path on the ground.

Buddy watched his mother. If he woke her up, she would know what to do about the thing, but he thought he'd wait until he saw it for sure before he shook her. She was pretty, sleeping, and he liked knowing he could look at her as long and close up as he wanted. He took a strand of her hair and held it in his hands as if it was the rein to a delicate beast. She was strong enough and could pull him along like the horse their name was.

Buddy had his mother's and his grandmother's name because his father had been a big mistake.

"They're all mistakes, even your father. But *you* are the best thing that ever happened to me."

That was what she said when he asked.

Even Kadie, the boyfriend crippled from being in a car wreck, was not as good a thing that had happened to his mother as Buddy was. "He was a medium-sized mistake," she said. "He's hurt and I shouldn't even say that, but it's the truth." At the moment, Buddy knew that being the best thing in his mother's life, he was also the reason they were hiding from the cops.

He wanted to touch the satin roses sewed on her pink tee-shirt, but he knew he shouldn't do that even in her sleep. If she woke up and found him touching the roses, she would say, "Quit that, Buddy." Sometimes she told him to stop hugging her like a gorilla. She never said that in the mean voice she used when he oppressed her, but when she said that he loosened up anyway.

There were times he felt like hugging her so hard and in such a special way that she would say to him, "Let's get married." There were also times he closed his eyes and wished that she would die, only a few times, but still it haunted him that his wish might come true. He and Uncle Lawrence would be left alone. Buddy wasn't worried, though, about his mother getting married to somebody else. She had said to her friend, Madonna, "All men suck," when she thought Buddy wasn't listening. He had made an uncertain sound, and when they heard him they took him in their arms.

"Except for you, Buddy," his mother said. "All except for you and maybe Uncle Lawrence, although he's pushing it."

"The cops suck the worst though," Buddy whispered to his mother's sleeping face, "because they're after us." He felt tired again, slumped down, and put his legs beneath the blanket. He closed his eyes and got the feeling that the cot was lifting up beneath him, that it was arching its canvas back and then traveling, traveling very fast and in the wrong direction for when he looked up he saw the three of them were advancing to meet the great metal thing with hooks and barbs and all sorts of sharp equipment to catch their bodies and draw their blood. He heard its insides as it rushed toward them, purring softly like a powerful motor and then they were right in its shadow. He pulled the reins as hard as he could and the beast reared, lifting him. His mother clapped her hand across his mouth.

"Okay," she said. "Lay low. They're outside and they're gonna hunt."

She touched his shoulder and Buddy leaned over with her to look through a crack in the boards.

They were out there all right, Albertine saw them. Two officers and that social worker woman. Vicki Koob. There had been no whistle, no dream, no voice to warn her that they were coming. There was only the crunching sound of cinders in the yard, the engine purring, the dust sifting off their car in a fine light brownish cloud and settling around them.

The three people came to a halt in their husk of metal—the car emblazoned with the North Dakota State Highway Patrol emblem which is the glowing profile of the Sioux policeman, Red Tomahawk, the one who killed Sitting Bull. Albertine gave Buddy the blanket and told him that he might have to wrap it around him and hide underneath the cot.

"We're gonna wait and see what they do." She took him in her lap and hunched her arms around him. "Don't you worry," she whispered against his ear. "Lawrence knows how to fool them."

Buddy didn't want to look at the car and the people. He felt his mother's heart beating beneath his ear so fast it seemed to push the satin roses in and out. He put his face to them carefully and breathed the deep, soft powdery woman smell of her. That smell was also in her little face cream bottles, in her brushes, and around the washbowl after she used it. The satin felt so unbearably smooth against his cheek that he had to press closer. She didn't push him away, like he expected, but hugged him still tighter, until he felt as close as he had ever been to back inside her again where she said he came from. Within the smells of her things, her soft skin and the satin of her roses, he closed his eyes then, and took his breaths softly and quickly with her heart.

They were out there, but they didn't dare get out of the car yet because of Lawrence's big, ragged dogs. Three of these dogs had loped up the dirt drive-way with the car. They were rangy, alert, and bounced up and down on their cushioned paws like wolves. They didn't waste their energy barking, but positioned themselves quietly, one at either car door and the third in front of the bellied-out screen door to Uncle Lawrence's house. It was six in the morning but the wind was up already, blowing dust, ruffling their short moth-eaten coats. The big brown one on Vicki Koob's side had unusual black and white markings, stripes almost, like a hyena and he grinned at her, tongue out and teeth showing.

"Shoo!" Miss Koob opened her door with a quick jerk.

The brown dog sidestepped the door and jumped before her, tiptoeing. Its dirty white muzzle curled and its eyes crossed suddenly as if it was zero-ing its cross-hair sights in on the exact place it would bite her. She ducked back and slammed the door.

"It's mean," she told Officer Brackett. He was printing out some type of form. The other officer, Harmony, a slow man, had not yet reacted to the car's halt. He had been sitting quietly in the back seat, but now he rolled down his window and with no change in expression unsnapped his holster and drew his pistol out and pointed it at the dog on his side. The dog smacked down on its belly, wiggled under the car and was out and around the back of the house before Harmony drew his gun back. The other dogs vanished with him. From wherever they had disappeared to they began to yap and howl, and the door to the low shoebox style house fell open.

"Heya, what's going on?"

Uncle Lawrence put his head out the door and opened wide the one eye he had in working order. The eye bulged impossibly wider in outrage when he saw the police car. But the eyes of the two officers and Miss Vicki Koob were wide open too because they had never seen Uncle Lawrence in his sleeping get up or, indeed, witnessed anything like it. For his ribs, which were cracked from a bad fall and still mending, Uncle Lawrence wore a thick white corset laced up the front with a striped sneakers lace. His glass eye and his set of dentures were still out for the night so his face puckered here and there, around its absences and scars, like a damaged but fierce little cake. Although he had a few gray streaks now, Uncle Lawrence's hair was still thick, and because he wore a special contraption of elastic straps around his head every night, two oiled waves always crested on either side of his middle part. All of this would have been sufficient to astonish, even without the most striking part of his outfit—the smoking jacket. It was made of black satin and hung open around his corset, dragging a tasseled belt. Gold thread dragons struggled up the lapels and blasted their furry red breath around his neck. As Lawrence walked down the steps, he put his arms up in surrender and the gold tassels in the inner seams of his sleeves dropped into view.

"My heavens, what a sight." Vicki Koob was impressed.

"A character," apologized Officer Harmony.

As a tribal police officer who could be counted on to help out the State Patrol, Harmony thought he always had to explain about Indians or get twice as tough to show he did not favor them. He was slow-moving and shy but two jumps ahead of other people all the same, and now, as he watched Uncle Lawrence's splendid approach, he gazed speculatively at the torn and bulging pocket of the smoking jacket. Harmony had been inside Uncle Lawrence's house before and knew that above his draped orange-crate shelf of war medals a blue-black German luger[1] was hung carefully in a net of flat-headed nails and fishing line. Thinking of this deadly exhibition, he got out of the car and shambled toward Lawrence with a dreamy little smile of welcome on his face. But when he searched Lawrence, he found that the bulging pocket held only the lonesome looking dentures from Lawrence's empty jaw. They were still dripping denture polish.

"I had been cleaning them when you arrived," Uncle Lawrence explained with acid dignity.

He took the toothbrush from his other pocket and aimed it like a rifle.

"Quit that, you old idiot." Harmony tossed the toothbrush away. "For once you ain't done nothing. We came for your nephew."

Lawrence looked at Harmony with a faint air of puzzlement.

"Ma Frere, listen," threatened Harmony amiably, "those two white peo-

---

1 **luger:** a pistol

ple in the car came to get him for the welfare. They got papers on your nephew that give them the right to take him."

"Papers?" Uncle Lawrence puffed out his deeply pitted cheeks. "Let me see them papers."

The two of them walked over to Vicki's side of the car and she pulled a copy of the court order from her purse. Lawrence put his teeth back in and adjusted them with busy workings of his jaw.

"Just a minute," he reached into his breast pocket as he bent close to Miss Vicki Koob. "I can't read these without I have in my eye."

He took the eye from his breast pocket delicately, and as he popped it into his face the social worker's mouth fell open in a consternated O.

"What is this," she cried in a little voice.

Uncle Lawrence looked at her mildly. The white glass of the eye was cold as lard. The black iris was strangely charged and menacing.

"He's nuts," Brackett huffed along the side of Vicki's neck. "Never mind him."

Vicki's hair had sweated down her nape in tiny corkscrews and some of the hairs were so long and dangly now that they disappeared into the zippered back of her dress. Brackett noticed this as he spoke into her ear. His face grew red and the backs of his hands prickled. He slid under the steering wheel and got out of the car. He walked around the hood to stand with Leo Harmony.

"We could take you in too," said Brackett roughly. Lawrence eyed the officers in what was taken as defiance. "If you don't cooperate, we'll get out the handcuffs," they warned.

One of Lawrence's arms was stiff and would not move until he'd rubbed it with witch hazel in the morning. His other arm worked fine though, and he stuck it out in front of Brackett.

"Get them handcuffs," he urged them. "Put me in a welfare home." Brackett snapped one side of the handcuffs on Lawrence's good arm and the other to the handle of the police car.

"That's to hold you," he said. "We're wasting our time. Harmony, you search that little shed over by the tall grass and Miss Koob and myself will search the house."

"My rights is violated!" Lawrence shrieked suddenly. They ignored him. He tugged at the handcuff and thought of the good heavy file he kept in his tool box and the German luger oiled and ready but never loaded, because of

Buddy, over his shelf. He should have used it on these bad ones, even Harmony in his big-time white man job. He wouldn't last long in that job anyway before somebody gave him what for.

"It's a damn scheme," said Uncle Lawrence, rattling his chains against the car. He looked over at the shed and thought maybe Albertine and Buddy had sneaked away before the car pulled into the yard. But he sagged, seeing Albertine move like a shadow within the boards. "Oh, it's all a damn scheme," he muttered again.

"I want to find that boy and salvage him," Vicki Koob explained to Officer Brackett as they walked into the house. "Look at his family life—the old man crazy as a bedbug, the mother intoxicated somewhere."

Brackett nodded, energetic, eager. He was a short, hopeful redhead who failed consistently to win the hearts of women. Vicki Koob intrigued him. Now, as he watched, she pulled a tiny pen out of an ornamental clip on her blouse. It was attached to a retractable line that would suck the pen back, like a child eating one strand of spaghetti. Something about the pen on its line excited Brackett to the point of discomfort. His hand shook as he opened the screen door and stepped in, beckoning Miss Koob to follow.

They could see the house was empty at first glance. It was only one rectangular room with whitewashed walls and a little gas stove in the middle. They had already come through the cooking lean-to with the other stove and washstand and rusty old refrigerator. That refrigerator had nothing in it but some wrinkled potatoes and a package of turkey necks. Vicki Koob noted that in her perfect-bound notebook. The beds along the walls of the big room were covered with quilts that Albertine's mother, Sophie, had made from bits of old wool coats and pants that the Sisters sold in bundles at the mission. There was no one hiding beneath the beds. No one was under the little aluminum dinette table covered with a green oilcloth, or the soft brown wood chairs tucked up to it. One wall of the big room was filled with neatly stacked crates of things—old tools and springs and small half-dismantled appliances. Five or six television sets were stacked against the wall. Their control panels spewed colored wires and at least one was cracked all the way across. Only the topmost set, with coathanger antenna angled sensitively to catch the bounding signals around Little Shell, looked like it could possibly work.

Not one thing escaped Vicki Koob's trained and cataloguing gaze. She made note of the cupboard that held only commodity flour and coffee. The unsanitary tin oil drum beneath the kitchen window, full of empty surplus pork cans and beer bottles, caught her eye as did Uncle Lawrence's physical and mental deteriorations. She quickly described these "benchmarks of alcoholic dependency within the extended family of Woodrow (Buddy) American Horse" as she walked around the room with the little notebook open, pushed against her belly to steady it. Although Vicki had been there before, Albertine's presence had always made it difficult for her to take notes.

"Twice the maximum allowable space between door and threshold," she wrote now. "Probably no insulation. 2–3 inch cracks in walls inadequately sealed with whitewash mud." She made a mental note but could see no point in describing Lawrence's stuffed reclining chair that only reclined, the shadeless lamp with its plastic orchid in the bubble glass base, or the three dimensional picture of Jesus that Lawrence had once demonstrated to her. When plugged in, lights rolled behind the water the Lord stood on so that he seemed to be strolling although he never actually went forward, of course, but only pushed the glowing waves behind him forever like a poor tame rat in a treadmill.

Brackett cleared his throat with a nervous rasp and touched Vicki's shoulder.

"What are you writing?"

She moved away and continued to scribble as if thoroughly absorbed in her work. "Officer Brackett displays an undue amount of interest in my person," she wrote. "Perhaps?"

He snatched playfully at the book, but she hugged it to her chest and moved off smiling. More curls had fallen, wetted to the base of her neck. Looking out the window, she sighed long and loud.

"All night on brush rollers for this. What a joke."

Brackett shoved his hands in his pockets. His mouth opened slightly, then shut with a small throttled cluck.

When Albertine saw Harmony ambling across the yard with his big brown thumbs in his belt, his placid smile, and his tiny black eyes moving back and forth, she put Buddy under the cot. Harmony stopped at the shed and stood quietly. He spread his arms wide to show her he hadn't drawn his big police gun.

"Ma Cousin," he said in the Michif dialect that people used if they were relatives or sometimes if they needed gas or a couple of dollars, "why don't you come out here and stop this foolishness?"

"I ain't your cousin," Albertine said. Anger boiled up in her suddenly. "I ain't related to no pigs."

She bit her lip and watched him through the cracks, circling, a big tan punching dummy with his boots full of sand so he never stayed down once he fell. He was empty inside, all stale air. But he knew how to get to her so much better than a white cop could. And now he was circling because he wasn't sure she didn't have a weapon, maybe a knife or the German luger that was the only thing that her father, Albert American Horse, had left his wife and daughter besides his name. Harmony knew that Albertine was a tall strong woman who took two big men to subdue when she didn't want to go in the drunk tank. She had hard hips, broad shoulders, and stood tall like her Sioux father, the American Horse who was killed threshing in Belle Prairie.

"I feel bad to have to do this," Harmony said to Albertine. "But for godsakes, let's nobody get hurt. Come on out with the boy why don't you. I know you got him in there."

Albertine did not give herself away this time. She let him wonder. Slowly and quietly she pulled her belt through its loops and wrapped it around and around her hand until only the big oval buckle with turquoise chunks shaped into a butterfly stuck out over her knuckles. Harmony was talking but she wasn't listening to what he said. She was listening to the pitch of his voice, the tone of it that would tighten or tremble at a certain moment when he decided to rush the shed. He kept talking slowly and reasonably, flexing the dialect from time to time, even mentioning her father.

"He was a damn good man. I don't care what they say, Albertine, I knew him."

Albertine looked at the stone butterfly that spread its wings across her fist. The wings looked light and cool, not heavy. It almost looked like it was ready to fly. Harmony wanted to get to Albertine through her father but she would not think about American Horse. She concentrated on the sky-blue stone.

Yet the shape of the stone, the color, betrayed her.

> She bit her lip and watched him through the cracks, circling, a big tan punching dummy with his boots full of sand so he never stayed down once he fell. He was empty inside, all stale air.

She saw her father suddenly, bending at the grill of their old grey car. She was small then. The memory came from so long ago it seemed like a dream—narrowly focused, snapshot clear. He was bending by the grill in the sun. It was hot summer. Wings of sweat, dark blue, spread across the back of his work shirt. He always wore soft blue shirts, the color of shade cloudier than this stone. His stiff hair had grown out of its short haircut and flopped over his forehead. When he stood up and turned away from the car, Albertine saw that he had a butterfly.

"It's dead," he told her. "Broke its wings and died on the grill."

She must have been five, maybe six, wearing one of the boy's tee-shirts Mama bleached in hilex-water.[2] American Horse took the butterfly, a black and yellow one, and rubbed it on Albertine's collarbone and chest and arms until the color and the powder of it were blended into her skin.

"For grace," he said.

And Albertine had felt a strange lightening in her arms, in her chest, when he did this and said, "For grace." The way he said it, grace meant everything the butterfly was. The sharp delicate wings. The way it floated over the grass. The way its wings seemed to breathe fanning in the sun. The wisdom of the way it blended into flowers or changed into a leaf. In herself she felt the same kind of possibilities and closed her eyes almost in shock or pain she felt so light and powerful at that moment.

Then her father had caught her and thrown her high into the air. She could not remember landing in his arms or landing at all. She only remembered the sun filling her eyes and the world tipping crazily behind her, out of sight.

"He was a damn good man," Harmony said again.

Albertine heard his starched uniform gathering before his boots hit the ground. Once, twice, three times. It took him four solid jumps to get right where she wanted him. She kicked the plank door open when he reached for the handle and the corner caught him on the jaw. He faltered, and Albertine hit him flat on the chin with the butterfly. She hit him so hard the shock of it went up her arm like a string pulled taut. Her fist opened, numb, and she let the belt unloop before she closed her hand on the tip end of it and sent the stone butterfly swooping out in a wide circle around her as if it was on the end of a leash. Harmony reeled backward as she walked toward him swinging the belt. She expected him to fall but he just stumbled. And then he took the gun from his hip.

---

2 **hilex-water:** "Hilex" is a brand of bleaching detergent.

Albertine let the belt go limp. She and Harmony stood within feet of each other, breathing. Each heard the human sound of air going in and out of the other person's lungs. Each read the face of the other as if deciphering letters carved into softly eroding veins of stone. Albertine saw the pattern of tiny arteries that age, drink, and hard living had blown to the surface of the man's face. She saw the spoked wheels of his iris and the arteries like tangled threads that sewed him up. She saw the living net of springs and tissue that held him together, and trapped him. She saw the random, intimate plan of his person.

She took a quick shallow breath and her face went strange and tight. She saw the black veins in the wings of the butterfly, roads burnt into a map, and then she was located somewhere in the net of veins and **sinew** that was the tragic complexity of the world so she did not see Officer Brackett and Vicki Koob rushing toward her, but felt them instead like flies caught in the same web, rocking it.

sinew: tendon; connective tissue

"Albertine!" Vicki Koob had stopped in the grass. Her voice was shrill and tight. "It's better this way, Albertine. We're going to help you."

Albertine straightened, threw her shoulders back. Her father's hand was on her chest and shoulders lightening her wonderfully. Then on wings of her father's hands, on dead butterfly wings, Albertine lifted into the air and flew toward the others. The light powerful feeling swept her up the way she had floated higher, seeing the grass below. It was her father throwing her up into the air and out of danger. Her arms opened for bullets but no bullets came. Harmony did not shoot. Instead, he raised his fist and brought it down hard on her head.

Albertine did not fall immediately, but stood in his arms a moment. Perhaps she gazed still farther back behind the covering of his face. Perhaps she was completely stunned and did not think as she sagged and fell. Her face rolled forward and hair covered her features, so it was impossible for Harmony to see with just what particular expression she gazed into the head-splitting wheel of light, or blackness, that overcame her.

Harmony turned the vehicle onto the gravel road that led back to town. He had convinced the other two that Albertine was more trouble than she was worth, and so they left her behind, and Lawrence too. He stood swearing in his cinder driveway as the car rolled out of sight. Buddy sat between the social worker and Officer Brackett. Vicki tried to hold Buddy fast and keep her arm down at the same time, for the words she'd screamed at Albertine had broken the seal of antiperspirant beneath her arms. She was sweating now as though she'd stored an ocean up inside of her. Sweat rolled down her back in a shallow river and pooled at her waist and between her breasts. A thin sheen of water came out on her forearms, her face. Vicki gave an irritated moan but Brackett seemed not to take notice, or take offense at least. Air-conditioned breezes were sweeping over the seat anyway, and very soon they would be comfortable. She smiled at Brackett over Buddy's head. The man grinned back. Buddy stirred. Vicki remembered the emergency chocolate bar she kept in her purse, fished it out, and offered it to Buddy. He did not react, so she closed his fingers over the package and peeled the paper off one end.

The car accelerated. Buddy felt the road and wheels pummeling each other and the rush of the heavy motor purring in high gear. Buddy knew that what he'd seen in his mind that morning, the thing coming out of the sky with barbs and chains, had hooked him. Somehow he was caught and held in the sour tin smell of the pale woman's armpit. Somehow he was pinned between their pounds of breathless flesh. He looked at the chocolate in his hand. He was squeezing the bar so hard that a thin brown trickle had melted down his arm. Automatically, he put the bar in his mouth.

As he bit down he saw his mother very clearly, just as she had been when she carried him from the shed. She was stretched flat on the ground, on her stomach, and her arms were curled around her head as if in sleep. One leg was drawn up and it looked for all the world like she was running full tilt into the ground, as though she had been trying to pass into the earth, to bury herself, but at the last moment something had stopped her.

There was no blood on Albertine, but Buddy tasted blood now at the sight of her, for he bit down hard and cut his own lip. He ate the chocolate, every bit of it, tasting his mother's blood. And when he had the chocolate down inside him and all licked off his hands, he opened his mouth to say thank you to the woman, as his mother had taught him. But instead of a thank you coming out he was astonished to hear a great rattling scream, and then another, rip out of him like pieces of his own body and whirl onto the sharp things all around him.

Responding to the Story

1. **LITERARY LENS** Using a two-column chart like the one below, list the characters, images, and attitudes in this story that represent Native American culture on one side and non-Indian culture on the other. Then write a statement that summarizes the relationship between the two cultures.

Native American Culture	Non-Indian Culture

2. Reread pages 383–384 in which Vicki Koob records details about Uncle Lawrence's dwelling. What do the details she writes down tell you about her?

3. The focus of the narrative shifts several times between Buddy, Albertine, and Vicki Koob. Why do you think the author shifts the narrative focus in this way?

4. Obviously, Buddy's family has its share of problems. In what ways does it work well nonetheless?

5. **THE AUTHOR'S STYLE** Read the quotation below. To use Erdrich's own words, how does "American Horse" rise, break, and fall?

Everything Into a Story

The people in our families made everything into a story . . . . People just sit and the stories start coming, one after another . . . I suppose that when you grow up constantly hearing the stories rise, break and fall, it gets into you somehow.

—Louise Erdrich, *Writer's Digest*

E. L. Doctorow
1931

About the Author

E. L. Doctorow grew up in New York, where he attended Bronx High School of Science. He recalls, "I had no business being there. I was no good in science or math and was completely out of step with the other kids ... so I drifted toward the school's literary magazine." It was there that he published his first fiction and poetry.

He went on to graduate from Kenyon College in Ohio and attend Columbia University, then worked in publishing as senior editor for the New American Library and editor-in-chief at Dial Press.

After a move to California, he published his third novel, *The Book of Daniel*, in 1971. It firmly established him as a major writer. He is also known for *Ragtime*, a novel in which actual figures from American history mingle with characters of his own creation. Published in 1975, it has been made into a film and musical. In *Writers on Writing* he is quoted as saying, "Good writing is supposed to evoke sensation in the reader—not the fact that it's raining but the feeling of being rained upon."

✴✴✴✴✴✴✴✴✴✴✴

The Author's Style

In many of his novels, the best known of which is probably *Ragtime*, Doctorow has illuminated what it means to succeed (or to try to succeed) in America. His characters are often preoccupied with money, property, social status, and other aspects of the American Dream. The unrecognized, unacknowledged tensions that lie beneath the surface of American life are central to Doctorow's purpose in writing. To reveal these tensions he often makes use of coincidence, highlights ironic connections between characters, and creates characters who are anxious to break free from the restrictions imposed by family or culture.

Doctorow develops character not only through description, but also by means of dialogue. He is adept at rendering the idiom, accent, and verbal gestures of his characters. This is a way of both making them come to life as individuals and marking them as members of specific families, ethnic groups, or social classes. Like Eudora Welty, Bobbie Ann Mason, and Raymond Carver, one of his interests as a writer is how family members communicate with one another.

LITERARY LENS Doctorow and other contemporary writers sometimes write *metafiction*, which is a fictional piece that contains within it a comment about, or reference to, the process of writing fiction. Watch for elements of metafiction in this story.

THE
WRITER
IN THE
FAMILY

E. L. DOCTOROW

n 1955 my father died with his ancient mother still alive in a nursing home. The old lady was ninety and hadn't even known he was ill. Thinking the shock might kill her, my aunts told her that he had moved to Arizona for his bronchitis. To the immigrant generation of my grandmother, Arizona was the American equivalent of the Alps, it was where you went if you had the money. Since my father had failed in all the business enterprises of his life, this was the aspect of the news my grandmother dwelled on, that he had finally had some success. And so it came about that as we mourned him at home in our stocking feet, my grandmother was bragging to her cronies about her son's new life in the dry air of the desert.

My aunts had decided on their course of action without consulting us. It meant neither my mother nor my brother nor I could

My brother Harold and I didn't mind—it was always a nightmare at the old people's home, where they all sat around staring at us while we tried to make conversation with Grandma. She looked terrible, had numbers of ailments, and her mind wandered.

visit Grandma because we were supposed to have moved west too, a family, after all. My brother Harold and I didn't mind—it was always a nightmare at the old people's home, where they all sat around staring at us while we tried to make conversation with Grandma. She looked terrible, had numbers of ailments, and her mind wandered. Not seeing her was no disappointment either for my mother, who had never gotten along with the old woman and did not visit when she could have. But what was disturbing was that my aunts had acted in the manner of that side of the family of making government on everyone's behalf, the true citizens by blood and the lesser citizens by marriage. It was exactly this attitude that had tormented my mother all her married life. She claimed Jack's family had never accepted her. She had battled them for twenty-five years as an outsider.

A few weeks after the end of our ritual mourning my Aunt Frances phoned us from her home in Larchmont. Aunt Frances was the wealthier of my father's sisters. Her husband was a lawyer, and both of her sons were at Amherst.[1] She had called to say that Grandma was asking why she didn't hear from Jack. I had answered the phone. "You're the writer in the family," my aunt said. "Your father had so much faith in you. Would you mind making up something? Send it to me and I'll read it to her. She won't know the difference."

That evening, at the kitchen table, I pushed my homework aside and composed a letter. I tried to imagine my father's response to his new life. He had never been west. He had never traveled anywhere. In his generation the great journey was from the working class to the professional class. He hadn't managed that either. But he loved New York, where he had been born and lived his life, and he was always discovering new things about it. He especially loved the old parts of the city below Canal Street, where he would find ships' chandlers[2] or firms that wholesaled in spices and teas. He was a sales-

---

1 **Amherst:** Amherst College in Massachusetts, a prestigious private college

2 **chandlers:** retailers who sell specialized items; in this case, items relating to ships

man for an appliance jobber with accounts all over the city. He liked to bring home rare cheeses or exotic foreign vegetables that were sold only in certain neighborhoods. Once he brought home a barometer,[3] another time an antique ship's telescope in a wooden case with a brass snap.

"Dear Mama," I wrote. "Arizona is beautiful. The sun shines all day and the air is warm and I feel better than I have in years. The desert is not as **barren** as you would expect, but filled with wildflowers and cactus plants and peculiar crooked trees that look like men holding their arms out. You can see

barren: lifeless

great distances in whatever direction you turn and to the west is a range of mountains maybe fifty miles from here, but in the morning with the sun on them you can see the snow on their crests."

My aunt called some days later and told me it was when she read this letter aloud to the old lady that the full effect of Jack's death came over her. She had to excuse herself and went out in the parking lot to cry. "I wept so," she said. "I felt such terrible longing for him. You're so right, he loved to go places, he loved life, he loved everything."

SOUTHERN ARIZONA, Maynard Dixon, 1941

We began trying to organize our lives. My father had borrowed money against his insurance and there was very little left. Some commissions were

---

3 **barometer:** an instrument used to measure atmospheric pressure, with the purpose of forecasting the weather

The Writer in the Family   **393**

still due but it didn't look as if his firm would honor them. There was a couple of thousand dollars in a savings bank that had to be maintained there until the estate was settled. The lawyer involved was Aunt Frances' husband and he was very proper. "The estate!" my mother muttered, gesturing as if to pull out her hair. "The estate!" She applied for a job part-time in the admissions office of the hospital where my father's terminal illness had been diagnosed, and where he had spent some months until they had sent him home to die. She knew a lot of the doctors and staff and she had learned "from bitter experience," as she told them, about the hospital routine. She was hired.

I hated that hospital, it was dark and grim and full of tortured people. I thought it was **masochistic** of my mother to seek out a job there, but did not tell her so.

masochistic:
self-punishing

We lived in an apartment on the corner of 175th Street and the Grand Concourse, one flight up. Three rooms. I shared the bedroom with my brother. It was jammed with furniture because when my father had required a hospital bed in the last weeks of his illness we had moved some of the living-room pieces into the bedroom and made over the living room for him. We had to navigate bookcases, beds, a gateleg table,[4] bureaus, a record player and radio console, stacks of 78 albums,[5] my brother's trombone and music stand, and so on. My mother continued to sleep on the convertible sofa in the living room that had been their bed before his illness. The two rooms were connected by a narrow hall made even narrower by bookcases along the wall. Off the hall were a small kitchen and dinette and a bathroom. There were lots of appliances in the kitchen—broiler, toaster, pressure cooker, counter-top dishwasher, blender—that my father had gotten through his job, at cost.[6] A treasured phrase in our house: *at cost*. But most of these fixtures went unused because my mother did not care for them. Chromium[7] devices with timers or gauges that required the reading of elaborate instructions were not for her. They were in part responsible for the awful clutter of our lives and now she wanted to get rid of them. "We're being buried," she said. "Who needs them!"

So we agreed to throw out or sell anything inessential. While I found boxes for the appliances and my brother tied the boxes with twine, my mother

---

4 **gateleg table:** a table with sides that can be raised and supported by moveable legs

5 **78 albums:** records designed to be played at 78 revolutions per minute

6 **at cost:** strictly what it costs to make the product, without fees for labor, taxes, shipping, etc.

7 **chromium:** a metallic element

opened my father's closet and took out his clothes. He had several suits because as a salesman he needed to look his best. My mother wanted us to try on his suits to see which of them could be altered and used. My brother refused to try them on. I tried on one jacket which was too large for me. The lining inside the sleeves chilled my arms and the vaguest scent of my father's being came to me.

"This is way too big," I said.

"Don't worry," my mother said. "I had it cleaned. Would I let you wear it if I hadn't?"

It was the evening, the end of winter, and snow was coming down on the windowsill and melting as it settled. The ceiling bulb glared on a pile of my father's suits and trousers on hangers flung across the bed in the shape of a dead man. We refused to try on anything more, and my mother began to cry.

The ceiling bulb glared on a pile of my father's suits and trousers on hangers flung across the bed in the shape of a dead man. We refused to try on anything more, and my mother began to cry.

"What are you crying for?" my brother shouted. "You wanted to get rid of things, didn't you?"

A few weeks later my aunt phoned again and said she thought it would be necessary to have another letter from Jack. Grandma had fallen out of her chair and bruised herself and was very depressed.

"How long does this go on?" my mother said.

"It's not so terrible," my aunt said, "for the little time left to make things easier for her."

My mother slammed down the phone. "He can't even die when he wants to!" she cried. "Even death comes second to Mama! What are they afraid of, the shock will kill her? Nothing can kill her. She's indestructible! A stake through the heart couldn't kill her!"

When I sat down in the kitchen to write the letter I found it more difficult than the first one. "Don't watch me," I said to my brother. "It's hard enough."

"You don't have to do something just because someone wants you to," Harold said. He was two years older than me and had started at City College; but when my father became ill he had switched to night school and gotten a job in a record store.

"Dear Mama," I wrote. "I hope you're feeling well. We're all fit as a fiddle. The life here is good and the people are very friendly and informal. Nobody wears suits and ties here. Just a pair of slacks and a short-sleeved shirt. Perhaps a sweater in the evening. I have bought into a very successful radio and record business and I'm doing very well. You remember Jack's Electric, my old place on Forty-third Street? Well, now it's Jack's Arizona Electric and we have a line of television sets as well."

I sent that letter off to my Aunt Frances, and as we all knew she would, she phoned soon after. My brother held his hand over the mouthpiece. "It's Frances with her latest review," he said.

"Jonathan? You're a very talented young man. I just wanted to tell you what a blessing your letter was. Her whole face lit up when I read the part about Jack's store. That would be an excellent way to continue."

"Well, I hope I don't have to do this anymore, Aunt Frances. It's not very honest."

Her tone changed. "Is your mother there? Let me talk to her."

"She's not here," I said.

"Tell her not to worry," my aunt said. "A poor old lady who has never wished anything but the best for her will soon die."

I did not repeat this to my mother, for whom it would have been one more in the family anthology of unforgivable remarks. But then I had to suffer it myself for the possible truth it might embody. Each side defended its position with **rhetoric**, but I, who wanted peace, rationalized the snubs and rebuffs each inflicted on the other, taking no stands, like my father himself.

Years ago his life had fallen into a pattern of business failures and missed opportunities. The great debate between his family on one side, and my mother Ruth on the other, was this: who was responsible for the fact that he had not lived up to anyone's expectations?

As to the **prophecies**, when spring came my mother's prevailed. Grandma was still alive.

One balmy Sunday my mother and brother and I took the bus to the Beth El cemetery in New Jersey to visit my father's grave. It was situated on a slight rise. We stood looking over rolling fields embedded with monuments. Here and there processions of black cars wound their way through the lanes, or clusters of people stood at open graves. My father's grave was planted with tiny shoots of evergreen but it lacked a headstone. We had chosen one and paid for it and then the stonecutters had gone on strike. Without a headstone my father did not seem to be honorably dead. He didn't seem to me properly buried.

rhetoric:
convincing words

prophecies:
mystical
predictions

My mother gazed at the plot beside his, reserved for her coffin. "They were always too fine for other people," she said. "Even in the old days on Stanton Street. They put on airs. Nobody was ever good enough for them. Finally Jack himself was not good enough for them. Except to get them things wholesale. Then he was good enough for them."

"Mom, please," my brother said.

"If I had known. Before I ever met him he was tied to his mama's apron strings. And Essie's apron strings were like chains, let me tell you. We had to live where we could be near them for the Sunday visits. Every Sunday, that was my life, a visit to mamaleh.[8] Whatever she knew I wanted, a better apartment, a stick of furniture, a summer camp for the boys, she spoke against it. You know your father, every decision had to be considered and reconsidered. And nothing changed. Nothing ever changed."

She began to cry. We sat her down on a nearby bench. My brother walked off and read the names on stones. I looked at my mother, who was crying, and I went off after my brother.

"Mom's still crying," I said. "Shouldn't we do something?"

"It's all right," he said. "It's what she came here for."

"Yes," I said, and then a sob escaped from my throat. "But I feel like crying too."

My brother Harold put his arm around me. "Look at this old black stone here," he said. "The way it's carved. You can see the changing fashion in monuments—just like everything else."

Somewhere in this time I began dreaming of my father. Not the **robust** father of my childhood, the handsome man with healthy pink skin and brown eyes and a mustache and the thinning hair parted in the middle. My dead father. We were taking him home from the hospital. It was understood that he had come back from death. This was amazing and joyous. On the other hand, he was terribly mysteriously damaged, or, more accurately, spoiled and unclean. He was very yellowed and debilitated by his death, and there were no guarantees that he wouldn't soon die again. He seemed aware of this and his entire personality was changed. He was angry and impatient with all of us. We were trying to help him in some way, struggling to get him home, but something prevented us, something we had to fix, a tattered suitcase that had sprung open, some mechanical thing: he had a car but it wouldn't start; or the car was made of wood; or

robust:
strong, vigorous

---

8 **mamaleh:** Yiddish for "mother"

He loved to walk. When I went walking with him he would say: "Hold your shoulders back, don't slump. Hold your head up and look at the world. Walk as if you meant it!"

his clothes, which had become too large for him, had caught in the door. In one version he was all bandaged and as we tried to lift him from his wheelchair into a taxi the bandage began to unroll and catch in the spokes of the wheelchair. This seemed to be some unreasonableness on his part. My mother looked on sadly and tried to get him to cooperate.

That was the dream. I shared it with no one. Once when I woke, crying out, my brother turned on the light. He wanted to know what I'd been dreaming but I pretended I didn't remember. The dream made me feel guilty. I felt guilty *in* the dream too because my enraged father knew we didn't want to live with him. The dream represented us taking him home, or trying to, but it was nevertheless understood by all of us that he was to live alone. He was this **derelict** back from death, but what we were doing was taking him to some place where he would live by himself without help from anyone until he died again.

derelict: good-for-nothing

At one point I became so fearful of this dream that I tried not to go to sleep. I tried to think of good things about my father and to remember him before his illness. He used to call me "matey." "Hello, matey," he would say when he came home from work. He always wanted us to go someplace—to the store, to the park, to a ball game. He loved to walk. When I went walking with him he would say: "Hold your shoulders back, don't slump. Hold your head up and look at the world. Walk as if you meant it!" As he strode down the street his shoulders moved from side to side, as if he was hearing some kind of cakewalk. He moved with a bounce. He was always eager to see what was around the corner.

The next request for a letter coincided with a special occasion in the house. My brother Harold had met a girl he liked and had gone out with her several times. Now she was coming to our house for dinner. We had prepared for this for days, cleaning everything in sight, giving the house a going-over, washing the dust of disuse from the glasses and good dishes. My mother came home early from work to get the dinner going. We opened the gateleg table in the living room and brought in the kitchen chairs. My mother spread the table with a laundered white cloth and put out her silver. It was the first family occasion since my father's illness.

I liked my brother's girlfriend a lot. She was a thin girl with very straight hair and she had a terrific smile. Her presence seemed to excite the air. It was amazing to have a living breathing girl in our house. She looked around and what she said was: "Oh, I've never seen so many books!" While she and my brother sat at the table my mother was in the kitchen putting the food into serving bowls and I was going from the kitchen to the living room, kidding around like a waiter, with a white cloth over my arm and a high style of service, placing the serving dish of green beans on the table with a flourish. In the kitchen my mother's eyes were sparkling. She looked at me and nodded and mimed the words: "She's adorable!"

My brother suffered himself to be waited on. He was wary of what we might say. He kept glancing at the girl—her name was Susan—to see if we met with her approval. She worked in an insurance office and was taking courses in accounting at City College. Harold was under a terrible strain but he was excited and happy too. He had bought a bottle of Concord-grape wine to go with the roast chicken. He held up his glass and proposed a toast. My mother said: "To good health and happiness," and we all drank, even I. At that moment the phone rang and I went into the bedroom to get it.

"Jonathan? This is your Aunt Frances. How is everyone?"

"Fine, thank you."

"I want to ask one last favor of you. I need a letter from Jack. Your grandma's very ill. Do you think you can?"

"Who is it?" my mother called from the living room.

"OK, Aunt Frances," I said quickly. "I have to go now, we're eating dinner." And I hung up the phone.

"It was my friend Louie," I said, sitting back down. "He didn't know the math pages to review."

The dinner was very fine. Harold and Susan washed the dishes and by the time they were done my mother and I had folded up the gateleg table and put it back against the wall and I had swept the crumbs up with the carpet sweeper. We all sat and talked and listened to records for a while and then my brother took Susan home. The evening had gone very well.

Once when my mother wasn't home my brother had pointed out something: the letters from Jack weren't really necessary. "What is this ritual?" he said, holding his palms up. "Grandma is almost totally blind, she's half deaf and crippled. Does the situation really call for a literary composition? Does it need **verisimilitude**? Would the old lady know the difference if she was read the phone book?

verisimilitude: the appearance of truth

"Then why did Aunt Frances ask me?"

"That is the question, Jonathan. Why did she? After all, she could write the letter herself—what difference would it make? And if not Frances, why not Frances' sons, the Amherst students? They should have learned by now to write."

"But they're not Jack's sons," I said.

"That's exactly the point," my brother said. "The idea is *service*. Dad used to bust his balls getting them things wholesale, getting them deals on things. Frances of Westchester really needed things at cost. And Aunt Molly. And Aunt Molly's husband, and Aunt Molly's ex-husband. Grandma, if she needed an errand done. He was always on the hook for something. They never thought his time was important. They never thought every favor he got was one he had to pay back. Appliances, records, watches, china, opera tickets, any goddamn thing. Call Jack."

"It was a matter of pride to him to be able to do things for them," I said. "To have connections."

"Yeah, I wonder why," my brother said. He looked out the window.

Then suddenly it dawned on me that I was being **implicated**.

implicated: involved; drawn in

"You should use your head more," my brother said.

Yet I had agreed once again to write a letter from the desert and so I did. I mailed it off to Aunt Frances. A few days later, when I came home from school, I thought I saw her sitting in her car in front of our house. She drove a black Buick Roadmaster, a very large clean car with whitewall tires. It was Aunt Frances all right. She blew the horn when she saw me. I went over and leaned in at the window.

"Hello, Jonathan," she said. "I haven't long. Can you get in the car?"

"Mom's not home," I said. "She's working."

"I know that. I came to talk to you."

"Would you like to come upstairs?"

"I can't, I have to get back to Larchmont. Can you get in for a moment, please?"

I got in the car. My Aunt Frances was a very pretty white-haired woman, very elegant, and she wore tasteful clothes. I had always liked her and from the time I was a child she had enjoyed pointing out to everyone that I looked more like her son than Jack's. She wore white gloves and held the steering wheel and looked straight ahead as she talked, as if the car was in traffic and not sitting at the curb.

"Jonathan," she said, "there is your letter on the seat. Needless to say I didn't read it to Grandma. I'm giving it back to you and I won't ever say a word to anyone. This is just between us. I never expected cruelty from you. I never thought you were capable of doing something so deliberately cruel and perverse."

I said nothing.

"Your mother has very bitter feelings and now I see she has poisoned you with them. She has always resented the family. She is a very strong-willed, selfish person."

"No she isn't," I said.

"I wouldn't expect you to agree. She drove poor Jack crazy with her demands. She always had the highest aspirations and he could never fulfill them to her satisfaction. When he still had his store he kept your mother's brother, who drank, on salary. After the war when he began to make a little money he had to buy Ruth a mink jacket because she was so desperate to have one. He had debts to pay but she wanted a mink. He was a very special person, my brother, he should have accomplished something special, but he loved your mother and devoted his life to her. And all she ever thought about was keeping up with the Joneses."

I watched the traffic going up the Grand Concourse. A bunch of kids were waiting at the bus stop at the corner. They had put their books on the ground and were horsing around.

"I'm sorry I have to descend to this," Aunt Frances said. "I don't like talking about people this way. If I have nothing good to say about someone, I'd rather not say anything. How is Harold?"

"Fine."

"Did he help you write this marvelous letter?"

"No."

After a moment she said more softly: "How are you all getting along?"

"Fine."

"I would invite you up for Passover[9] if I thought your mother would accept."

---

9 **Passover:** the Jewish holiday commemorating the Hebrews' freedom from slavery in Egypt

I didn't answer.

She turned on the engine. "I'll say good-bye now, Jonathan. Take your letter. I hope you give some time to thinking about what you've done."

That evening when my mother came home from work I saw that she wasn't as pretty as my Aunt Frances. I usually thought my mother was a good-looking woman, but I saw now that she was too heavy and that her hair was undistinguished.

"Why are you looking at me?" she said.

"I'm not."

> *We* came up with two things, a Victory medal, which my brother said everyone got for being in the service during the Great War, and an astounding sepia photograph of my father and his shipmates on the deck of a ship.

"I learned something interesting today," my mother said. "We may be eligible for a V.A. pension because of the time your father spent in the Navy."

That took me by surprise. Nobody had ever told me my father was in the Navy.

"In World War I," she said, "he went to Webb's Naval Academy on the Harlem River. He was training to be an ensign. But the war ended and he never got his commission."

After dinner the three of us went through the closets looking for my father's papers, hoping to find some proof that could be filed with the Veterans Administration. We came up with two things, a Victory medal, which my brother said everyone got for being in the service during the Great War, and an astounding **sepia** photograph of my father and his shipmates on the deck of a ship. They were dressed in bell-bottoms and T-shirts and armed with mops and pails, brooms and brushes.

sepia:
brown-toned

"I never knew this," I found myself saying. "I never knew this."

"You just don't remember," my brother said.

I was able to pick out my father. He stood at the end of the row, a thin, handsome boy with a full head of hair, a mustache, and an intelligent smiling **countenance**.

countenance:
facial expression

"He had a joke," my mother said. "They called their training ship the S.S.

Constipation because it never moved."

Neither the picture nor the medal was proof of anything, but my brother thought a duplicate of my father's service record had to be in Washington some-

CENTRAL NEVADA, Maynard Dixon, 1941

where and that it was just a matter of learning how to go about finding it.

"The pension wouldn't amount to much," my mother said. "Twenty or thirty dollars. But it would certainly help."

I took the picture of my father and his shipmates and propped it against the lamp at my bedside. I looked into his youthful face and tried to relate it to the Father I knew. I looked at the picture a long time. Only gradually did my eye connect it to the set of Great Sea Novels in the bottom shelf of the bookcase a few feet away. My father had given that set to me: it was uniformly bound in green with gilt lettering and it included works by Melville, Conrad, Victor Hugo and Captain Marryat. And lying across the top of the books, jammed in under the sagging shelf above, was his old ship's telescope in its wooden case with the brass snap.

imperceptive: dense; undiscerning

I thought how stupid, and **imperceptive**, and self-centered I had been never to have understood while he was alive what my father's dream for his life had been.

On the other hand, I had written in my last letter from Arizona—the one that had so angered Aunt Frances—something that might allow me, the writer in the family, to soften my judgment of myself. I will conclude by giving the letter here in its entirety.

> Dear Mama,
>
> This will be my final letter to you since I have been told by the doctors that I am dying.
>
> I have sold my store at a very fine profit and am sending Frances a check for five thousand dollars to be deposited in your account. My present to you, Mamaleh. Let Frances show you the passbook.
>
> As for the nature of my ailment, the doctors haven't told me what it is, but I know that I am simply dying of the wrong life. I should never have come to the desert. It wasn't the place for me.
>
> I have asked Ruth and the boys to have my body cremated and the ashes scattered in the ocean.
>
> Your loving son
> Jack

Responding to the Story

1. **LITERARY LENS** Consider the letters that Jonathan composed as the "writer in the family." What do these letters say about the interplay between lies and the truth in fiction?

2. Explain the conflicts and tensions between the narrator's immediate family and his father's extended family.

3. What feelings are not expressed in the scene on page 395 when the mother encourages her sons to try on their dead father's clothes?

4. Play psychologist for a moment. How would you interpret the dream on pages 397–398?

5. Aunt Frances thinks the final letter Jonathan writes is perverse and cruel. What did you think of it?

6. **THE AUTHOR'S STYLE** A common theme for Doctorow is what it means to succeed, or try to succeed, in America. In what ways was the narrator's father both a failure and a success?

Russell Banks
1940

About the Author

Born in Massachusetts to a working-class family, Russell Banks was the eldest of four children and the first in his family to finish college. He intended to become a plumber like his father until his mother convinced him to go to college and study English. "The idea of being a writer was like the idea of being a butterfly," he has said.

Banks worked as a shoe salesman and window trimmer before becoming an editor, publisher, and writer. A world traveler who has lived in the Caribbean, he is perhaps best known for his novels *Continental Drift* and *Cloudsplitter*, both finalists for the Pulitzer Prize. Later novels *Affliction* and *The Sweet Hereafter* were adapted for the screen, the latter of which won the International Critics Prize at the 1997 Cannes Film Festival.

****

The Author's Style

The fiction of Banks usually involves people who confront bleak economic realities and are desperate for basic necessities and a better life. These characters are often part of conflicts involving race and social class. They are also affected by both their physical surroundings and the darker moods and motives behind human behavior.

Banks' characters are often feisty and resilient, but not particularly talkative or eloquent. They learn from experience about the terrible potential for disaster in everyday life and find themselves waiting, enduring, and trying to heal. Some Banks stories read like contemporary allegories or fables, suggesting broad implications from relatively simple events.

Banks conveys all this through concrete, factual descriptions and unemotional statements. He focuses on the gritty details of the physical world. The close attention he pays to the rough lives of working class Americans has led some readers to compare his writing to that of other writers, including Raymond Carver, Bobbie Ann Mason, and Tobias Wolff.

LITERARY LENS A *fable* is a brief tale featuring fantastic events meant to convey a useful truth or to satirize human foibles. Political satirists have been known to hide criticism of political leaders within a fable. Watch for elements of the fable in this unusual short story.

THE
FISH

Russell Banks

When Colonel Tung's first attempt to destroy the fish failed, everyone, even the Buddhists, was astonished. On the colonel's orders, a company of soldiers under the command of a young lieutenant named Han marched out from the village early one summer morning as far as the bridge. Departing from the road there, the soldiers made their way in single file through the bamboo groves and shreds of golden mist to a clearing, where they stepped with care over spongy ground to the very edge of the pond, which was then the size of a soccer field. Aiming automatic weapons into the water, the troopers waited for the fish to arrive. A large crowd from the village gathered behind them and, since most of the people were Buddhists, **fretted** and scowled at the soldiers, saying, "Shame! Shame!" Even some Catholics from the village joined the scolding, though it had been their complaints that first

fretted:
pestered

407

had drawn the colonel's attention to the existence of the huge fish and had obliged him to attempt to destroy it, for pilgrimages to view the fish had come to seem like acts of opposition to his administration. In great numbers, the Buddhists from other districts were visiting the Buddhists in his district, sleeping in local homes, buying food from local vendors, and trading goods of various kinds, until it had begun to seem to Colonel Tung that there were many more Buddhists in his district than Catholics, and this frightened him. Thus his opinion that the pilgrimages to view the fish were acts of political opposition, and thus his determination to destroy the fish.

Shortly after the soldiers lined up at the shore, the fish broke the surface of the water halfway across the pond. It was a silver swirl in the morning sun, a clean swash of movement, like a single brushstroke, for the fish was thought to be a reincarnation of Rad, the painter, an early disciple of Buddha. The soldiers readied their weapons. Lieutenant Han repeated his order: "Wait until I say to fire," he said, and there was a second swirl, a lovely arc of silver bubbles, closer to shore this time. The crowd had gone silent. Many were moving their lips in prayer; all were straining to see over and around the line of soldiers at the shore. Then there it was, a few feet out and hovering in the water like a cloud in the sky, one large dark eye watching the soldiers as if with curiosity, delicate fins fluttering gently in the dark water like **translucent** leaves. "Fire!" the lieutenant cried. The soldiers obeyed, and their weapons roared for what seemed a long time. The pond erupted and boiled in white fury, and when finally the water was still once again, everyone in the crowd rushed to the shore and searched for the remains of the fish. Even the lieutenant and his band of soldiers pushed to the mud at the edge of the water and looked for the fish, or what everyone thought would be chunks of the fish floating on the still surface of the pond. But they saw nothing, not a scrap of it, until they noticed halfway across the pond a swelling in the water, and the fish rolled and dove, sending a wave sweeping in to shore, where the crowd cried out

> Then there it was, a few feet out and hovering in the water like a cloud in the sky, one large dark eye watching the soldiers as if with curiosity, delicate fins fluttering gently in the dark water like translucent leaves. "Fire!" the lieutenant cried.

translucent: see-through

joyfully and the soldiers and the young lieutenant cursed, for they knew that Colonel Tung was not going to like this, not at all.

They were correct. Colonel Tung took off his sunglasses and glared at the lieutenant, then turned in his chair to face the electric fan for a moment. Finally, replacing his glasses, he said, "Let us assume .that in that pond an enemy submarine is surfacing at night to send spies and saboteurs[1] into our midst. Do you have the means to destroy it?" He tapped a cigarette into an ebony holder and lighted it. The lieutenant, like the colonel a man trained at

> *L*et us assume that in that pond an enemy submarine is surfacing at night to send spies and saboteurs into our midst. Do you have the means to destroy it?"

the academy but rapidly adapting his skills to life in the provinces, said yes, he could destroy such an enemy. He would mine the pond, he said, and detonate the mines from shore. "Indeed," the colonel said. "That sounds like a fine idea," and he went back to work.

From a rowboat, the soldiers placed in the pond ten pie-sized mines connected by insulated wires to one another and to a detonator and battery, and when everything was ready and the area had been cleared of civilians, Lieutenant Han set off the detonator from behind a mound of earth they had heaped up for this purpose. There was a deep, convulsive rumble and the surface of the pond blew off, causing a wet wind that had the strength of a gale[2] and tore leaves from the trees and bent the bamboo stalks to the ground. Immediately after the explosion, everyone from the village who was not already at the site rushed to the pond and joined the **throng** that encircled it. Everything that had ever lived in or near the pond seemed to be dead and floating on its surface—carp, crayfish, smelts, catfish, eels, tortoises, frogs, egrets, woodcocks, peccaries, snakes, feral dogs, lizards, doves, shellfish and all the plants from the bottom, the long grasses, weeds, and reeds, and the banyans, mangroves and other trees rooted in the water and the flowering bushes and the lilies that had floated on the surface of the pond—everything once alive seemed dead. Many people wept openly, some prayed, burned incense, chanted, and others, more practical, rushed about with baskets, gathering up the unexpected harvest. The lieutenant and his soldiers walked

throng: crowd

---

1 **saboteurs:** those who intend to sabotage, or damage

2 **gale:** a strong wind

*S*oon the settlement surrounding the pond was as large as the village where the colonel's district headquarters was located. Naturally, this alarmed the colonel, for these pilgrims were Buddhists, many of them fanatics, and he, a Catholic, was no longer sure he could rule them.

intently around the pond, searching for the giant fish. When they could not find it, they rowed out to the middle of the pond and searched there. But still, amongst the hundreds of dead fish and plants, birds and animals floating in the water, they saw no huge silver fish, no carcass that could justify such carnage. Then, as they began to row back toward shore, the lieutenant, who was standing at the bow, his hand shading his eyes from the milky glare of the water, saw before them once again the rolling, shiny side of the giant fish, its dorsal fin like a black knife slicing **obliquely** across their bow, when it disappeared, only to reappear off the stern[3] a ways, swerving back and suddenly heading straight at the small, crowded boat. The men shouted in fear, and at the last possible second the fish looped back and dove into the dark waters below. The crowd at the shore had seen it, and a great cheer went up, and in seconds there were drums and cymbals and all kinds of song joining the cheers, as the soldiers rowed slowly, glumly, in to shore.

obliquely: diagonally

The reputation of the fish and its miraculous powers began to spread rapidly across the whole country, and great flocks of believers undertook pilgrimages to the pond, where they set up tents and booths on the shore. Soon the settlement surrounding the pond was as large as the village where the colonel's district headquarters was located. Naturally, this alarmed the colonel, for these pilgrims were Buddhists, many of them fanatics, and he, a Catholic, was no longer sure he could rule them. "We must destroy that fish," he said to the lieutenant, who suggested this time that he and his soldiers pretend to join the believers and scatter pieces of bread over the waters to feed the fish, as had become the custom. They would do this from the boat, he said, and with specially sweetened chunks of bread, and when the fish was used to being fed this way and approached the boat carelessly close, they

---

3 **stern:** the rear end of a boat

would lob hand grenades painted white as bread into the water, and the fish, deceived, would swallow one or two or more whole, as it did the bread, and that would be that. Colonel Tung admired the plan and sent his man off to **implement** it instantly. Lieutenant Han's inventiveness surprised the colonel and pleased him, though he foresaw problems, for if the plan worked, he would be obliged to promote the man, which would place Han in a position where he could begin to **covet** his superior's position as district commander. This damned fish, the colonel said to himself, may be the worst thing to happen to me.

It soon appeared that Lieutenant Han's plan was working, for the fish, which seemed recently to have grown to an even more gigantic size than before and was now almost twice the size of the boat, approached the boat without fear and rubbed affectionately against it, or so it seemed, whenever the soldiers rowed out to the middle of the pond and scattered large chunks of bread, which they did twice a day. Each time, the fish gobbled the chunks, cleared the water entirely and swam rapidly away. The throng on shore cheered, for they, too, had taken the bait—they believed that the soldiers,

implement:
carry out

covet:
envy; desire

RETURN TO THE BEGINNING, IN MEMORY OF GINGER, Joseph Raffael, 1981

"If this time we succeed in destroying the fish," a soldier said, "the people may not let us get back to shore. There are now thousands of them, Catholics as well as Buddhists, and but ten of us."

under the colonel's orders, had come to appreciate the fish's value to the district as a whole, to Catholics as much as to Buddhists, for everyone, it seemed, was profiting from its presence—tentmakers, carpenters, farmers, storekeepers, clothiers, woodchoppers, scribes, entrepreneurs of all types, entertainers, even, musicians and jugglers, and of course the manufacturers of altars and religious images and also of paintings and screens purported to have been made by the original Rad, the artist and early disciple of Buddha, now reincarnated as the giant fish.

balked:
hesitated;
refused

When finally Lieutenant Han gave the order to float the specially prepared grenades out with the bread, several soldiers **balked**. They had no objections to blowing up the fish, but they were alarmed by the size of the crowd now more or less residing on the shore and, as usual, watching them in hopes of seeing the fish surface to feed. "If this time we succeed in destroying the fish," a soldier said, "the people may not let us get back to shore. There are now thousands of them, Catholics as well as Buddhists, and but ten of us." The lieutenant pointed out that the crowd had no weapons and they had automatic rifles that could easily clear a path from the shore to the road and back to the village. "And once the fish is gone, the people will go away, and things will settle back into their normal ways again." The soldiers took heart and proceeded to drop the grenades into the water with an equal number of chunks of bread. The fish, large as a house, had been lurking peacefully off the stern of the boat and now swept past, swooping up all the bread and the grenades in one huge swallow. It turned away and rolled, exposing its silver belly to the sun, as if in gratitude, and the crowd cried out in pleasure. The music rose, with drums, cymbals, flutes joining happily and floating to the sky on swirling clouds of incense, while the soldiers rowed furiously for shore. The boat scraped gravel, and the troopers jumped out, dragged the boat up onto the mud and made their way quickly through the throng toward the road. As they reached the road, they heard the first of the explosions, then the others in rapid succession, a tangled knot of bangs as all the grenades went off, in the air, it seemed, out of the water and certainly not inside the fish's belly. It was as if the fish were spitting the grenades out just as they were about to explode, creating the effect of a fireworks display above the pond, which must have been what caused the people gathered at the shore to break into sustained, **awestruck** applause and then, long into the day and the following night, song.

awestruck: amazed; reverential

Now the reputation of the miraculous fish grew **tenfold**, and busloads of pilgrims began to arrive from as far away as Saigon and Bangkok. People on bicycles, on donkeys, in trucks and in oxcarts made their way down the dusty road from the village to the pond, where as many of them as could find a spot got down to the shore and prayed to the fish for help, usually against disease and injury, for the fish was thought to be especially effective in this way. Some prayed for wealth or for success in love or for revenge against their enemies, but these requests were not thought likely to be answered, though it surely did no harm to try. Most of those who came now took away with them containers filled with water from the pond. They arrived bearing bowls, buckets, fruit tins, jars, gourds, even cups, and they took the water with them back to their homes in the far corners of the country, where many of them were able to sell off small vials of the water for surprisingly high prices to those unfortunate neighbors and loved ones unable to make the long overland journey to the pond. Soldiers, too, whenever they passed through Colonel Tung's district, came to the pond and filled their canteens with the magical waters. More than once a helicopter landed on the shore, and a troop of soldiers jumped out, ran to the pond, filled their canteens and returned to the helicopter and took off again. Thus, when Lieutenant Han proposed to Colonel Tung that this time they try to destroy the fish by poisoning the water in the pond, the colonel demurred. "I think that instead of trying to kill the fish, we learn how to profit from it ourselves. It's too dangerous now," he observed, "to risk offending the people by taking away what has become their main source of income. What I have in mind, my boy, is a levy, a tax on the water that is taken away from this district. A modest levy, not enough to discourage the pilgrims, but more than enough to warrant the efforts and costs of collection." The colonel smiled slyly and set his lieutenant to the task. There will be no promotions now, he said to himself, for there are no heroics in tax collecting.

tenfold: ten times

And so a sort of calm and orderliness settled over the district, which pleased everyone, Colonel Tung most of all, but also Lieutenant Han, who managed to collect the tax on the water so effectively that he was able without detection to cut a small percentage out of it for himself, and the soldiers, who felt much safer collecting taxes than trying to destroy a miraculous and beloved fish, and the people themselves, who, because they now paid a fee for the privilege of taking away a container of pond water, no longer doubted the water's magical power to cure illness and injury, to let the blind see, the lame walk, the deaf hear, the dumb talk. The summer turned into fall, the fall became winter, and there were no changes in the district, until the spring, when it became obvious to everyone that the pond was much smaller in diameter than it had been in previous springs. The summer rains that year were heavy, though not unusually so, and the colonel hoped that afterwards the pond would be as large as before, but it was not. In September, when the dry season began, the colonel tried to restrict the quantity of water taken from the pond. This proved impossible, for by now too many people had too many reasons to keep on taking water away. A powerful black market operated in several cities, and at night tanker trucks edged down to the shore, where they sucked thousands of gallons of water out, and the next morning the surface of the pond would be yet another foot lower than before and encircling it would be yet another mud aureole[4] inside the old shoreline.

At last there came the morning when the pond was barely large enough to hold the fish. The colonel, wearing sunglasses, white scarf, and cigarette holder, and Lieutenant Han and the soldiers and many of the pilgrims walked across the drying mud to the edge of the water, where they lined up around the tiny pool, little more than a puddle now, and examined the fish. It lay on its side, half exposed to the sun. One gill, blood-red inside, opened and closed, but no water ran through. One eye was above water, one below, and the eye above was clouded over and fading to white. A pilgrim who happened to be carrying a pail leaned down, filled his pail and splashed the water over the side of the fish. Another pilgrim with a gourd joined him, and two soldiers went back to the encampment and returned with a dozen containers of various types and sizes, which they distributed to the others, even including the colonel. Soon everyone was dipping his container into the water and splashing it over the silvery side of the huge, still fish. By midday, however, the sun had evaporated most of the water, and the containers were filled with more mud than moisture, and by sunset they had buried the fish.

---

4 **aureole:** ring; circle

Responding to the Story

1. **LITERARY LENS** The moral of this fable is not summarized at the end, as in more traditional fables. How would you state the moral of this tale? If it works for you, try using Banks' satirical tone in stating your moral.

2. The fish means different things to different people and groups. Using a chart like the one below, summarize what the fish means to those listed. Then answer the question for yourself: What does the fish mean to you?

Person or Group	Meaning
The colonel	*The fish is a threat because it attracts Buddhists to the area of control.*
The pilgrims	
The soldiers	

3. What shortcomings of humankind does this story reveal?

4. The time and place of this story is kept somewhat vague but many of the details point to Vietnam during the 20th century. Taking this into consideration, answer the following question: What possible meaning might the tale have if the setting were the Vietnam War?

5. **THE AUTHOR'S STYLE** At times, "The Fish" has a surreal (intense, irrational, and dreamlike) quality. Find examples of events in the story that could not happen in real life. How do these surreal passages contribute to the story?

****

Garrison Keillor
1942

About the Author

Garrison Keillor grew up in small-town Minnesota, part of a large family that belonged to a fundamentalist church called The Plymouth Brethren. After attending the University of Minnesota, where he studied English, Keillor used his small-town, Midwestern background in his radio work. In 1974, he began the radio show *A Prairie Home Companion* for Minnesota Public Radio as a Saturday afternoon variety show. The show focuses on Lake Wobegon, a town Keillor made up, modeling its oddball characters and small town rituals and landmarks after the people and places with which he grew up.

Keillor's writing career stemmed in part from the leisurely monologues he delivered on the show, which began to be broadcast nationally in 1980. He is the author of several novels and volumes of short stories, not all of them focused on Lake Wobegon. *Lake Wobegon Days*, however, is one of his best-known books. His signature line is, "That's the news from Lake Wobegon, where all the women are strong, the men are good-looking, and all the children are above average."

****

The Author's Style

Keillor's stories about his fictional hometown of Lake Wobegon, Minnesota, are written in the American comic tradition of Mark Twain. Like Twain's writing in *Huckleberry Finn*, the stories ask us to consider the meanings of family and home. Keillor's people are a little "above average" yet far from perfect. Almost always they are forgivable and endearing. His comic wit is honest but sympathetic.

    Keillor presents the citizens of Lake Wobegon as quirky individuals who are ultimately familiar as character types—stubborn, quietly proud, modestly talented, and tied to habits and traditions like everyone else.

    In fact, the controlling metaphor for Keillor's stories is Lake Wobegon itself. The out-of-the-way community represents much of America in its need for comforting rituals and the company of friends who understand each other's odd behavior. Lake Wobegon people are often quiet, but occasionally just blurt out a chunk of what they think in language that is simple, straightforward, and not nessarily grammatically correct. Keillor's anecdotal style is characterized by simple sentences based on subject-verb constructions, and compound sentences created by adding a comma and a clarifying phrase. The sentences often add up to paragraph-long lists of down-to-earth observations and opinions that seem hard for anyone to dispute.

LᴵᵀᴇRARY LENS Keillor is a legendary storyteller on the radio program *Prairie Home Companion*. His weekly stories, of which "Truckstop" is an example, usually focus on the lives of ordinary people from the fictional town of Lake Wobegon in rural Minnesota. Watch for ways he develops the two main characters of this story.

TRUCKSTOP

GARRISON KEILLOR

t has been a quiet week in Lake Wobegon. Florian and Myrtle Krebsbach left for Minneapolis on Tuesday, a long haul for them. They're no spring chickens, and it was cold and raining, and he hates to drive anyway. His eyesight is poor and his '66 Chev only has 47,000 miles on her, just like new, and he's proud of it. But Myrtle had to go down for a checkup. She can't get one from Dr. DeHaven or the doctors in Saint Cloud because she's had checkups from them recently and they say she is all right. She is pretty sure she might have cancer. She reads "Questions and Answers on Cancer" in the paper and has seen symptoms there that sound familiar, so when she found a lump on the back of her head last week and noticed blood on her toothbrush, she called a clinic in Minneapolis, made an appointment,

BURGER CHEF, Ralph Goings, 1970

and off they went. He put on his good carcoat and a clean Pioneer Seed Corn cap, Myrtle wore a red dress so she would be safe in Minneapolis traffic. He got on Interstate 94 in Avon and headed south at forty miles an hour, hugging the right side, her clutching her purse, peering out of her thick glasses, semis blasting past them, both of them upset and scared, her about brain tumors, him about semis. Normally she narrates a car trip, reading billboards, pointing out interesting sights, but not now. When they got beyond the range of the "Rise 'N Shine" show, just as Bea and Bob were coming to the "Swap 'N Shop" feature, a show they've heard every morning for thirty years, they felt awful, and Florian said, "If it was up to me, I'd just as soon turn around and go home."

It was the wrong thing to say, with her in the mood she was in, and she was expecting him to say it and had worked up a speech in her mind in case he did. "Well, of course. I'm sure you would rather turn around. You don't care. You don't care one tiny bit, and you never have, so I'm not surprised that you don't now. You don't care if I live or die. You'd probably just as soon I died right now. That'd make you happy, wouldn't it? You'd just clap your hands if I died. Then you'd be free of me, wouldn't you—then you'd be free to go off and do your dirty business, wouldn't you."

Florian, with his '66 Chev and 47,003 miles on it, wouldn't strike most people as a candidate for playboyhood, but it made sense to her—forty-eight years of marriage and she had finally figured him out, the rascal. She wept. She blew her nose.

He said, "I would too care if you died."

She said, "Oh yeah, how much? You tell me."

Florian isn't good at theoretical questions. After a couple minutes she said, "Well, I guess that answers *my* question. The answer is, you don't care a bit."

It was his idea to stop at the truckstop, he thought coffee would calm him down, and they sat and drank a couple cups apiece, and then the pie looked good so they had some, banana cream and lemon meringue, and more coffee. They sat by the window, not a word between them, watching the rain fall on the gas pumps. They stood up and went and got in the car, then he decided to use the men's room. While he was gone, she went to the ladies' room. And while she was gone, he got in behind the wheel, started up, checked the side mirror, and headed out on the freeway. Who knows how this sort of thing happens, he just didn't notice, his mind was on other things, and Florian is a man who thinks slowly so he won't have to go back and think it over again. He was still thinking about how much he'd miss her if she was gone, how awful he'd feel, how empty the house would be with him lying alone in bed at night, and all those times when you want to turn to someone and say, "You won't believe what happened to me," or "Did you read this story in the newspaper about the elk in Oregon?" or "Boy, Johnny Carson is looking old, ain't he? And Ed[1] too," and she wouldn't be there for him to point this out to—and he turned to tell her how much he'd miss her and she wasn't there. The seat was empty. You could have knocked him over with a stick.

He took his foot off the gas and coasted to a stop. He hadn't noticed her crawl into the backseat, but he looked and she wasn't there. She hadn't jumped—he would've noticed that. (Wouldn't he?) It couldn't've been angels taking her away. He thought of the truckstop. He was a good ways from there, he knew that. He must've gone twenty miles. Then, when he made a U-turn, he noticed he wasn't on the freeway anymore. There was no median strip. He was on a Highway 14, whatever that was.

He drove a few miles and came to a town named Bolivia. He never knew there was a Bolivia, Minnesota, but there it was. Went into a Pure Oil station, an old man was reading a Donald Duck comic book. Florian asked, "How far to the Interstate?" He didn't look up from his comic. A pickup came in, the bell dinged, the old man kept reading. Florian went down the street into a café, Yaklich's Café, and asked the woman where the Interstate was. She said,

---

1 **Johnny Carson . . . Ed:** the host of *The Tonight Show*, from 1962 until 1992, and his sidekick, Ed McMahon

Truckstop   **419**

The waitress said, "You mean the lady in the blue coat?" Florian didn't remember what color Myrtle's coat was. He wasn't sure exactly how to describe her except as *real mad*, probably.

"Oh, that's nowheres around here."

"Well, it must be," he said, "I was just on it. I just came from there."

"Oh," she says, "that's a good ten miles from here."

"Which way?"

"East, I think."

"Which way's east?"

"What way you come in?"

"That way!"

"That way is northeast. You want to go that way and then a little southeast when you get to the Y in the road. Then keep to your left. It's about two miles the other side of that old barn with Red Man on the side. Red Man Chewing Tobacco. On your left. You'll see it."

There was a funny look about her: her eyes bulged, and her lips were purplish. Her directions weren't good either. He drove that way and never saw the barn, so he turned around and came back and looked for the barn on the right side, but no barn, so he headed back to Bolivia, but Bolivia wasn't there anymore. It was getting on toward noon.

It was four o'clock before he ever found the truckstop. He had a long time to think up something to tell Myrtle, but he still had no idea what to say. But she wasn't there anyway. The waitress said, "You mean the lady in the blue coat?" Florian didn't remember what color Myrtle's coat was. He wasn't sure exactly how to describe her except as *real mad*, probably. "*Ja*, that's the lady in the blue coat," she said. "Oh, she left here hours ago. Her son came to get her."

Florian sat and had a cup of coffee and a piece of apple pie. "Can you tell me the quickest way to get to Lake Wobegon from here?" he asked. "Lake what?" she said. "I never heard of it. It can't be around here."

But it was, not too far away, and once he got off the freeway he found his way straight home, although it was dark by then. He stopped at the Sidetrack for a quick bump. He felt he owed it to himself after all he'd been through and what with what he was about to go through. "Where's the old lady?" asked Wally. "Home, waiting for me," he said.

He headed south and saw his house, and kept going. Carl's pickup was in the driveway and he couldn't see facing the both of them. He parked on the crossroad and sat, just beyond Roger Hedlund's farm, where he could watch his house. It was dark except a light was on in the kitchen and one in the bathroom. Roger's house was lit up. What if Roger should see him and come out to investigate? Out there in the country, a parked car stands out more than a little bit, you might as well be towing a searchlight behind you. It's considered unusual for a man to sit in his car in the evening on a crossroad an eighth of a mile from his own house, just sit there. If Roger came out, Florian thought he'd explain that he was listening to the radio and it was a Lutheran show so the old lady wouldn't have it in the house—Roger was Lutheran, he'd like that.

He ducked down as a car came slowly past, its headlights on high beam. The preacher on the radio might be Lutheran, he didn't know. It sure wasn't the Rosary. The man was talking about sinners who had wandered away from the path, and it seemed to Florian to fit the situation. "Broad is the road that leadeth to destruction, and narrow is the path of righteousness"—that seemed to be true too, from what he knew of freeways. The preacher mentioned forgiveness, but Florian wasn't sure about that. He wondered what this preacher would do if *he* had forgotten his wife at a truckstop and gotten lost; the preacher knew a lot about forgiveness theoretically but what would he do in Florian's situation? A woman sang, "Softly and tenderly Jesus is calling, calling for you and for me. See by the portals he's waiting and watching. Calling, O sinner come home."

Come home, come home—
Ye who are weary come home.

Florian felt weary. Seventy-two is old to get yourself in such a ridiculous situation. He waited as long as he could for Carl to leave, and then the coffee inside him reached the point of no return and he started up the engine. Taking a leak in another man's field: he drew the line at that. He turned on his headlights, and right when he did he saw Carl's headlights far away light up and the beams swung around across the yard and Carl headed back toward town.

Florian coasted up his driveway with the headlights out. He still did not have a speech ready. He was afraid. He also had to pee. Outside, on the porch, he smelled supper: breaded fish fillets. He was surprised that the door was unlocked—they never have locked it but he thought she might if she thought he was coming.

He hung up his coat in the mud room and looked around the corner. She was at the stove, her back to him, stirring something in a pan. He cleared his throat. She turned. She said, "Oh thank God." She dropped the spoon on the floor and ran to him on her old legs and said, "Oh Daddy, I was so scared. Oh Daddy, don't ever leave me again. I'm sorry I said what I did. I didn't mean it. I didn't mean to make you so angry at me. Don't leave me again like that."

Tears came to his eyes. To be so welcome—in his own home. He was about to tell her that he hadn't left her, he'd forgotten her; then she said, "I love you, Daddy. You know that."

He was going to tell her, but he didn't. It occurred to him that leaving her on account of passionate anger might be better than forgetting her because of being just plain dumb. There wasn't time to think this through clearly. He squeezed her and whispered, "I'm sorry. I was wrong. I promise you that I'll never do a dumb thing like that again."

She felt good at supper and put on the radio; she turned it up when she heard "The Saint Cloud Waltz." *Sometimes I dream of a mansion afar but there's no place so lovely as right where we are, here on a planet that's almost a star, we dance to the Saint Cloud Waltz.* That night he lay awake, **incredulous**. That she thought he was capable of running away, like a John Barrymore or something. Seventy-two years old, married forty-eight years, and she thought that maybe it hadn't worked out and he might fly the coop like people do in songs? Amazing woman. He got up at six o'clock, made scrambled eggs and sausage and toast, and felt like a new guy. She felt better too. The lump on her head felt like all the other lumps and there was no blood on her toothbrush. She said, "I wonder if I hadn't ought to call down there about that appointment." "Oh," he said, "I think by now they must know you're all right."

incredulous:
disbelieving

Responding to the Story

1. LITERARY LENS Select a detail from the story that reveals the character of either Florian or Myrtle Krebsbach. Explain how the detail helps you understand who this character is.

2. What three words would you use to describe the relationship between the couple?

3. Why does Florian park down the road from his farmhouse when he finally gets home?

4. Keillor is a homespun humorist, gently satirizing, while at the same time honoring, the very believable characters he creates. What is the basis of the humor in this story?

5. Garrison Keillor's work has often been compared to that of Mark Twain. From what you know about Twain, do you find this to be a good comparison? Explain.

6. THE AUTHOR'S STYLE Keillor tells his radio stories in a relaxed, anecdotal style. An *anecdote* is a minor incident that is told because it is interesting, amusing, or makes a good point. There are many linked anecdotes in this story. Find one and tell why you think it was included.

Amy Tan
1952

About the Author

Born in California to Chinese immigrant parents, Amy Tan wore a clothespin on her nose as a teenager in hopes of making it slimmer. She also hoped to have plastic surgery one day to make herself look more Western. As she matured, however, her Chinese heritage became an honored and important part of her work.

When Tan was an adolescent, both her brother and father died of brain tumors. Following the deaths, Tan, her mother, and her other brother moved to Switzerland, where she went to high school and found that the Swiss were more interested in her Asian heritage than her fellow Americans had been. After graduation she attended college back home in California and began work as a freelance writer. The short story you are about to read was originally written so that she could be accepted into a writer's workshop at Squaw Valley in California. Eventually it became part of her novel *The Joy Luck Club,* which won the National Book Award in 1989 and was made into a movie in 1993. In her free time, Tan sings in a garage band, The Rock Bottom Remainders, with novelist Stephen King and columnist Dave Barry; the group raises money for literacy and first amendment rights groups.

****

The Author's Style

The interaction between Chinese immigrant and American cultures is a key concern of Tan's fiction. She is particularly interested in the impact this interaction has on individuals and families. An important focus is the mother-daughter relationship, especially the conflicts that arise from the relationship between culture and gender. Her young characters often struggle with what it means to be a Chinese American girl.

As Tan shows us through family dialogue, the effectiveness of mother-daughter communication often depends upon how well mothers and daughters use language themselves and how well they listen to each other. Both the mothers and the daughters attempt to express their identities by establishing their voices and stories within the family. Tan is particularly adept at capturing the choppy, uneven English of immigrant mothers and the breezy, California speech of their daughters. In *The Joy Luck Club* she accomplishes this by conveying their first person points of view in alternating sections.

Tan incorporates into her fiction the ways in which people work out what it might mean to be "American" and which set of "rules" ought to be followed. Her stories explore everyday aspects of culture such as food, language, and dating, showing how these can become the focus of tension and conflict. Characters in her stories often seem ambivalent about both cultures.

LITERARY LENS Consider the meaning of the title as you read.

Rules
of the
Game

Amy Tan

was six when my mother taught me the art of invisible strength. It was a strategy for winning arguments, respect from others, and eventually, though neither of us knew it at the time, chess games.

"Bite back your tongue," scolded my mother when I cried loudly, yanking her hand toward the store that sold bags of salted plums. At home, she said, "Wise guy, he not go against the wind. In Chinese we say, Come from South, blow with wind— poom!—North will follow. Strongest wind cannot be seen."

The next week I bit back my tongue as we entered the store with the forbidden candies. When my mother finished her shopping, she quietly plucked a small bag of plums from the rack and put it on the counter with the rest of the items.

My mother imparted her daily truths so she could help my older brothers and me rise above our circumstances. We lived in San Francisco's Chinatown. Like most of the other Chinese children who played in the back alleys of restaurants and curio shops,[1] I didn't think we were poor. My bowl was always full, three five-course meals every day, beginning with a soup of mysterious things I didn't want to know the names of.

We lived on Waverly Place, in a warm, clean, two-bedroom flat that sat above a small Chinese bakery specializing in steamed pastries and dim sum.[2] In the early morning, when the alley was still quiet, I could smell fragrant red beans as they were cooked down to a pasty sweetness. By daybreak, our flat was heavy with the odor of fried sesame balls and sweet curried chicken crescents. From my bed, I would listen as my father got ready for work, then locked the door behind him, one-two-three clicks.

At the end of our two-block alley was a small sandlot playground with swings and slides well-shined down the middle with use. The play area was bordered by wood-slat benches where old-country people sat cracking roasted watermelon seeds with their golden teeth and scattering the husks to an impatient gathering of gurgling pigeons. The best playground, however, was the dark alley itself. It was crammed with daily mysteries and adventures. My brothers and I would peer into the medicinal herb shop, watching old Li dole out onto a stiff sheet of white paper the right amount of insect shells, saffron-colored seeds, and pungent leaves for his ailing customers. It was said that he once cured a woman dying of an ancestral curse that had eluded the best of American doctors. Next to the pharmacy was a printer who specialized in gold-embossed wedding invitations and festive red banners.

Farther down the street was Ping Yuen Fish Market. The front window displayed a tank crowded with doomed fish and turtles struggling to gain footing on the slimy green-tiled sides. A hand-written sign informed tourists, "Within this store, is all for food, not for pet." Inside, the butchers with their bloodstained white smocks deftly gutted the fish while customers cried out their orders and shouted, "Give me your freshest," to which the butchers always protested, "All are freshest." On less crowded market days, we would inspect the crates of live frogs and crabs which we were warned not to poke, boxes of dried cuttlefish,[3] and row upon row of iced prawns,[4] squid, and

---

1 **curio shops:** shops containing novelty and gift items

2 **dim sum:** a variety of traditional Chinese foods

3 **cuttlefish:** 10-armed fish that are related to squid

4 **prawns:** large shrimp

slippery fish. The sanddabs[5] made me shiver each time; their eyes lay on one flattened side and reminded me of my mother's story of a careless girl who ran into a crowded street and was crushed by a cab. "Was smash flat," reported my mother.

At the corner of the alley was Hong Sing's, a four-table café with a recessed stairwell in front that led to a door marked "Tradesmen." My brothers and I believed the bad people emerged from this door at night. Tourists never went to Hong Sing's, since the menu was printed only in Chinese. A Caucasian man with a big camera once posed me and my playmates in front of the restaurant. He had us move to the side of the picture window so the photo would capture the roasted duck with its head dangling from a juice-covered rope. After he took the picture, I told him he should go into Hong Sing's and eat dinner. When he smiled and asked me what they served, I shouted, "Guts and duck's feet and octopus gizzards!" Then I ran off with my friends, shrieking with laughter as

GIRL WITH BANGS, Mary Heussenstamm

we scampered across the alley and hid in the entryway grotto of the China Gem Company, my heart pounding with hope that he would chase us.

My mother named me after the street that we lived on: Waverly Place Jong, my official name for important American documents. But my family called me Meimei, "Little Sister." I was the youngest, the only daughter. Each morning before school, my mother would twist and yank on my thick black hair until she had formed two tightly wound pigtails. One day, as she struggled to weave a hard-toothed comb through my disobedient hair, I had a sly thought.

I asked her, "Ma, what is Chinese torture?" My mother shook her head. A bobby pin was wedged between her lips. She wetted her palm and

---

5 **sanddabs:** fish that are a type of flounder

smoothed the hair above my ear, then pushed the pin in so that it nicked sharply against my scalp.

"Who say this word?" she asked without a trace of knowing how wicked I was being. I shrugged my shoulders and said, "Some boy in my class said Chinese people do Chinese torture."

"Chinese people do many things," she said simply. "Chinese people do business, do medicine, do painting. Not lazy like American people. We do torture. Best torture."

My older brother Vincent was the one who actually got the chess set. We had gone to the annual Christmas party held at the First Chinese Baptist Church at the end of the alley. The missionary ladies had put together a Santa bag of gifts donated by members of another church. None of the gifts had names on them. There were separate sacks for boys and girls of different ages.

One of the Chinese parishioners had donned a Santa Claus costume and a stiff paper beard with cotton balls glued to it. I think the only children who thought he was the real thing were too young to know that Santa Claus was not Chinese. When my turn came up, the Santa man asked me how old I was. I thought it was a trick question; I was seven according to the American formula and eight by the Chinese calendar. I said I was born on March 17, 1951. That seemed to satisfy him. He then solemnly asked if I had been a very, very good girl this year and did I believe in Jesus Christ and obey my parents. I knew the only answer to that. I nodded back with equal **solemnity**.

solemnity: seriousness; earnestness

Having watched the older children opening their gifts, I already knew that the big gifts were not necessarily the nicest ones. One girl my age got a large coloring book of biblical characters, while a less greedy girl who selected a smaller box received a glass vial of lavender toilet water. The sound of the box was also important. A ten-year-old boy had chosen a box that jangled when he shook it. It was a tin globe of the world with a slit for inserting money. He must have thought it was full of dimes and nickels, because when he saw that it had just ten pennies, his face fell with such undisguised disappointment that his mother slapped the side of his head and led him out of the church hall, apologizing to the crowd for her son who had such bad manners he couldn't appreciate such a fine gift.

As I peered into the sack, I quickly fingered the remaining presents, testing their weight, imagining what they contained. I chose a heavy, compact one that was wrapped in shiny silver foil and a red satin ribbon. It was a twelve-pack of Life Savers and I spent the rest of the party arranging and rearranging the candy tubes in the order of my favorites. My brother Winston chose wisely as well. His present turned out to be a box of intricate plastic parts; the instructions on the box proclaimed that when they were properly assembled he would have an authentic miniature replica of a World War II submarine.

Vincent got the chess set, which would have been a very decent present to get at a church Christmas party, except it was obviously used and, as we discovered later, it was missing a black pawn and a white knight. My mother graciously thanked the unknown benefactor, saying, "Too good. Cost too much." At which point, an old lady with fine white, wispy hair nodded toward our family and said with a whistling whisper, "Merry, merry Christmas."

Vincent at first refused to let me play, but when I offered my Life Savers as replacements for the buttons that filled in for the missing pieces, he relented.

When we got home, my mother told Vincent to throw the chess set away. "She not want it. We not want it," she said, tossing her head stiffly to the side with a tight, proud smile. My brothers had deaf ears. They were already lining up the chess pieces and reading from the dog-eared instruction book.

I watched Vincent and Winston play during Christmas week. The chessboard seemed to hold elaborate secrets waiting to be untangled. The chessmen were more powerful than old Li's magic herbs that cured ancestral curses. And my brothers wore such serious faces that I was sure something was at stake that was greater than avoiding the tradesmen's door to Hong Sing's.

"Let me! Let me!" I begged between games when one brother or the other would sit back with a deep sigh of relief and victory, the other annoyed, unable to let go of the outcome. Vincent at first refused to let me play, but when I offered my Life Savers as replacements for the buttons that filled in for the missing pieces, he relented. He chose the flavors: wild cherry for the black pawn and peppermint for the white knight. Winner could eat both.

As our mother sprinkled flour and rolled out small doughy circles for the steamed dumplings that would be our dinner that night, Vincent explained the rules, pointing to each piece. "You have sixteen pieces and so do I. One king and queen, two bishops, two knights, two castles, and eight pawns. The pawns can only move forward one step, except on the first move. Then they can move two. But they can only take men by moving crossways like this, except in the beginning, when you can move ahead and take another pawn."

"Why?" I asked as I moved my pawn. "Why can't they move more steps?"

"Because they're pawns," he said.

"But why do they go crossways to take other men? Why aren't there any women and children?"

"Why is the sky blue? Why must you always ask stupid questions?" asked Vincent. "This is a game. These are the rules. I didn't make them up. See. Here in the book." He jabbed a page with a pawn in his hand. "Pawn. P-A-W-N. Pawn. Read it yourself."

My mother patted the flour off her hands. "Let me see book," she said quietly. She scanned the pages quickly, not reading the foreign English symbols, seeming to search deliberately for nothing in particular.

"This American rules," she concluded at last. "Every time people come out from foreign country, must know rules. You not know, judge say, Too bad go back. They not telling you why so you can use their way go forward. They say, Don't know why, you find out yourself. But they knowing all the time. Better you take it, find out why yourself. But they knowing all the time. Better you take it, find out why yourself. She tossed her head back with a satisfied smile.

I found out about all the whys later. I read the rules and looked up all the big words in a dictionary. I borrowed books from the Chinatown library. I studied each chess piece, trying to absorb the power each contained.

I learned about opening moves and why it's important to control the center early on; the shortest distance between two points is straight down the middle. I learned about the middle game and why tactics between two **adversaries** are like clashing ideas; the one who plays better has the clearest plans for both attacking and getting out of traps. I learned why it is essential in the endgame to have foresight, a mathematical understanding of all possible moves, and patience; all weaknesses and advantages become evident to a strong adversary and are **obscured** to a tiring opponent. I discovered that for the whole game one must gather invisible strengths and see the endgame before the game begins.

I also found out why I should never reveal "why" to others. A little knowledge withheld is a great advantage one should store for future use. That

adversaries:
opponents

obscured:
concealed

is the power of chess. It is a game of secrets in which one must show and never tell.

I loved the secrets I found within the sixty-four black and white squares. I carefully drew a handmade chessboard and pinned it to the wall next to my bed, where I would stare for hours at imaginary battles. Soon I no longer lost any games or Life Savers, but I lost my adversaries. Winston and Vincent decided they were more interested in roaming the streets after school in their Hopalong Cassidy cowboy hats.

On a cold spring afternoon, while walking home from school, I detoured through the playground at the end of our alley. I saw a group of old men, two seated across a folding table playing a games of chess, others smoking pipes, eating peanuts, and watching. I ran home and grabbed Vincent's chess set, which was bound in a cardboard box with rubber bands. I also carefully selected two prized rolls of Life Savers. I came back to the park and approached a man who was observing the game.

"Want to play?" I asked him. His face widened with surprise and he grinned as he looked at the box under my arm.

"Little sister, been a long time since I play with dolls," he said, smiling **benevolently**. I quickly put the box down next to him on the bench and displayed my **retort**.

Lau Po, as he allowed me to call him, turned out to be a much better player than my brothers. I lost many games and many Life Savers. But over the weeks, with each diminishing roll of candies, I added new secrets. Lau Po gave me the names. The Double Attack from the East and West Shores. Throwing Stones on the Drowning Man. The Sudden Meeting of the Clan. The Surprise from the Sleeping Guard. The Humble Servant Who Kills the King. Sand in the Eyes of Advancing Forces. A Double Killing Without Blood.

There were also the fine points of chess **etiquette**. Keep captured men in neat rows, as well-tended prisoners. Never announce "Check" with vanity, **lest** someone with an unseen sword slit your throat. Never hurl pieces into the sandbox after you have lost a game, because then you must find them again, by yourself, after apologizing to all around you. By the end of the summer, Lau Po had taught me all he knew, and I had become a better chess player.

A small weekend crowd of Chinese people and tourists would gather as I played and defeated my opponents one by one. My mother would join the

benevolently:
kindly

retort:
sharp reply

etiquette:
manners; protocol

lest:
for fear that

crowds during these outdoor exhibition games. She sat proudly on the bench, telling my admirers with proper Chinese humility, "Is luck."

A man who watched me play in the park suggested that my mother allow me to play in local chess tournaments. My mother smiled graciously, an answer that meant nothing. I desperately wanted to go, but I bit back my tongue. I knew she would not let me play among strangers. So as we walked home I said in a small voice that I didn't want to play in the local tournament. They would have American rules. If I lost, I would bring shame on my family.

"Is shame you fall down nobody push you," said my mother.

During my first tournament, my mother sat with me in the front row as I waited for my turn. I frequently bounced my legs to unstick them from the cold metal seat of the folding chair. When my name was called, I leapt up. My mother unwrapped something in her lap. It was her *chang*, a small tablet of red jade which held the sun's fire. "Is luck," she whispered, and tucked it into my dress pocket. I turned to my opponent, a fifteen-year-old boy from Oakland. He looked at me, wrinkling his nose.

As I began to play, the boy disappeared, the color ran out of the room, and I saw only my white pieces and his black ones waiting on the other side. A light wind began blowing past my ears. It whispered secrets only I could hear.

"Blow from the South," it murmured. "The wind leaves no trail." I saw a clear path, the traps to avoid. The crowd rustled. "Shhh! Shhh!" said the corners of the room. The wind blew stronger. "Throw sand from the East to distract him." The knight came forward ready for the sacrifice. The wind hissed, louder and louder. "Blow, blow, blow. He cannot see. He is blind now. Make him lean away from the wind so he is easier to knock down."

"Check," I said, as the wind roared with laughter. The wind died down to little puffs, my own breath.

My mother placed my first trophy next to a new plastic chess set that the neighborhood Tao society had given to me. As she wiped each piece with a soft cloth, she said, "Next time win more, lose less."

"Ma, it's not how many pieces you lose," I said. "Sometimes you need to lose pieces to get ahead."

"Better to lose less, see if you really need."

At the next tournament, I won again, but it was my mother who wore the triumphant grin.

"Lost eight piece this time. Last time was eleven. What I tell you? Better off lose less!" I was annoyed, but I couldn't say anything.

I attended more tournaments, each one farther away from home. I won all games, in all divisions. The Chinese bakery downstairs from our flat displayed my growing collection of trophies in its window, amidst the dust-covered cakes that were never picked up. The day after I won an important regional tournament, the window encased a fresh sheet cake with whipped-cream frosting and red script saying "Congratulations, Waverly Jong, Chinatown Chess Champion." Soon

The day they took the magazine picture I wore neatly plaited braids clipped with plastic barrettes trimmed with rhinestones. I was playing in a large high school auditorium that echoed with phlegmy coughs and the squeaky rubber knobs of chair legs sliding across freshly waxed wooden floors.

after that, a flower shop, headstone engraver, and funeral parlor offered to sponsor me in national tournaments. That's when my mother decided I no longer had to do the dishes. Winston and Vincent had to do my chores.

"Why does she get to play and we do all the work," complained Vincent.

"Is new American rules," said my mother. "Meimei play, squeeze all her brains out for win chess. You play, worth squeeze towel."

By my ninth birthday, I was a national chess champion. I was still some 429 points away from grand-master status, but I was **touted** as the Great American Hope, a child prodigy and a girl to boot. They ran a photo of me in *Life* magazine next to a quote in which Bobby Fischer said, "There will never be a woman grand master." "Your move, Bobby," said the caption.

touted: acclaimed

The day they took the magazine picture I wore neatly plaited braids clipped with plastic barrettes trimmed with rhinestones. I was playing in a large high school auditorium that echoed with phlegmy coughs and the squeaky rubber knobs of chair legs sliding across freshly waxed wooden floors. Seated across from me was an American man, about the same age as Lau Po, maybe fifty. I remember that his sweaty brow seemed to weep at my every move. He wore a dark, **malodorous** suit. One of his pockets was stuffed with a great white kerchief on which he wiped his palm before sweeping his hand over the chosen chess piece with great flourish.

malodorous: foul-smelling

In my crisp pink-and-white dress with scratchy lace at the neck, one of two my mother had sewn for these special occasions, I would clasp my hands under my chin, the delicate points of my elbows poised lightly on the table in the manner my mother had shown me for posing for the press. I would swing my patent leather shoes back and forth like an impatient child riding on a school bus. Then I would pause, suck in my lips, twirl my chosen piece in midair as if undecided, and then firmly plant it in its new threatening place, with a triumphant smile thrown back at my opponent for good measure.

I no longer played in the alley of Waverly Place. I never visited the playground where the pigeons and old men gathered. I went to school, then directly home to learn new chess secrets, cleverly concealed advantages, more escape routes.

But I found it difficult to concentrate at home. My mother had a habit of standing over me while I plotted out my games. I think she thought of herself as my protective **ally**. Her lips would be sealed tight, and after each move I made, a soft "Hmmmmph" would escape from her nose.

ally: supporter; collaborator

"Ma, I can't practice when you stand there like that," I said one day. She retreated to the kitchen and made loud noises with the pots and pans. When the crashing stopped, I could see out of the corner of my eye that she was standing in the doorway. "Hmmmmph!" Only this one came out of her tight throat.

My parents made many concessions to allow me to practice. One time I complained that the bedroom I shared was so noisy that I couldn't think. Thereafter, my brothers slept in a bed in the living room facing the street. I said I couldn't finish my rice; my head didn't work right when my stomach was too full. I left the table with half-finished bowls and nobody complained. But there was one duty I couldn't avoid. I had to accompany my mother on Saturday market days when I had no tournament to play. My mother would proudly walk with me, visiting many shops, buying very little. "This is my daughter Wave-ly Jong," she said to whoever looked her way.

One day after we left a shop I said under my breath, "I wish you wouldn't do that, telling everybody I'm your daughter." My mother stopped walking. Crowds of people with heavy bags pushed past us on the sidewalk, bumping into first one shoulder, then another.

"Aiii-ya. So shame be with mother?" She grasped my hand even tighter as she glared at me.

I looked down. "It's not that, it's just so obvious. It's just so embarrassing."

"Embarrass you be my daughter?" Her voice was cracking with anger.

"That's not what I meant. That's not what I said."

"What you say?"

I knew it was a mistake to say anything more, but I heard my voice speaking, "Why do you have to use me to show off? If you want to show off, then why don't you learn to play chess?"

My mother's eyes turned into dangerous black slits. She had no words for me, just sharp silence.

I felt the wind rushing around my hot ears. I jerked my hand out of my mother's tight grasp and spun around, knocking into an old woman. Her bag of groceries spilled to the ground.

"Aii-ya! Stupid girl!" my mother and the woman cried. Oranges and tin cans **careened** down the sidewalk. As my mother stooped to help the old woman pick up the escaping food, I took off.

careened: swayed

I raced down the street, dashing between people, not looking back as my mother screamed shrilly, "Meimei! Meimei!" I fled down an alley, past dark, curtained shops and merchants washing the grime off their windows. I sped into the sunlight, into a large street crowded with tourists examining trinkets and souvenirs. I ducked into another dark alley, down another street, up another alley. I ran until it hurt and I realized I had nowhere to go, that I was not running from anything. The alleys contained no escape routes.

My breath came out like angry smoke. It was cold. I sat down on an upturned plastic pail next to a stack of empty boxes, cupping my chin with my hands, thinking hard. I imagined my mother, first walking briskly down one street or another looking for me, then giving up and returning home to await my arrival. After two hours, I stood up on creaking legs and slowly walked home.

The alley was quiet and I could see the yellow lights shining from our flat like two tiger's eyes in the night. I climbed the sixteen steps to the door, advancing quietly up each so as not to make any warning sounds. I turned the knob; the door was locked. I heard a chair moving, quick steps, the locks turning—click! click! click!—and then the door opened.

"About time you got home," said Vincent. "Boy, are you in trouble."

He slid back to the dinner table. On a platter were the remains of a large fish, its fleshy head still connected to bones swimming upstream in vain

escape. Standing there waiting for my punishment, I heard my mother speak in a dry voice.

"We not concerning this girl. This girl not having concerning for us."

Nobody looked at me. Bone chopsticks clinked against the inside of bowls being emptied into hungry mouths.

I walked into my room, closed the door, and lay down on my bed. The room was dark, the ceiling filled with shadows from the dinnertime lights of neighboring flats.

In my head, I saw a chessboard with sixty-four black and white squares. Opposite me was my opponent, two angry black slits. She wore a triumphant smile. "Strongest wind cannot be seen," she said.

Her black men advanced across the plane, slowly marching to each successive level as a single unit. My white pieces screamed as they scurried and fell off the board one by one. As her men drew closer to my edge, I felt myself growing light. I rose up into the air and flew out the window. Higher and higher, above the alley, over the tops of tiled roofs, where I was gathered up by the wind and pushed up toward the night sky until everything below me disappeared and I was alone.

I closed my eyes and pondered my next move.

GRANT AVENUE
1992
Martin Wong

Responding to the Story

1. LITERARY LENS Besides chess, to what might "Rules of the Game" refer?

2. Why do you think the author spends so much time describing San Francisco's Chinatown before she gets into the action of the story?

3. What are some of the ways Waverly attempts to establish her identity?

4. Which mother-daughter problems depicted in the story are common in all cultures, and which are more specifically Chinese American?

5. Using a chart like the one below, list the ways Tan reveals the differences and similarities of the two main characters in this story—Waverly and her Chinese-born mother. Consider dialogue, motivation, and any other elements of characterization you might find.

Characterization	Waverly	Waverly's Mother
Dialogue		
Motivation		

6. THE AUTHOR'S STYLE In conventional plots, the conflict is resolved one way or another by the end of the story. In this story, however, the plot remains unresolved. Why do you think Tan leaves the story so open-ended?

Experiencing

1. Consider "The Sky Is Gray," "Everything Stuck to Him," and "American Horse." What is your reaction to realistic fiction that explores social problems such as alcoholism, racism, and divorce?

2. Success is a common theme in literature. Using the point of view of the father in "The Writer in the Family" and the mother in "Rules of the Game," write two definitions of success in America.

Interpreting

3. The solitary walk is the basis of many stories. On a deeper level, the solitary walk represents a rite of passage from childhood to maturity. Consider "The Flowers" and "The Key"—two stories in which the main character takes a solitary walk. Using a chart like the one below, compare the two journeys.

Main Character	The Key	The Flowers
State before walk		
What she encounters		
How she is changed		

4. In both "Everything Stuck to Him" and "Detroit Skyline, 1949," a seemingly ordinary event triggers a moment of clarity. Pinpoint when the moment occurs in each story, and interpret what the impact is on the character.

5. What elements in a story that examines a social problem distinguish it from a treatise or piece of propaganda on the same topic?

Evaluating

6. The style and subject matter of O'Brien has been compared to that of Hemingway, whom you read in the first unit. Whose style do you find more appealing and why?

7. The guardian angel is an important image in "Detroit Skyline, 1949" in this unit and in "Angel Levine" in the previous unit. Compare and contrast the way this symbol is handled in the two stories.

WRITING ABOUT THE LITERATURE

The Real vs. the Fantastic

Realism and fantasy literature are often pitted against each other. Realism is often considered depressing; fantasy is often considered escapist. Consider one of the realistic stories you have read so far, such as "The Sky Is Gray" or "He," and one of the stories with elements of fantasy, such as "The Fish" or "The Veldt." Write a persuasive essay that tells which one you feel best succeeds at conveying its message.

WRITING WITH STYLE

Choose one of these two assignments:

Are we there yet?

In the style of "Detroit Skyline, 1949" write an account of a trip taken in your own growing up years. As Bobbie Ann Mason does, use details such as TV shows, songs, or historical incidents to evoke the era of your story.

The Keillor Style

Keillor's anecdotal style often relies on simple sentences based on subject-verb constructions and compound sentences with clarifying phrases. Consider this example.

A pickup came in, the bell dinged, the old man kept reading.
Florian went down the street into a café, Yaklich's Café,
and asked the woman there where the interstate was.

Create your own Keilloresque sentences by filling in the blanks in the pattern below.

A __noun__ __verb__, the __noun__ __verb__, the __noun__ __verb__.
__Noun__ __verb__ __prepositional phrase__ __qualifying phrase__,
__conjunction__ __verb__ __noun__ __verb phrase__.

★★

IN YOUR OWN STYLE

Try your own hand at realistic literature by writing a fictional scene that deals with a social issue or an "ism"—for example, racism, sexism, ageism, war, or poverty.

UNIT FOUR

LITERATURE FROM THE 1990s

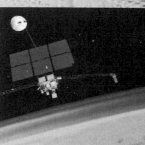

Literature from the 1990s

The 1990s provided an opportunity to look back on the 20th century and forward to a new millennium. In a scenario that was eerily reminiscent of the fallout shelter mania of the sixties, there were doomsday predictions that the turn of the century would cause a worldwide computer-related meltdown. The last days of 1999 found some Americans stocking up on water, food, and cash—unnecessarily, as it turned out. The frenzy heightened an awareness that the world is a global village.

In the nineties the technological revolution thrived, demonstrating that international communication, commerce, technology, and travel make all of us citizens not just of the countries we live in, but of the world. That realization intensified in the waning years of the century when violence seemed to be on the rise internationally—hijackings, car bombings, terrorist attacks. New versions of old conflicts and increasingly sophisticated kinds of warfare signaled that for better or worse, we are all in this together.

All of this imposed a new kind of anxiety on contemporary life. American writers such as Paul Theroux and Robert Olen Butler told stories of American characters as they made their way around the world. These authors confirmed that the personal and local are never far removed from the national and international. Meanwhile, writers reflected on the worldwide marketing of American products and popular culture. Millions around the world became consumers of a wide range of American products, from hamburgers to television sitcoms to vacation cruises. Even as the world's largest shopping mall, The Mall of America, was erected in Minnesota in 1992 with 400 stores and a full-sized Ferris wheel, American writers were asking questions about the integrity and stability of a consumer culture that was constantly reinventing itself and touting new products.

top to bottom:
The breakup of the Soviet Union continued into the 1990s. Russians, intent on moving in new directions, cast out Mikhail Gorbachev in favor of Boris Yeltsin, who became the first elected president of the Russian Federation. ★ Tensions grew in the Middle East, especially between Israelis and Palestinians. ★ 1995: Firefighter Chris Fields, with the body of a child in his arms, symbolized the tragedy of the Murrah Federal Building bombing in Oklahoma City.

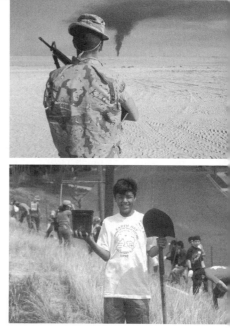

Although television and interstates homogenized America in some ways, writers were more aware than ever of living in a diverse democratic culture, especially as immigrants flooded into the country in record numbers. From Louisiana to Lake Wobegon, writers examined what it meant to be a man or woman belonging to a particular race or social class. Writer Sherman Alexie used an irreverent tone to remind readers that a rich Native American culture existed long before the mainstream American culture evolved. He and others used points of view outside the white middle-class majority, nudging readers to look at America through different lenses.

At the same time, writers such as Joyce Carol Oates and T. Coraghessan Boyle carried on the time-honored tradition of Edgar Allan Poe by mesmerizing readers with nightmarish and grotesque tales set in all too familiar settings. In contrast, writers of realistic everyday life such as Andre Dubus, Barbara Kingsolver, and Tobias Wolff continued to work in the tradition of John Steinbeck, Katherine Anne Porter, and John Updike. It was clear that morality and ethics were still fundamental concerns.

Whatever their styles, writers of the short story in the 1990s often focused on how people behave at specific moments, and whether or not they treat each other with dignity and respect. Although Americans may still be too close to this decade to make conclusions about its literature, it seems clear that an overall theme was how to live a life that matters in a world turned upside down.

top to bottom: Talk show host Oprah Winfrey with her friend and mentor, the author Maya Angelou. ★ 1991–95: The breakup of the former Yugoslavia caused prolonged conflict over territory, ethnicity, and religion. ★ 1991: A U.S. soldier on patrol during the Persian Gulf War. The war, which lasted less than two months, was in response to Iraq's invasion of its neighbor, Kuwait. ★ Concern over the environment continued to grow, especially among young people. ★ 1990: The Hubble Space Telescope was launched and began its remarkable quest to unlock the secrets of the universe.

Joyce Carol Oates
1938

About the Author

Born in Lockport, New York, to a middle-class family, Joyce Carol Oates submitted her first manuscript for publication when she was 15. It was rejected, but at the age of 25 she published a collection of short stories, *By the North Gate*. Since then she has produced a flood of novels, stories, poems, and critical essays, averaging two or three books a year. Oates' speed is linked to her belief that much rewriting is avoidable and unnecessary.

Among her more important novels are *A Garden of Earthly Delights*, *THEM* (winner of a National Book Award) and *Do With Me What You Will*. A frequent contributor to periodicals such as *The New York Times*, Oates has also written suspense novels under the pseudonym Rosamond Smith. She teaches at Princeton University.

****

The Author's Style

One of the most prolific contemporary American writers, Oates often writes in the romantic tradition represented in American literature as early as the work of Edgar Allan Poe. Like Poe's tales, Oates' stories often develop from gothic situations involving hostile environments or isolated individuals. Her characters exhibit distorted physical or psychological extremes, and they often succumb to impulses and perversions that lead to dread and violence. Oates has been both criticized and praised for bringing the grotesque into the presumably safe havens of suburban, middle-class America.

The threatening aura of Oates' stories is created through the use of ironic situations, internal monologues that reveal the working of her characters' minds, and the strategy of repeating words and phrases until they become ominous. She uses ellipses (. . .) to lead the reader to the verge of a disastrous event or appalling revelation. In many stories the ironic contrast between what characters believe (or want to believe) and what is actually taking place adds to the level of fear. In "Ladies and Gentlemen:" Oates' use of the second person intensifies a disturbing situation in which the captain seems not only to be addressing the cruise customers directly, but also the reader. The combination of grimness, helplessness, and bitterness turns many of her stories into dark fables.

LITERARY LENS Notice the way the tension builds in this story.

LADIES AND GENTLEMEN:

JOYCE CAROL OATES

adies and gentlemen: A belated but heartfelt welcome aboard our cruise ship S.S. *Ariel*. It's a true honor and a privilege for me, your captain, to greet you all on this lovely sun-warmed January day—as balmy, isn't it, as any June morning back north? I wish I could claim that we of the *Ariel* arranged personally for such splendid weather, as compensation of sorts for the—shall we say—somewhat rocky weather of the past several days. But at any rate it's a welcome omen indeed and bodes well for the remainder of the cruise and for this morning's excursion, ladies and gentlemen, to the island you see us rapidly approaching, a small but remarkably beautiful island the natives of these waters call the Island of Tranquility or, as some translators prefer, the Island of

Repose. For those of you who've become virtual sailors with a keen eye for navigating, you'll want to log our longitude at 155 degrees East and our latitude at 5 degrees North, approximately twelve hundred miles north and east of New Guinea. Yes, that's right! We've come so far! And as this is a rather crucial morning, and your island adventure an important event not only on this cruise but in your lives, ladies and gentlemen, I hope you will quiet just a bit—just a bit!—and give me, your captain, your fullest attention. Just for a few minutes, I promise! Then you disembark.

As to the problems some of you have experienced: let me take this opportunity, as your captain, ladies and gentlemen, to apologize, or at least to explain. It's true for instance that certain of your staterooms are not *precisely* as the advertising brochures depicted them, the portholes are not quite so large; in some cases the portholes are not in evidence. This is not the fault of any of the *Ariel* staff; indeed, this has been a sore point with us for some years, a matter of misunderstandings and embarrassments out of our control, yet I, as your captain, ladies and gentlemen, offer my apologies and my profoundest sympathies. Though I am a bit your junior in age, I can well understand the special disappointment, the particular hurt, outrage, and dismay that attend one's sense of having been cheated on what, for some of you, probably, is perceived as being the last time you'll be taking so prolonged and exotic a trip—thus, my profoundest sympathies! As to the toilets that have been reported as malfunctioning or out of order entirely, and the loud throbbing or "tremors" of the engines that have been keeping some of you awake, and the **negligent** or even rude service, the overcooked or undercooked food, the high tariffs on mineral water, alcoholic beverages, and cigarettes, the reported sightings of rodents, cockroaches, and other vermin on board ship— perhaps I should explain, ladies and gentlemen, that this is the final voyage of the S.S. *Ariel* and it was the owners' decision, and a justifiably **pragmatic** decision, to cut back on repairs, services, expenses, and the like. Ladies and gentlemen, I am sorry for your inconvenience, but the *Ariel is* an old ship, bound for dry dock in Manila and the fate of many a veteran seagoing vessel that has outlived her time. God bless her! We'll not see her likes again!

Ladies and gentlemen, may I have some quiet—please, just five minutes more?—before the stewards help you prepare for your disembarkment? Thank you.

Yes, the *Ariel* is bound for Manila next. But have no fear, you won't be aboard.

negligent:
careless;
inattentive

pragmatic:
practical; expedient

Joyce Carol Oates

Ladies and gentlemen, *please*. This murmuring and muttering begins to annoy.

(Yet, as your captain, I'd like to note that, amid the usual whiners and complainers and the just plain bad-tempered, it's gratifying to see a number of warm, friendly, *hopeful* faces and to know that there are men and women determined to enjoy life, not quibble and harbor suspicions. Thank *you*!)

Now to our business at hand: ladies and gentlemen, do you know what you have in common?

You can't guess?

You *can* guess?

No? Yes?

No?

Well, yes sir, it's true that you are all aboard the S.S. *Ariel*; and yes, sir—excuse me, *ma'am*—it's certainly true that you are all of "retirement" age. (Though "retirement" has come to be a rather vague term in the past decade or so, hasn't it? For the youngest among you are in their late fifties—the result, I would guess, of especially generous early-retirement programs—and the eldest among you are in their mid-nineties. Quite a range of ages!)

Yes, it's true you are all Americans. You have expensive cameras, even in some cases video equipment, for recording this South Seas adventure; you have all sorts of tropical-cruise **paraphernalia**, including some extremely attractive bleached-straw hats; some of you have quite a supply of sun-protective lotions; and most of you have a considerable quantity and variety of pharmacological supplies. And quite a store of paperbacks, magazines, cards, games, and crossword puzzles. Yet there is one primary thing you have in common, ladies and gentlemen, which has determined your presence here this morning, at longitude 155 degrees East and latitude 5 degrees North: your fate, as it were. Can't you guess?

Ladies and gentlemen: *your children*.

Yes, you have in common the fact that this cruise on the S.S. *Ariel* was originally your children's idea and that they arranged for it, if you'll recall. (Though you have probably paid for your own passages, which weren't cheap.) Your children—who are "children" only technically, for of course they are fully grown, fully adult, a good number of them parents themselves (having made you proud grandparents—yes, haven't you been proud!)—these sons and daughters, if I may speak frankly, are *very* tired of waiting for their inheritances.

paraphernalia: gear

Yes, and *very* impatient, some of them, *very* angry, waiting to come into control of what they believe is their due.

Ladies and gentlemen, please! I'm asking for quiet, and I'm asking for respect. As captain of the *Ariel*, I am not accustomed to being interrupted.

I believe you did hear me correctly, sir. And you too, sir.

Yes and you, ma'am. And *you*. (Most of you aren't nearly so deaf as you pretend!)

Let me speak candidly. While your children are in many cases, or at least in some cases, genuinely fond of you, they are simply impatient with the prospect of waiting for your "natural" deaths.

Let me speak **candidly**. While your children are in many cases, or at least in some cases, genuinely fond of you, they are simply impatient with the prospect of waiting for your "natural" deaths. Ten years, fifteen? Twenty? With today's medical technology, who knows; you might outlive *them*!

Of course it's a surprise to you, ladies and gentlemen. It's a *shock*. Thus you, sir, are shaking your head in disbelief, and you, sir, are muttering just a little too loudly, "Who does that fool think he is, making such bad jokes?"—and you, ladies, are giggling like teenaged girls, not knowing what to think. But remember: your children have been living lives of their own, in a very difficult, very competitive corporate America; they are, on the face of it, well-to-do, even affluent; yet they want, in some cases desperately need, *your* estates—not in a dozen years but *now*.

That is to say, as soon as your wills can be probated.

For, however your sons and daughters appear in the eyes of their neighbors, friends, and business colleagues, even in the eyes of their own offspring, you can be sure that *they have not enough money*. You can be sure that they suf-

fer keenly certain financial jealousies and yearnings—and who dares **calibrate** another's suffering? Who dares peer into another's heart? Without betraying anyone's confidence, I can say that there are several youngish men, beloved sons of couples in your midst, ladies and gentlemen, who are nearly bankrupt; men of integrity and "success" whose worlds are about to come tumbling about their heads—unless they get money or find themselves in the position of being able to borrow money against their parents' estates, *fast*. Investment bankers, lawyers, a college professor or two—some of them already in debt. Thus they decided to take severe measures.

Ladies and gentlemen, it's pointless to protest. As captain of the *Ariel*, I merely **expedite** orders.

And you must know that it's pointless to express disbelief or incredulity, to roll your eyes as if *I* (of all people) were a bit cracked, to call out questions or demands, to shout, weep, sob, beg, rant and rave and mutter—"If this is a joke it isn't a very funny joke!" "As if my son/daughter would ever do such a thing to me/us!"—in short, it's pointless to express any and all of the reactions you're expressing, which have been expressed by other ladies and gentlemen on past *Ariel* voyages to the South Seas.

Yes, it's the best thing, to cooperate. Yes, in an orderly fashion. It's wisest not to provoke the stewards (whose nerves are a bit ragged these days—the crew is only human, after all) into using force.

Ladies and gentlemen, these *are* lovely **azure** waters—exactly as the brochures promised!—but shark-infested, so take care.

As, yes, those dorsal fins slicing the waves, just beyond the surf: observe them closely.

No, we're leaving no picnic baskets with you today. Nor any bottles of mineral water, Perrier water, champagne.

For why delay what's inevitable? Why cruelly protract anguish?

Ladies and gentlemen, maybe it's a simple thing, maybe it's a self evident thing, but consider: you are the kind of civilized men and women who brought babies into the world not by crude, primitive, anachronistic chance but by systematic deliberation. You planned your futures; you planned, as the expression goes, your parenthood. You are all of that American economic class called "upper middle"; you are educated, you are cultured, you are stable; nearly without exception, you showered love upon your sons and daughters, who knew themselves, practically in the cradle, privileged. The very best—the most exclusive—nursery schools, private schools, colleges, universities. Expensive toys and gifts of all kinds; closets of clothing, ski equipment, stereo equipment, racing bicycles; tennis lessons, riding lessons, snorkeling lessons, private tutoring, trips to the Caribbean, to Mexico, to Tangier, to Tokyo, to Switzerland; junior years abroad in Paris, in Rome, in London; yes, and their teeth were perfect, or were made to be; yes, and they had cosmetic surgery if necessary, or nearly necessary; yes, and you gladly

paid for their abortions or their tuition for law school, medical school, business school; yes, and you paid for their weddings; yes, and you loaned them money "to get started," certainly you helped them with their mortgages, or their second cars, or their children's orthodontic bills; nothing was too good or too expensive for them, for what, ladies and gentlemen, would it have been?

And always the more you gave your sons and daughters, the more you seemed to be holding in reserve; the more generous you displayed yourself, the more generous you were hinting you might be in the future. But so far in the future—when your wills might be probated, after your deaths.

Ladies and gentlemen, you rarely stopped to consider your children as other than *your* children, as men and women growing into maturity distinct from you. Rarely did you pause to see how patiently they were waiting to inherit their due—and then, by degrees, how impatiently. What anxieties **besieged** them, what nightmare speculations—for what if you squandered your money in medical bills? nursing home bills? the **melancholic impedimenta** of age in America? What if—worse yet!—addle-brained, suffering from Alzheimer's disease (about which they'd been reading suddenly, it seemed, everywhere) you turned against them, disinherited them, remarried someone younger, healthier, more cunning than they, rewrote your wills, as elderly fools are always doing?

Ladies and gentlemen, your children declare that they want only *what's theirs*.

They say laughingly, *they* aren't going to live forever.

(Well, yes: I'll confide in you, off the cuff, in several instances it was an *in-law* who looked into the possibility of a cruise on the S.S. *Ariel*; your own son/daughter merely cooperated, after the fact as it were. Of course, that isn't the same thing!)

Ladies and gentlemen, as your captain, about to bid you farewell, let me say I *am* sympathetic with your plight. Your stunned expressions, your staggering-swaying gait, your damp eyes, working mouths—"This is a bad joke!" "This is intolerable!" "This is a nightmare!" "No child of mine could be so cruel—inhuman—monstrous" et cetera—all this is touching, wrenching to the heart, altogether *natural*. One might almost say *traditional*. Countless others, whose bones you may discover should you have the energy and spirit to explore the Island of Tranquility (or Repose), reacted in more or less the same way.

Thus do not despair, ladies and gentlemen, for your emotions, however painful, are time-honored; but do not squander the few precious remaining hours of your life, for such emotions are futile.

Ladies and gentlemen: the Island of Tranquility upon which you now stand shivering in the steamy morning heat is approximately six kilometers in circumference, ovoid in shape, with a curious archipelago of giant metamorphic rocks trailing off to the north, a pounding hallucinatory surf, and horizon, vague, dreamy, and distant, on all sides. Its soil is an admixture of volcanic ash, sand, rock, and peat; its jungle interior is pocked with treacherous bogs of quicksand.

besieged:
attacked

melancholic:
sad; depressing

impedimenta:
obstacles

habituated: accostomed; used to

ubiquitous: unavoidable; pervasive

iridescent: lustrous; rainbowlike

It *is* a truly exotic island, but fairly quickly most of you will become **habituated** to the ceaseless winds that ease across the island from several directions simultaneously, air intimate and warmly stale as exhaled breaths, caressing, narcotic. You'll become habituated to the **ubiquitous** sand flies, the glittering dragonflies with their eighteen-inch **iridescent** wings, the numerous species of snakes (the small quicksilver orange-speckled *baya* snake is the most venomous, you'll want to know); the red-beaked carnivorous macaw and its ear-piercing shriek; bullfrogs the size of North American jackrabbits; two-hundred-pound tortoises with pouched, intelligent eyes; spider monkeys playful as children; tapirs; tarantulas; and, most colorful of all, the comical cassowary birds with their bony heads, gaily-hued wattles, and stunted wings—these ungainly birds whom millions of years of evolution, on this island lacking mammal predators, have rendered flightless.

And orchids: some of you have already noticed the lovely, bountiful orchids growing everywhere, dozens of species, every imaginable color, some the size of grapes and others the size of a man's head, unfortunately inedible.

And the island's smells, are they fragrances or odors? Is it rampant, fresh-budding life or jungle-rancid decay? Is there a difference?

By night (and the hardiest among you should survive numerous nights, if past history prevails), you'll contemplate the tropical moon, so different from our North American moon, hanging heavy and luminous in the sky like an overripe fruit; you'll be moved to smile at the sport of fiery-phosphorescent fish frolicking in the waves; you'll be lulled to sleep by the din of insects, the cries of nocturnal birds, your own prayers perhaps.

Some of you will cling together, like terrified herd animals; some of you will wander off alone, dazed, refusing to be touched, even comforted, by a spouse of fifty years.

Ladies and gentlemen, I, your captain, speak for the crew of the S.S. *Ariel*, bidding you farewell.

Ladies and gentlemen, your children have asked me to assure you that they *do* love you—but circumstances have intervened.

Ladies and gentlemen, your children have asked me to recall to you those years when they were in fact *children*—wholly innocent as you imagined them, adoring you as gods.

reverential: expressing profound respect

Ladies and gentlemen, I now bid farewell to you as children do, waving goodbye not once but numerous times, solemn, **reverential**. Goodbye, goodbye, goodbye.

Responding to the Story

1. **LITERARY LENS** Satire is a form of literature that exposes and
   condemns human vices. What vice or vices are being satirized
   in this piece?

2. What commentary does this story make on the American upper-
   middle class?

3. A *euphemism* is a figure of speech in which a name or term masks a
   more direct, or brutal, fact. For example, the phrase "senior citizens"
   is a euphemism for "old people." What euphemisms are employed
   in this story and what truth do they mask?

4. Oates' stories often juxtapose the safe, daylight lives of the upper-
   middle class with the dark, nightmarish underside of American life.
   Using a chart such as the one below, list the elements of the
   story as well as aspects of Oates' style that contribute to
   the juxtaposition.

Safe, Daylight Life	Dark, Nightmarish Underside
Retirees are on a cruise	*The cruise ship is decrepit*

5. **THE AUTHOR'S STYLE** An author's style is often related to his or
   her vision of life. Consider the vision of American life presented in
   Oats' satire "Ladies and Gentlemen:." Do you think that this is in any
   way an accurate view of American life? Why or why not?

Barbara Kingsolver
1955

About the Author

Born in Kentucky, Barbara Kingsolver has remained connected to her roots all of her life. The area where she grew up, "in the middle of an alfalfa field," is mentioned in many of her works. From an early age, however, she was a world traveler. Her father was a doctor who took his family along when he practiced medicine in the Congo (now called Zaire) and St. Lucia, a Caribbean island.

Always the keeper of a journal, Kingsolver traveled and studied biology and ecology for several years before writing her first novel. She wrote it in the middle of the night when she was suffering from insomnia during a pregnancy. *The Bean Trees* became a bestseller.

Besides winning many awards herself, Kingsolver has also established a literary award called the Bellwether, which is given to unpublished authors who address issues of social injustice in their writing. She says of her work, "I want an English professor to understand the symbolism while at the same time I want the people I grew up with—who may not often read anything but the Sears catalogue—to read my books."

****

The Author's Style

Kingsolver was born in eastern Kentucky, but has also lived in Indiana and Arizona; she has lived in and written about Africa and the Congo. These experiences and her work as a biological researcher, an archaeologist, and a scientific writer incline her to see multiple points of view. She approaches the human dilemmas that are created by social, political, cultural, and personal differences with generous sympathy.

The emphasis in Kingsolver's fiction is on the personal relationships of families and communities. She focuses particularly on "average" people who find themselves in unusual or extreme situations but use love, endurance, and common sense in working toward solutions. She writes in straightforward, declarative prose, using down-to-earth language and figures of speech. Her particular emphasis is on the lives of girls and women, with female characters combining toughness, humor, and hopefulness to overcome anxiety and fear, especially after some catastrophic experience. They then carry on with their lives sensibly and responsibly. Her sensitive presentation of working-class people has led some readers to compare her writing to that of Bobbie Ann Mason and Russell Banks.

LITERARY LENS See what you can learn from the interior monologue of the main character in this story.

Fault Lines

BARBARA KINGSOLVER

Randall is moving away from his living wife. With the reckless, innocent grace of a liberated animal he scrambles toes-and-hands up the face of a huge rock; this must be Africa because none of the trees look right. The two boys are little and hold onto her hands, watching their father. When he straddles the top, Randall turns around to wave at the three of them. She's about to tell him to be careful, but then he jumps off, just jumps on purpose, as if he means to amuse the boys. It's much too high. His body bounces several times with a dull energy like an old tennis ball. He lies still, and then looks up at her sorrowfully because he knows he's going to die.

SAN FRANCISCO LANDSCAPE, Wayne Thiebaud, 1976

Grace wakes up with her breath quick in her throat. It's exactly 5:00 A.M. She gets up to check on the boys, who are breathing, as they've been doing steadily for more than a decade and will surely continue to do. She wishes she could believe it. Her new friends in California tell her to "trust the universe," but Grace sees nothing trustworthy about the universe; it's full of exploding stars. Randall didn't die in Africa but in Louisville, two miles from home, when a drill bit broke in the machine shop where he worked. His employer called it a freak accident. Grace considers it a freak accident that anyone ever makes it through life in one piece. When the life insurance came through she thought it would help her mind-set to get away from Kentucky, so they moved to Oakland. Now she has earthquakes to consider.

She goes back to bed but sits up against the headboard waiting for the sun to come up and the boys to stir and another day to happen. The blue shirt she hugs around herself is Randall's, going threadbare at the elbows, wearing out without him. Maybe she dreamed of Randall out of guilt, because she's going on her first date tonight. A blind date—the term alone sounds hazardous. A redhead named Fiona in her grieving group is setting

Barbara Kingsolver

Grace up with her brother. Grace would rather pass, but Fiona has that California air of calling everything between here and New York "the Midwest," in a pitying way, and organizing your whole life for you over the phone before you know what's hit you. Fiona also likes to brag that her apartment is located exactly on the San Andreas Fault.

Grace's relatives have reminded her that Kentucky gets earthquakes too—in 1812 one hit that made the Mississippi run backward. "There's nothing new under the sun to worry about," her cousin Rita declared. Grace is amazed at the things people will say, supposedly to be helpful. When she was pregnant, both times, women would stop her in the grocery to describe their own pregnancies, always disastrous. "Don't do what I did," someone actually told her once in frozen foods at Kroger's. "I went into labor in the fifth month and had a boy that's blind and retarded. He's at the Lexington Shriner's Home." Grace was exactly five months along with Jacob then. It was Christmas Eve. She went straight home to bed, not daring to carry in the groceries from the car. When Randall got home the ice cream had melted into a huge puddle in the bottom of the trunk and then refrozen. He tried to make her laugh about it: he called it the Neapolitan skating rink. Randall always trusted the universe. And he ended up with a drill bit in his femoral artery. Grace wipes her eyes on his shirtsleeve. The people in her grieving group say she's in the denial phase, but she's not denying anything. She knows he's dead. She just wishes she could go back and start life over. She'd meet Randall again and they'd move into a safe-deposit box.

In the parking lot after work Grace has an attack of despair. Her job is not the cause. It's a position she secured with the help of her former boss, before moving here: she's a secretary for a company that sells high-pressure liquid chromatography systems to scientists everywhere. She's not clear on what high-pressure liquid chromatography is, but Kareema, the cheeky receptionist who shares the front office, has even less of an idea, and she's been there over a year. "Do I look like a rocket scientist?" she asks Grace.

She doesn't. She looks like an exotic paintbrush. She wears black tights and has dyed her hair fuchsia on the ends and somehow persuades it to reach for the stars. She gives Grace wardrobe tips and tells her she envies her petite figure and undamaged hair. This is one more concern Grace hasn't much considered before: hair damage. When she confided this afternoon that she had a date after work, Kareema offered the loan of her lucky earrings.

So Grace has a pair of little silver snakes biting her earlobes now, but she has no idea what good luck would bring her, if she came into any. She doesn't want to drive to U.C. Berkeley and fall in love tonight. She wants to go home and find Randall in the driveway shooting baskets, missing on purpose so Jacob can win a round of Horse. Puberty is turning Matthew's face into an exact replica of his father's. He'll never even know what they look like, she thinks. When he died they still had preteen baby faces, no jawbones, no real noses yet, just stamped-out cookie dough faces like all kids have till they've lived long enough to reveal their family secrets. She pulls the car off the street and crumples around the pain in her stomach. She thinks of Randall's face in her dream, so pleased, before he jumped. Why Africa? Where is he trying to take her? How can she hold back what happens next? She lies curled on the front seat, staring up at the darkening sky and a neon fish blinking its way to no particular reward. People have told her she's taking his death too personally. She wonders what options she has; if she were a plant, she'd take it like a plant. She sits up again, fixes her eyes, and drives.

> *People have told her she's taking his death too personally. She wonders what options she has; if she were a plant, she'd take it like a plant. She sits up again, fixes her eyes, and drives.*

Fiona's brother Loren turns out to be fortyish and tall, with long black hair and pale blue eyes and a blue tattoo in Chinese that curls around his wrist like a suicide scar. If you saw this guy on the street, Grace thinks, you'd expect him to ask for a quarter or steal your purse, but now here he is, her date.

Parking is a problem so they leave her car in his reserved space at the university and walk to the restaurant. Grace never knows what to make of Berkeley's cleverness: a stationer's shop called Avant Card; a coffeehouse called Sufficient Grounds.

"In the town where I grew up," she confesses, "nobody would even get these jokes." It's true. Grace barely remembers what she once expected to find here: trolley cars and the ocean. Now she isn't sure whether she's come up in the world or just moved to a city of pretenders. If these people have the answers, why are they living on a fault line? Also, they're dying like crazy: a great, sad wave of them. Loren touches her arm and they both stop to let a blind young man pass by—his sight taken, Grace now understands, by AIDS. She's learned about retinitis and pneumocystis[1] and the other devastations from three different people in her grieving group; she often feels she's being introduced to her new home through the tragedy channel.

They arrive at their destination, the China Doll. The menu is printed in Chinese with hesitant-looking translations in pencil. Grace laughs at an item called "Funny-Tasting Eggplant." "Who'd order that?" she asks Loren. "It sounds like you'd get salmonella."

He smiles. "My sister forced you into this, didn't she?"

"No, it's okay. She's trying to help me take charge of my life. She thinks I'm lonely."

"Are you?" Loren watches her. Up close he's going a little gray and seems more respectable than she'd first thought.

"No. I've got two boys. Did she tell you that? Teenagers in the house are like living in a buffalo herd." His face registers a tiny shock. People here always do that, she's noticed. It's one more backward thing she's done with her life, had kids before she was twenty.

"I'm envious," he says. "My life is too quiet. Nothing ever happens. Maybe one of my books might fall off the shelf."

Grace doesn't believe for a minute that this man's life is too quiet. It dawns on her that the envies people claim on her—undamaged hair, rowdy teenagers—are stretching it; they're being nice to a widow from East Jesus Nowhere. She looks around the restaurant and wonders if everybody has already guessed this is a first date going on here. She and Loren are both practically glowing with miserable goodwill. "What kind of, what are you at the university?" she asks. "Fiona said an associate professor."

"Of Chinese history," he says, and her eyes inadvertently go to the tattoo on his wrist. He looks down too, then draws up his sleeve and displays it for her. "It says, Beware of funny-tasting eggplant."

Grace laughs, feeling grateful. Even if she never sees him again, she'll remember that he helped her get through this day. "So can you read this whole menu?" she asks.

They're interrupted by a peppy blond waiter wearing checked pants and a moppy haircut something like Dennis the Menace. "Can I answer any ques-

---

[1] **retinitis . . . pneumocystis:** inflamation of the retina, or lining of the eye . . . a type of pneumonia that attacks weakened immune systems

tions for you tonight?" he asks.

"Sure," says Loren. "What is the meaning of life?"

"Enjoy it. You don't die with your assets; you die with your memories."

Grace is amazed. She doesn't think she'll ever be witty enough to live here. When the waiter is gone, she asks, "What does it really say? Your tattoo. I'll bet it's some girl."

"Worse than that. It's a quote from the I Ching that I considered momentous when I was seventeen."

"You don't die with your assets; you die with your memories?"

"Something along those lines. Never get a tattoo."

The waiter brings their wine and they stare into their glasses. Then they both glance up as the blind man who passed them earlier comes into the restaurant with a companion and is seated at a far table. "Everything that happens to you is like a tattoo," Grace says quietly. "It might not show on the outside, but it's permanent."

"Or it shows up later," Loren says.

Grace wonders if he's thinking of AIDS. "You know what I keep imagining? Whenever I come over here to Berkeley I see all these guys blinded, in wheelchairs, and I think they're home from some war nobody knows about."

"Everybody knows about it; they just wish they didn't."

"No, I don't think so. There's lots of little towns like the one I grew up in where they're still in the dark."

"They haven't heard?"

"Oh, they've *heard*. But they scrub behind their ears and go to church and count on being saved. My cousin told me somebody I used to know was back there visiting his mother and went swimming at the Country Club pool. After he'd left, the city council found out he was HIV positive. They revoked his mother's membership and drained the swimming pool."

Loren appears to choke, or laugh. "Drained the pool?"

"Yes. Can you imagine? They don't have any idea of how big a disaster it is. I guess they figure they had a near miss, but it's all under control now."

"People don't believe in disasters."

"I do," Grace vows.

"No, I mean real Cecil B. DeMille natural disasters, epidemics and floods and locust plagues. People believe in individual will. They think they can control what happens to them. Drain the pool, hell, drain the ocean. Uncontrollable **pestilence** and boils are things that happened a million years ago, to Moses, not to people who possess microchip technology."

"Right. Here's to pestilence and boils," Grace says, raising her glass. She's aware that this may be the unsexiest conversation in the history of dating.

pestilence: devastating, infectious disease

Matthew is asleep when she gets home, but Jacob is still up working on an experiment with goldfish he's conducting for a science fair. Grace is amazed at the difference between Kentucky and California school systems. Last year Jacob pasted photos of endangered species on a poster and won first prize; this year he's worked every night for weeks to make something Grace thinks ought to go on *Nova*, and he says it's terrible— a lot of kids have better projects. It stuns her to realize she's brought her sons to a place where they'll grow up feeling second-rate, as she does. So many things in life she has failed to predict.

Jacob's experiment involves electricity, but he swears it doesn't hurt the goldfish. Grace believes it, because he's named them: Madonna and Goldilocks. Jacob has the softest heart of any fourteen-year-old she's ever heard of. He's been obsessed with endangered species all his life. *Jacob believes in disasters*, Grace knows. Adults walk around making jokes about the hole in the ozone, even Johnny Carson does, but Jacob looks up at the sky and chews the skin around his cuticles.

"They do this in Germany to test the drinking water," he explained to her on the day he brought home the fish and a box of electrodes. "They keep all these goldfish in a tank of city water downtown and they monitor the current. The fish give off so many electrical impulses per minute when the water's pure. If there's too much zinc or cadmium or stuff like that in it, then they give off less. It makes a power shortage, and that sets off an alarm at the headquarters."

Jacob's experiment only shows the electrical emissions from happy fish. His teacher told him he would need to show both control and polluted conditions for a chance at the prize, but Jacob said no. His room is papered with endangered cheetahs and great dying whales. He's not going to poison Madonna and Goldilocks with zinc.

On Saturday morning Grace feels an unsteadiness in her kitchen she suspects of being a tremor. Two minutes later the phone rings and she's pretty sure it will be Fiona telling her to go stand under a doorway. It's Fiona, all right, but she just wants a report on the date. Grace runs down the details, including the menu of China Doll; there's not a lot more to tell.

"No electricity," Fiona concludes, and Grace laughs, thinking of Jacob's goldfish. Maybe we're swimming through too much pollution, she thinks, and then on impulse decides to tell Fiona about her dream. "Your brother's sweet, but I'm still too attached to Randall to see another man," she says, describing how her heart was pounding, how she woke up feeling guilty.

"He *bounced* when he fell? That sounds almost whimsical."

"It wasn't whimsical," Grace says, shocked. "It was awful. He looked down at us and then he just jumped. On purpose."

"Sounds like you're holding him responsible for his death," Fiona says. Fiona has been through so much therapy she feels qualified to say things that normal people would consider extremely none of their business. She and her husband got a no-fault divorce and lived for one year as best friends before he died of a drug overdose. But this grieving group is only the latest of a long series of groups for Fiona.

"I don't hold him responsible," Grace says. "It was an industrial accident. I blame OSHA."[2]

"But you blame him for being there. You've told me yourself you wished he'd finished his night courses and been a CPA."[3]

Grace regrets bringing up the dream. She knows Fiona could be partly right. "I just feel abandoned sometimes. Not that it's his fault. Just mad that we got left behind."

"It's natural to want to blame somebody."

"I know. Your brother said people don't believe in disasters, they believe in individual will."

Fiona laughs. "Loren's a little intense. But it's true, it's the modern age— Grace, we all act like we were born with some certificate saying we're going to have perfect, happy lives, guaranteed. So if you slip on a bar of soap, you sue Procter and Gamble."

"I saw a show about that on *Oprah*," Grace says, hoping to change the

---

2 **OSHA:** Occupational Safety and Health Organization

3 **CPA:** Certified Public Accountant

subject. "This woman got window cleaner in her eye and went blind. She sued the window-cleaner company, and then she turned around and sued her maid for taking the day off."

"It's a totally American phenomenon," Fiona says. "We refuse to accept bad luck."

After work on Monday, Grace drives into San Francisco to pick up Jacob from the science fair. Matthew will come home on the bus alone and log in a few more hours as a Latchkey Child. He's thirteen and seems tough beyond his years, with his spiked haircut and heavy high-topped sneakers, but Grace still worries.

"Mom, I think there's going to be an earthquake today," Jacob reports from the backseat as they're transporting Goldilocks and Madonna home. They won third prize.

"Why's that?" Grace asks, not doubting it a bit.

"All the experiments with white rats messed up today. They wouldn't go through the mazes or anything; they all just huddled up together in their boxes. It was lucky for me—that's the only reason I won a prize."

"You think white rats know when an earthquake's coming?"

"All mammals do. Except people. They can smell the positive ions that get released into the air."

"If that's so," Grace says, "They ought to have a big cage of rats downtown at the fire station, like your German goldfish."

"They do have rats downtown," Jacob says. "But nobody's keeping an eye on them."

Grace smiles. She believes Jacob is a near-genius, something she always felt about Randall too, even though he worked in an auto plant. He didn't want to be a CPA, he wanted to make cars. He just had his own crazy way of looking at the world. "So how come we can't smell the positive ions like other animals do?"

"I don't know," he says, and Grace can tell he's looking out the window thinking about this. They're approaching the eastbound on-ramp to the Bay Bridge. The double-decker traffic makes her nervous, with all those westbound commuters whizzing by above them, but both boys love crossing the water. She tries to relax and see the bridge as they do: an intricate forest of I-beams.

Finally he says, "I guess we're tracking so many other stimuli that we don't notice the positive ions. We're too busy doing our own stuff."

Isn't that the truth, Grace thinks, and then suddenly her car is out of control. "Oh God," she says. "Oh my God, I've got a flat tire. I've got *two* flat tires." She pulls as hard as she can on the steering wheel and the car sways less and less violently and finally comes to a stop as far over to the right as she can get on the cramped bridge. She jumps out and looks under the car. She can't see a thing wrong with the tires on this side. She walks around to the other side, and then sees Jacob getting out of the car, laughing. He points behind Grace and she turns around.

A hundred other cars are pulled over, a hundred other drivers all bent over staring at their tires. It's taking everybody quite a while to realize this isn't a personal problem.

She finds the scene hilarious. She thinks again of Randall, catching her eye, spreading his arms wide to embrace the air. It *is* whimsical; nobody knows what's going to happen next. That's where he's trying to take her—that far and no farther. There are only two choices in the "what happens next" department: to pretend it's your job to know or to admit you don't have a clue.

The steel cables over Grace's head hum strangely and then suddenly go slack. Somewhere the structure has broken. Lots of drivers have raised their hoods and are waiting for a tow truck, civilized salvation, hoping they still might make their appointments. For once Grace feels like the only person around who's getting the joke. It will be hours, if not tomorrow, before they're all off the bridge. "Forget it!" she says aloud. "Nobody's coming. This is the mess we're in."

The concrete is still trembling under her shoes and Grace laughs so hard she can't stop. There are stalled cars over her head and the dancing bay below and Jacob is hugging her. She decides to trust the universe.

Responding to the Story

1. LITERARY LENS Consider the repartee in the story. What do these exchanges reveal about the narrator's character?

2. Other than the obvious reference to a geological fault line, what other meanings might the title have?

3. Kingsolver is adept at sketching minor characters in a line or two. Of Grace's friend, she writes, "Fiona also likes to brag that her apartment is located exactly on the San Andreas Fault." What does this tell you about the character of Fiona?

4. Fiona says the refusal to accept bad luck is a "totally American phenomenon." Do you agree? Explain.

5. THE AUTHOR'S STYLE "Fault Lines" might be seen as a story of ideas and attitudes toward life. Trace the different attitudes expressed in the story. Which idea or attitude best sums up the message of the story?

T. Coraghessan Boyle
1948

About the Author

T. Coraghessan Boyle stands a wiry six foot, three inches. His red hair spikes up from his head and out from his goatee, and he can usually be found in torn jeans, lots of earrings, and a wrinkled T-shirt that advertises the name of his latest book. Born in Peekskill, New York, the grandson of Irish immigrants, he studied English and history at the State University of New York at Potsdam.

He says that to avoid service in Vietnam, he taught for several years at his high school alma mater. Subsequently, he attended the University of Iowa Writers' Workshop. A flamboyant speaker, Boyle often goes on book tours and appears on talk shows. He is known for making comments that are outrageously immodest, such as this one in an interview for *Passion and Craft*: "I think all my novels are a complete and utter joy and I can't understand why everyone in America isn't reading them instead of John Grisham."

Among his best-known works are the short story collection *Greasy Lake* and the novels *The Road to Wellville*, which was made into a film, and *The Tortilla Curtain*.

****

The Author's Style

Boyle writes comic satire that provides an unforgiving look at human folly—the way supposedly smart people turn into pathetic fools and make victims of themselves and others in their pursuit of pleasure, comfort, security, and order. In Boyle's work, characters are undone by the fundamental human weaknesses of pride, greed, and anger. They also come to grief because of a smug belief that their intelligence, education, and money will protect them from harm.

Boyle is noted for his eerily inventive and sometimes quirky use of language. He has an ability to splice together the normal and the bizarre, the humorous and the horrifying.

The prevailing tone of Boyle's stories is irony; a typical mood is dread. He puts characters in extreme situations of which they are blissfully ignorant until it is too late. Since Boyle's characters are often unaware of their weaknesses and of the power of social, political, and natural laws and forces around them, they push forward almost obsessively, oblivious to warning signs—even as these signs become increasingly clear to the reader. At times their situations are calamitous to the point of absurdity, yet the characters are so hapless that they evoke laughter as well as sympathy.

LITERARY LENS Listen for the tone of this story.

Top
of the
Food Chain

T. Coraghessan Boyle

The thing was, we had a little problem with the insect **vector** there, and believe me, your tamer stuff, your Malathion and pyrethrum[1] and the rest of the so-called environmentally safe products didn't begin to make a dent in it, not a dent, I mean it was utterly useless—we might as well have been spraying with Chanel No. 5 for all the good it did. And you've got to realize these people were literally covered with insects day and night—and the fact that they hardly wore any clothes just compounded the problem. Picture if you can, gentlemen, a naked little two-year-old boy so black with flies and mosquitoes it looks like he's wearing long johns, or the young mother so racked with the malarial shakes she can't even lift a diet Coke to her lips—it was

vector:
disease-spreading organism

| **Malathion and pyrethrum:** insecticides that are said to be nontoxic to mammals

pathetic, just pathetic, like something out of the Dark Ages. . . . Well, anyway, the decision was made to go with DDT. In the short term. Just to get the situation under control, you understand.

Yes, that's right, Senator, *DDT*: Dichlorodiphenyltrichloroethan.

Yes, I'm well aware of that fact, sir. But just because *we* banned it domestically, under pressure from the birdwatching contingent and the hopheads down at the EPA, it doesn't necessarily follow that the rest of the world—especially the developing world—is about to jump on the bandwagon. And that's the key word here, Senator: *developing*. You've got to realize this is Borneo we're talking about here, not Port Townsend or Enumclaw.[2] These people don't know from square one about sanitation, disease control, pest eradication—or even personal hygiene, if you want to come right down to it. It rains a hundred and twenty inches a year, minimum. They dig up roots in the jungle. They've still got headhunters along the Rajang River, for god's sake.

And please don't forget they *asked* us to come in there, practically begged us—and not only the World Health Organization but the Sultan of Brunei and the government in Sarawak too. We did what we could to accommodate them and reach our objective in the shortest period of time and by the most direct and effective means. We went to the air. Obviously. And no one could have foreseen the consequences, no one, not even if we'd gone out and generated a hundred environmental-impact statements—it was just one of those things, a freak occurrence, and there's no defense against that. Not that I know of, anyway. . . .

Caterpillars? Yes, Senator, that's correct. That was the first sign: caterpillars.

But let me backtrack a minute here. You see, out in the bush they have these roofs made of thatched palm leaves—you'll see them in the towns too, even in Bintulu or Brunei—and they're really pretty effective, you'd be surprised. A hundred and twenty inches of rain, they've got to figure a way to keep it out of the hut, and for centuries, this was it. Palm leaves. Well, it was about a month after we sprayed for the final time and I'm sitting at my desk in the trailer thinking about the drainage project at Kuching, enjoying the fact that for the first time in maybe a year I'm not smearing mosquitoes all over the back of my neck, when there's a knock at the door. It's this elderly

---

2 **Borneo . . . Port Townsend . . . Enumclaw:** a large island near the Philippines; a port city on Washington's coast; an inland city in Washington

gentleman, tattooed from head to toe, dressed only in a pair of running shorts—they love those shorts, by the way, the shiny material and the tight machine-stitching, the whole country, men and women and children, they can't get enough of them. . . . Anyway, he's the headman of the local village and he's very excited, something about the roofs—*atap*, they call them. That's all he can say, *atap, atap*, over and over again.

It's raining, of course. It's always raining. So I shrug into my rain slicker, start up the 4 x 4 and go have a look. Sure enough, all the *atap* roofs are collapsing, not only in his village, but throughout the target area. The people are all huddled there in their running shorts, looking pretty miserable, and one after another the roofs keep falling in, it's bewildering, and gradually I realize the headman's **diatribe** has begun to feature a new term I was unfamiliar with at the time—the word for caterpillar, as it turns out, in the Iban dialect. But who was to make the connection between three passes with the crop duster and all these staved-in roofs?

Our people finally sorted it out a couple weeks later. The chemical, which, by the way, cut down the number of mosquitoes exponentially, had the unfortunate side effect of killing off this little wasp—I've got the scientific name for it somewhere in my report here, if you're interested—that preyed on a type of caterpillar that in turn ate palm leaves. Well, with the wasps gone, the caterpillars hatched out with nothing to keep them in check and chewed the roofs to pieces, and that was unfortunate, we admit it, and we had a real cost overrun on replacing those roofs with tin . . . but the people were happier, I think, in the long run, because let's face it, no matter how tightly you weave those palm leaves, they're just not going to keep the water out like tin. Of course, nothing's perfect, and we had a lot of complaints about the rain drumming on the panels, people unable to sleep and what-have-you. . . .

Yes, sir, that's correct—the flies were next.

Well, you've got to understand the magnitude of the fly problem in Borneo, there's nothing like it here to compare it with, except maybe a garbage strike in New York. Every minute of every day you've got flies everywhere, up your nose, in your mouth, your ears, your eyes, flies in your rice, your Coke, your Singapore sling and your gin rickey. It's enough to drive you to distraction, not to mention the diseases these things carry, from dysentery to typhoid to cholera and back round the loop again. And once the mosquito

diatribe:
bitter complaint

population was down, the flies seemed to breed up to fill in the gap—Borneo wouldn't be Borneo without some damned insect blackening the air.

Of course, this was before our people had tracked down the problem with the caterpillars and the wasps and all of that, and so we figured we'd had a big success with the mosquitoes, why not a series of ground sweeps, mount a fogger in the back of a Suzuki Brat and sanitize the huts, not to mention the open sewers, which as you know are nothing but a breeding ground for flies, chiggers and biting insects of every sort. At least it was an error of commission rather than omission. At least we were trying.

I watched the flies go down myself. One day they were so thick in the trailer I couldn't even *find* my paperwork, let alone attempt to get through it, and the next they were collecting on the windows, bumbling around like they were drunk. A day later they were gone. Just like that. From a million flies in the trailer to none. . . .

Well, no one could have foreseen that, Senator.

The geckos ate the flies, yes. You're all familiar with geckos, I assume, gentlemen? These are the lizards you've seen during your trips to Hawaii, very colorful, patrolling the houses for roaches and flies, almost like pets, but of course they're wild animals, never lose sight of that, and just about as unsanitary as anything I can think of, except maybe flies.

Yes, well don't forget sir, we're viewing this with twenty-twenty hindsight, but at the time no one gave a thought to geckos or what they ate—they were just another fact of life in the tropics. Mosquitoes, lizards, scorpions, leeches—you name it, they've got it. When the flies began piling up on the windowsills like drift, naturally the geckos feasted on them, stuffing themselves till they looked like sausages crawling up the walls. Where before they moved so fast you could never be sure you'd seen them, now they waddled across the floor, laid around in the corners, clung to the air vents like magnets—and even then no one paid much attention to them till they started turning belly-up in the streets. Believe me, we confirmed a lot of things there about the buildup of these products as you move up the food chain and the **efficacy**—or lack thereof—of certain methods, no doubt about that. . . .

efficacy:
effectiveness

The cats? That's where it got sticky, really sticky. You see, nobody really lost any sleep over a pile of dead lizards—though we did the tests routinely and the tests confirmed what we'd expected, that is, the product had been concentrated in the geckos because of the sheer number of contaminated flies they'd consumed. But lizards are one thing and cats are another. These people really have an affection for their cats—no house, no hut, no matter how primitive, is without at least a couple of them. Mangy-looking things, long-legged and scrawny, maybe, not at all the sort of animal you'd see here, but there it was: they loved their cats. Because the cats were functional, you understand—without them, the place would have been swimming in rodents inside of a week.

You're right there, Senator, yes—that's exactly what happened.

You see, the cats had a field day with these feeble geckos—you can imagine, if any of you have ever owned a cat, the kind of joy these animals must have experienced to see their **nemesis**, this ultra-quick lizard, and it's just barely creeping across the floor like a bug. Well, to make a long story short, the cats ate up every dead and dying gecko in the country, from snout to tail, and then the cats began to die . . . which to my mind would have been no great loss if it wasn't for the rats. Suddenly there were rats everywhere— you couldn't drive down the street without running over half-a-dozen of them at a time. They fouled the grain supplies, fell in the wells and died, bit infants as they slept in their cradles. But that wasn't the worst, not by a long shot. No, things really went down the tube after that. Within the month we were getting scattered reports of bubonic plague, and of course we tracked them all down and made sure the people got a round of treatment with antibiotics, but still we lost a few and the rats kept coming. . . .

It was my plan, yes. I was brainstorming one night, rats scuttling all over the trailer like something out of a cheap horror film, the villagers in a panic over the threat of the plague and the stream of nonstop hysterical reports from the interior—people were turning black, swelling up and bursting, that sort of thing—well, as I say, I came up with a plan, a stopgap, not perfect, not cheap; but at this juncture, I'm sure you'll agree, something had to be implemented.

We wound up going as far as Australia for some of the cats, cleaning out the SPCA[3] facilities and what-have-you, though we rounded most of them up in Indonesia and Singapore—approximately fourteen thousand in all. And yes, it cost us—cost us upfront purchase money and aircraft fuel and pilots' overtime and all the rest of it—but we really felt there was no alternative. It was like all nature had turned against us.

And yet still, all things considered, we made a lot of friends for the U.S.A. the day we dropped those cats, and you should have seen them, gentlemen,

nemesis: formidable rival

---

3 **SPCA:** Society for the Prevention of Cruelty to Animals

the little parachutes and harnesses we'd tricked up, fourteen thousand of them, cats in every color of the rainbow, cats with one ear, no ears, half a tail, three-legged cats, cats that could have taken pride of show in Springfield, Massachusetts, and all of them twirling down out of the sky like great big oversized snowflakes. . . .

It was something. It was really something.

Of course, you've all seen the reports. There were other factors we hadn't counted on, adverse conditions in the paddies and manioc fields—we don't to this day know what predatory species were inadvertently killed off by the initial sprayings, it's just a mystery—but the weevils and whatnot took a pretty

THE TOP OF THE FOOD CHAIN, Caty Bartholomew, 1993

heavy toll on the crops that year, and by the time we dropped the cats, well, the people were pretty hungry, and I suppose it was inevitable that we lost a good proportion of them right then and there. But we've got a CARE[4] program going there now, and something hit the rat population—we still don't know what, a virus, we think—and the geckos, they tell me, are making a comeback.

So what I'm saying is, it could be worse, and to every cloud a silver lining, wouldn't you agree, gentlemen?

---

4 **CARE:** Cooperative for Assistance and Relief Everywhere

T. Coraghessan Boyle

Responding to the Story

1. **LITERARY LENS** In what ways is "Top of the Food Chain" ironic?

2. Reread the first sentence of the story. What does it tell you about the narrator and the situation that is about to unfold?

3. What is being satirized in "Top of the Food Chain"?

4. Some critics consider both Joyce Carol Oates and T. Coraghessan Boyle harsh and unforgiving judges of contemporary American morals and values. Discuss why you agree or disagree.

5. At one point, the narrator justifies sweeping the ground with a fog of pesticides this way: "At least it was an error of commission rather than omission. At least we were trying." If you were a member of the committee before which he is testifying, how would you respond?

6. Using evidence from the text, find two adjectives to describe the narrator's attitude toward the developing world.

7. **THE AUTHOR'S STYLE** Boyle is said to have a gift for pairing the familiar with the frightening and the normal with the bizarre. Find two such pairings in "Top of the Food Chain." How do they add to the story?

Robert Olen Butler
1945

About the Author

Robert Olen Butler grew up in Granite City, Illinois, majored in theatre at Northwestern University, and then studied playwriting at the University of Iowa. In 1971, he went to Vietnam as a counter-intelligence special agent and later as a translator; he was fluent in Vietnamese because the Army had sent him to language school the year before.

During an interview at Powells City of Books in Portland, Oregon, in 1996, he said that while serving in Vietnam, "My favorite thing in the world to do was to wander out into the back alleys of Saigon, where nobody seemed to sleep. I did this almost every night. In those back alleys I would crouch with the people and talk with them. The Vietnamese people as a group are the most open and generous-spirited people in the world. Invariably they would invite me into their homes, their culture, and their lives."

Although Butler is known primarily for writing about Vietnam, he has written on a variety of topics, publishing nine novels and two volumes of short fiction, as well as screenplays and teleplays, since 1981. In 1993 his collection of short stories, *A Good Scent from a Strange Mountain*, was awarded the Pulitzer Prize. He is a professor at Florida State University.

★★★★★★★★★★★

The Author's Style

Butler served as an army linguist during the Vietnam War. His command of the language of Vietnam and his familiarity with its climate, geography, and people are central to much of his fiction. Butler's stories are concerned with individuals whose lives continue to be affected by their experiences in the war and by the sharp differences between American and Vietnamese culture. He is remarkably adept at conveying the language, tone, and points of view of both male and female characters and both Americans and Vietnamese. He has won an award from fellow veterans for outstanding contributions to American culture by a Vietnam veteran.

His work makes clear many fascinating and appealing aspects of Vietnamese life. It also shows how frustratingly different that life can be from life in the United States. His characters' struggles with one or another aspect of American culture reveal why their post-war lives are characterized by both new opportunities and painful betrayals. The lasting emotional and physical wounds suffered by both civilians and former soldiers help explain the urgency behind the first-person stories they tell.

LITERARY LENS Look for the symbols in this story.

LETTERS
FROM
MY FATHER

ROBERT OLEN BUTLER

look through the letters my father sent to me in Saigon and I find this: "Dear Fran. How are you? I wish you and your mother were here with me. The weather here is pretty cold this time of year. I bet you would like the cold weather." At the time, I wondered how he would know such a thing. Cold weather sounded very bad. It was freezing, he said, so I touched the tip of my finger to a piece of ice and I held it there for as long as I could. It hurt very bad and that was after only about a minute. I thought, How could you spend hours and days in weather like that?

It makes no difference that I had misunderstood the cold weather. By the time he finally got me and my mother out of Vietnam, he had moved to a place where it almost never got very cold. The point is that in his letters to me he often said this and that about the weather. It is cold today. It is hot today. Today there are clouds in the sky. Today there are no clouds. What did that have to do with me?

He said, "Dear Fran" because my name is Fran. That's short for Francine and the sound of Fran is something like a Vietnamese name, but it isn't really. So I told my friends in Saigon that my name was Trán, which was short for Hôn Trán, which means "a kiss on the forehead." My American father lived in America but my Vietnamese mother and me lived in Saigon, so I was still a Saigon girl. My mother called me Francine, too. She was happy for me to have this name. She said it was not just American, it was also French. But I wanted a name for Saigon and Trán was it.

I was a child of dust. When the American fathers all went home, including my father, and the communists took over, that's what we were called, those of us who had faces like those drawings you see in some of the book-stalls on Nguyen Huê Street. You look once and you see a beautiful woman sitting at her mirror, but then you look again and you see the skull of a dead person, no skin on the face, just the wide eyes of the skull and the bared teeth. We were like that, the children of dust in Saigon. At one look we were Vietnamese and at another look we were American and after that you couldn't get your eyes to stay still when they turned to us, they kept seeing first one thing and then another.

Last night I found a package of letters in a footlocker that belongs to my father. It is in the storage shack at the back of our house here in America. I am living now in Lake Charles, Louisiana, and I found this package of letters outside—many packages, hundreds of letters—and I opened one, and these are all copies he kept of letters he sent trying to get us out of Vietnam. I look through these letters my father wrote and I find this: "What is this crap that you're trying to give me now? It has been nine years, seven months, and fifteen days since I last saw my daughter, my own flesh-and-blood daughter."

This is an angry voice, a voice with feeling. I have been in this place now for a year. I am seventeen and it took even longer than nine years, seven months, fifteen days to get me out of Vietnam. I wish I could say something about that, because I know anyone who listens to my story would expect me right now to say how I felt. My mother and me were left behind in Saigon. My father went on ahead to America and he thought he could get some paperwork done and prepare a place for us, then my mother and me would be leaving for America very soon. But things happened. A different footlocker was lost and some important papers with it, like their marriage license and my birth certificate. Then the country of South Vietnam fell to the communists, and even those who thought it might happen thought it happened pretty fast, really. Who knew? My father didn't.

I look at a letter he sent me in Saigon after it fell and the letter says: "You can imagine how I feel. The whole world is let down by what happened." But I could not imagine that, if you want to know the truth, how my father felt. And I knew nothing of the world except Saigon, and even that wasn't the way the world was, because when I was very little they gave it a different name, calling it Hô´Chí Minh City. Now, those words are a man's name, you know, but the same words have several other meanings, too, and I took the name like everyone took the face of a child of dust: I looked at it one way and it meant one thing and then I looked at it a different way and it meant something else. Hô´Chí Minh also can mean "very intelligent starch-paste," and that's what we thought of the new name, me and some friends of mine who also had American fathers. We would meet at the French cemetery on Phan Thanh Gian´ Street and talk about our city—Hô´, for short; starch-paste. We would talk about our lives in Starch-Paste City and we had this game where we'd hide in the cemetery, each in a separate place, and then we'd keep low and move slowly and see how many of our friends we would find. If you saw the other person first, you would get a point. And if nobody ever saw you, if it was like you were invisible, you'd win.

The cemetery made me sad, but it felt very comfortable there somehow. We all thought that, me and my friends. It was a ragged place and many of the names were like Couchet, Picard, Vernet, Believeau, and these graves never had any flowers on them. Everybody who loved these dead people had gone home to France long ago. Then there was a part of the cemetery that had Vietnamese dead. There were some flowers over there, but not very many. The grave markers had photos, little oval frames built into the stone, and these were faces of the dead, mostly old people, men and women, the wealthy Vietnamese, but there were some young people, too, many of them dead in 1968 when there was much killing in Saigon. I would always hide over in this section and there was one boy, very cute, in sunglasses, leaning

> *I* found her when I was about ten or so and she was very beautiful, with long black hair and dark eyes and a round face. I would always go to her grave and I wanted to be just like her, though I knew my face was different from hers.

on a motorcycle, his hand on his hip. He died in February of 1968, and I probably wouldn't have liked him anyway. He looked cute but very conceited. And there was a girl nearby. The marker said she was fifteen. I found her when I was about ten or so and she was very beautiful, with long black hair and dark eyes and a round face. I would always go to her grave and I wanted to be just like her, though I knew my face was different from hers. Then I went one day—I was almost her age at last—and the rain had gotten into the little picture frame and her face was nearly gone. I could see her hair, but the features of her face had faded until you could not see them, there were only dark streaks of water and the picture was curling at the edges, and I cried over that. It was like she had died.

Sometimes my father sent me pictures with his letters. "Dear Fran," he would say. "Here is a picture of me. Please send me a picture of you." A friend of mine, when she was about seven years old, got a pen pal in Russia. They wrote to each other very simple letters in French. Her pen pal said, "Please send me a picture of you and I will send you one of me." My friend put on her white aó dài[1] and went downtown and had her picture taken before the big banyan tree in the park on Le′ Thánh Tôn. She sent it off and in return she got a picture of a fat girl who hadn't combed her hair, standing by a cow on a collective farm.

My mother's father was some government man, I think. And the communists said my mother was an agitator or collaborator. Something like that. It was all mostly before I was born or when I was just a little girl, and whenever my mother tried to explain what all this was about, this father across the sea and us not seeming to ever go there, I just didn't like to listen very much and my mother realized that, and after a while she didn't say any more. I put his picture up on my mirror and he was smiling, I guess. He was outside somewhere and there was a lake or something in the background and he had a T-shirt on and I guess he was really more squinting than smiling. There

---

I **aó dài:** a traditional Vietnamese dress

were several of these photographs of him on my mirror. They were always outdoors and he was always squinting in the sun. He said in one of his letters to me: "Dear Fran, I got your photo. You are very pretty, like your mother. I have not forgotten you." And I thought: I am not like my mother. I am a child of dust. Has he forgotten that?

One of the girls I used to hang around with at the cemetery told me a story that she knew was true because it happened to her sister's best friend. The best friend was just a very little girl when it began. Her father was a soldier in the South Vietnam Army and he was away fighting somewhere secret, Cambodia or somewhere. It was very secret, so her mother never heard from him and the little girl was so small when he went away that she didn't even remember him, what he looked like or anything. But she knew she was supposed to have a daddy, so every evening, when the mother would put her daughter to bed, the little girl would ask where her father was. She asked with such a sad heart that one night the mother made something up.

There was a terrible storm and the electricity went out in Saigon. So the mother went to the table with the little girl clinging in fright to her, and she lit an oil lamp. When she did, her shadow suddenly was thrown upon the wall and it was very big, and she said, "Don't cry, my baby, see there?" She pointed to the shadow. "There's your daddy. He'll protect you." This made the little girl very happy. She stopped shaking from fright immediately and the mother sang the girl to sleep.

The next evening before going to bed, the little girl asked to see her father. When the mother tried to say no, the little girl was so upset that the mother gave in and lit the oil lamp and cast her shadow on the wall. The little girl went to the wall and held her hands before her with the palms together and she bowed low to the shadow. "Good night, Daddy," she said, and she went to sleep. This happened the next evening and the next and it went on for more than a year.

Then one evening, just before bedtime, the father finally came home. The mother, of course, was very happy. She wept and she kissed him and she said to him, "We will prepare a thanksgiving feast to honor our ancestors. You go in to our daughter. She is almost ready for bed. I will go out to the market and get some food for our celebration."

So the father went in to the little girl and he said to her, "My pretty girl, I am home. I am your father and I have not forgotten you."

But the little girl said, "You're not my daddy. I know my daddy. He'll be here soon. He comes every night to say good night to me before I go to bed."

The man was shocked at his wife's faithlessness, but he was very proud, and he did not say anything to her about it when she got home. He did not say anything at all, but prayed briefly before the shrine of their ancestors and picked up his bag and left. The weeks passed and the mother grieved so badly that one day she threw herself into the Saigon River and drowned.

The father heard news of this and thought that she had killed herself from shame. He returned home to be a father to his daughter, but on the first night, there was a storm and the lights went out and the man lit the oil lamp, throwing his shadow on the wall. His little girl laughed in delight and went and bowed low to the shadow and said, "Good night, Daddy." When the man saw this, he took his little girl to his own mother's house, left her, and threw himself into the Saigon River to join his wife in death.

My friend says this story is true. Everyone in the neighborhood of her sister's friend knows about it. But I don't think it's true. I never did say that to my friend, but for me, it doesn't make sense. I can't believe that the little girl would be satisfied with the shadow father. There was this darkness on the wall, just a flatness, and she loved it. I can see how she wouldn't take up with this man who suddenly walks in one night and says, "I'm your father, let me tell you good night." But the other guy, the shadow—he was no father either.

When my father met my mother and me at the airport, there were people with cameras and microphones and my father grabbed my mother with this enormous hug and this sound like a shout and he kissed her hard and all the people with microphones and cameras smiled and nodded. Then he let go of my mother and he looked at me and suddenly he was making this little choking sound, a kind of gacking in the back of his throat like a rabbit makes when you pick him up and he doesn't like it. And my father's hands just flut-

SEPARATION, Larry Yung

tered before him and he got stiff-legged coming over to me and the hug he gave me was like I was soaking wet and he had on his Sunday clothes, though he was just wearing some silly T-shirt.

All the letters from my father, the ones I got in Saigon, and the photos, they're in a box in the back of the closet of my room. My closet smells of my perfume, is full of nice clothes so that I can fit in at school. Not everyone can say what they feel in words, especially words on paper. Not everyone can look at a camera and make their face do what it has to do to show a feeling. But years of flat words, grimaces at the sun, these are hard things to forget. So I've been sitting all morning today in the shack behind our house, out here with the tree roaches and the carpenter ants and the smell of mildew and rotting wood and I am sweating so hard that it's dripping off my nose and chin. There are many letters in my lap. In one of them to the U.S. government my father says: "If this was a goddamn white woman, a Russian ballet dancer and her daughter, you people would have them on a plane in twenty-four hours. This is my wife and my daughter. My daughter is so beautiful you can put her face on your dimes and quarters and no one could ever make change again in your goddamn country without stopping and saying, Oh my God, what a beautiful face."

I read this now while I'm hidden in the storage shack, invisible, soaked with sweat like it's that time in Saigon between the dry season and the rainy season, and I know my father will be here soon. The lawn mower is over there in the corner and this morning he got up and said that it was going to be hot today, that there were no clouds in the sky and he was going to have to mow the lawn. When he opens the door, I will let him see me here, and I will ask him to talk to me like in these letters, like when he was so angry with some stranger that he knew what to say.

Responding to the Story

1. **LITERARY LENS** Consider the unusual analogies and comparisons the narrator uses in telling her story. With a chart like the one below, examine several of these comparisons and what they mean to Fran. Then write a short description of Fran based on the analogies she uses.

Comparison	Meaning to Fran
Hô' Chí Minh can mean "very intelligent starch-paste."	The name of the city could be taken the same way that some people take the faces of the children of dust.

2. What are some of the ways you see Fran struggling for her identity in this story?

3. What do you think is the significance of the game the children play at the cemetery in Vietnam?

4. Why do you think Fran became so attached to the girl whose photograph was framed on the headstone in the cemetery?

5. Do you think Butler, an American adult male, is convincing when writing in the voice of a young Vietnamese girl? Explain your reaction.

6. **THE AUTHOR'S STYLE** In telling Fran's story, Butler uses bits and pieces of her past such as photos, paintings, letters, memories, and even an urban legend. Which of these do you think best defines Fran's character?

★★

Sherman Alexie
1966

About the Author

A Spokane/Coeur d'Alene Indian, Sherman Alexie grew up on the Spokane Reservation in Washington, but chose to attend high school in a nearby town. There, as he puts it, he was the only Indian except the mascot. After high school he went on to Washington State University, where he stumbled into a poetry class and found what he was looking for.

A stand-up comedian as well as a three-time world heavyweight poetry slam champion and writer of stories and novels, Alexie is a funny writer who is nonetheless very serious about his work and its focus on Indian concerns. In a July 2, 1998 interview in *Salon*, he said, "I'm not trying to speak for everybody. I'm one individual heavily influenced by my tribe. And good art doesn't come out of assimilation—it comes out of tribalism." (*Assimilation* is the process of being absorbed into a culture or group.)

Alexie's best-known works include the poetry collection *The Business of Fancydancing* and *The Lone Ranger and Tonto Fistfight in Heaven*, a series of linked stories that won a Hemingway Foundation/PEN Award.

★★★★★★★★★★★

The Author's Style

Alexie writes with sensitivity and energetic wit about the everyday lives of Indians. One of his concerns is the interaction between traditional tribal culture and mainstream, contemporary American life. The dreams, hopes, and visions of his characters are linked to Native American oral storytelling, and are in constant conflict with elements of the non-Indian world. His stories examine Indian stereotypes, dependence on government food and housing, and exploitation of Indian culture.

Alexie's stories and novels often use flashbacks and are written in brief sections or episodes that enable Alexie to point out the ironies of contemporary Indian life. Alexie's stories are marked by a poet's use of symbols and figures of speech.

Alexie is a comic writer in that his stories are simultaneously funny and sad; he is hopeful, but not optimistic. The quick dialogue and biting wit of his characters contain serious messages, and have been successfully rendered in the film *Smoke Signals*. The film was adapted from *The Lone Ranger and Tonto Fistfight in Heaven*, which drew particularly from the story you are about to read.

LITERARY **L**ENS Watch for the flashbacks (abrupt scene changes to earlier times) in this story.

THIS IS WHAT IT MEANS TO SAY PHOENIX, ARIZONA

SHERMAN ALEXIE

J ust after Victor lost his job at the BIA,[1] he also found out that his father had died of a heart attack in Phoenix, Arizona. Victor hadn't seen his father in a few years, only talked to him on the telephone once or twice, but there still was a genetic pain, which was soon to be pain as real and immediate as a broken bone.

Victor didn't have any money. Who does have money on a reservation, except the cigarette and fireworks salespeople? His father had a savings account waiting to be claimed, but Victor needed to find a way to get to Phoenix. Victor's mother was just as poor as he was, and the rest of his family didn't have any use at all for him. So Victor called the Tribal Council.

---

1 **BIA:** Bureau of Indian Affairs, a federal government department that administers programs and policies for Native American people and reservations

"Listen," Victor said. "My father just died. I need some money to get to Phoenix to make arrangements."

"Now, Victor," the council said. "You know we're having a difficult time financially."

"But I thought the council had special funds set aside for stuff like this."

"Now, Victor, we do have some money available for the proper return of tribal members' bodies. But I don't think we have enough to bring your father all the way back from Phoenix."

"Well," Victor said. "It ain't going to cost all that much. He had to be cremated. Things were kind of ugly. He died of a heart attack in his trailer and nobody found him for a week. It was really hot, too. You get the picture."

"Now, Victor, we're sorry for your loss and the circumstances. But we can really only afford to give you one hundred dollars."

"That's not even enough for a plane ticket."

"Well, you might consider driving down to Phoenix."

"I don't have a car. Besides, I was going to drive my father's pickup back up here."

"Now, Victor," the council said. "We're sure there is somebody who could drive you to Phoenix. Or is there somebody who could lend you the rest of the money?"

"You know there ain't nobody around with that kind of money."

"Well, we're sorry, Victor, but that's the best we can do."

Victor accepted the Tribal Council's offer. What else could he do? So he signed the proper papers, picked up his check, and walked over to the Trading Post to cash it.

While Victor stood in line, he watched Thomas Builds-the-Fire standing near the magazine rack, talking to himself. Like he always did. Thomas was a storyteller that nobody wanted to listen to. That's like being a dentist in a town where everybody has false teeth.

Victor and Thomas Builds-the-Fire were the same age, had grown up and played in the dirt together. Ever since Victor could remember, it was Thomas who always had something to say.

Once, when they were seven years old, when Victor's father still lived with the family, Thomas closed his eyes and told Victor this story: "Your father's heart is weak. He is afraid of his own family. He is afraid of you. Late at night he sits in the dark. Watches the television until there's nothing but that white noise. Sometimes he feels like he wants to buy a motorcycle and ride away. He wants to run and hide. He doesn't want to be found."

Thomas Builds-the-Fire had known that Victor's father was going to leave, knew it before anyone. Now Victor stood in the Trading Post with a one-hundred-dollar check in his hand, wondering if Thomas knew that Victor's father was dead, if he knew what was going to happen next.

Just then Thomas looked at Victor, smiled, and walked over to him.

"Victor, I'm sorry about your father," Thomas said.

"How did you know about it?" Victor asked

"I heard it on the wind. I heard it from the birds. I felt it in the sunlight. Also, your mother was just in here crying."

"Oh," Victor said and looked around the Trading Post. All the other Indians stared, surprised that Victor was even talking to Thomas. Nobody talked to Thomas anymore because he told the same damn stories over and over again. Victor was embarrassed, but he thought that Thomas might be able to help him. Victor felt a sudden need for tradition.

"I can lend you the money you need," Thomas said suddenly. "But you have to take me with you."

"I can't take your money," Victor said. "I mean, I haven't hardly talked to you in years. We're not really friends anymore."

"I didn't say we were friends. I said you had to take me with you."

"Let me think about it."

Victor went home with his one hundred dollars and sat at the kitchen table. He held his head in his hands and thought about Thomas Builds-the-Fire, remembered little details, tears and scars, the bicycle they shared for a summer, so many stories.

Thomas Builds-the-Fire sat on the bicycle, waited in Victor's yard. He was ten years old and skinny. His hair was dirty because it was the Fourth of July.

"Victor," Thomas yelled. "Hurry up. We're going to miss the fireworks."

After a few minutes, Victor ran out of his house, jumped the porch railing, and landed gracefully on the sidewalk.

"And the judges award him a 9.95, the highest score of the summer," Thomas said, clapped, laughed.

"That was perfect, cousin," Victor said. "And it's my turn to ride the bike."

Thomas gave up the bike and they headed for the fairgrounds. It was nearly dark and the fireworks were about to start.

"You know," Thomas said. "It's strange how us Indians celebrate the Fourth of July. It ain't like it was *our* independence everybody was fighting for."

He counted his one hundred dollars again and again. He knew he needed more to make it to Phoenix and back. He knew he needed Thomas Builds-the-Fire.

"You think about things too much," Victor said. "It's just supposed to be fun. Maybe Junior will be there."

"Which Junior? Everybody on this reservation is named Junior."

And they both laughed.

The fireworks were small, hardly more than a few bottle rockets and a fountain. But it was enough for two Indian boys. Years later, they would need much more.

Afterwards, sitting in the dark, fighting off mosquitoes, Victor turned to Thomas Builds-the-Fire.

"Hey," Victor said. "Tell me a story."

Thomas closed his eyes and told this story: "There were these two Indian boys who wanted to be warriors. But it was too late to be warriors in the old way. All the horses were gone. So the two Indian boys stole a car and drove to the city. They parked the stolen car in front of the police station and then hitchhiked back home to the reservation. When they got back, all their friends cheered and their parents' eyes shone with pride. *You were very brave*, everybody said to the two Indian boys. *Very brave*."

"Ya-hey," Victor said. "That's a good one. I wish I could be a warrior."

"Me, too," Thomas said.

They went home together in the dark, Thomas on the bike now, Victor on foot. They walked through shadows and light from streetlamps.

"We've come a long ways," Thomas said. "We have outdoor lighting."

"All I need is the stars," Victor said. "And besides, you still think about things too much."

They separated then, each headed for home, both laughing all the way.

Victor sat at his kitchen table. He counted his one hundred dollars again and again. He knew he needed more to make it to Phoenix and back. He knew he needed Thomas Builds-the-Fire. So he put his money in his wallet and opened the front door to find Thomas on the porch.

"Ya-hey, Victor," Thomas said. "I knew you'd call me."

Thomas walked into the living room and sat down on Victor's favorite chair.

Sherman Alexie

"I've got some money saved up," Thomas said. "It's enough to get us down there, but you have to get us back."

"I've got this hundred dollars," Victor said. "And my dad had a savings account I'm going to claim."

"How much in your dad's account?"

"Enough. A few hundred."

"Sounds good. When we leaving?"

When they were fifteen and had long since stopped being friends, Victor and Thomas got into a fistfight. That is, Victor was really drunk and beat Thomas up for no reason at all. All the other Indian boys stood around and watched it happen. Junior was there and so were Lester, Seymour, and a lot of others. The beating might have gone on until Thomas was dead if Norma Many Horses hadn't come along and stopped it.

"Hey, you boys," Norma yelled and jumped out of her car. "Leave him alone."

If it had been someone else, even another man, the Indian boys would've just ignored the warnings. But Norma was a warrior. She was powerful. She could have picked up any two of the boys and smashed their skulls together. But worse than that, she would have dragged them all over to some tipi and made them listen to some elder tell a dusty old story.

The Indian boys scattered, and Norma walked over to Thomas and picked him up.

"Hey, little man, are you okay?" she asked.

Thomas gave her a thumbs up.

"Why they always picking on you?"

Thomas shook his head, closed his eyes, but no stories came to him, no words or music. He just wanted to go home, to lie in his bed and let his dreams tell his stories for him.

Thomas Builds-the-Fire and Victor sat next to each other in the air plane, coach section. A tiny white woman had the window seat. She was busy twisting her body into pretzels. She was flexible.

"I have to ask," Thomas said, and Victor closed his eyes in embarrassment.

"Don't," Victor said.

This Is What It Means to Say Phoenix, Arizona   **489**

"Excuse me, miss," Thomas asked. "Are you a gymnast or something?"

"There's no something about it," she said. "I was first alternate on the 1980 Olympic team."

"Really?" Thomas asked.

"Really."

"I mean, you used to be a world-class athlete?" Thomas asked.

"My husband still thinks I am."

Thomas Builds-the-Fire smiled. She was a mental gymnast, too. She pulled her leg straight up against her body so that she could've kissed her kneecap.

"I wish I could do that," Thomas said.

Victor was ready to jump out of the plane. Thomas, that crazy Indian storyteller with ratty old braids and broken teeth, was flirting with a beautiful Olympic gymnast. Nobody back home on the reservation would ever believe it.

"Well," the gymnast said. "It's easy. Try it."

Thomas grabbed at his leg and tried to pull it up into the same position as the gymnast. He couldn't even come close, which made Victor and the gymnast laugh.

"Hey," she asked. "You two are Indian, right?"

"Full-blood," Victor said.

"Not me," Thomas said. "I'm half magician on my mother's side and half clown on my father's."

They all laughed.

"What are your names?" she asked.

"Victor and Thomas."

"Mine is Cathy. Pleased to meet you all."

The three of them talked for the duration of the flight. Cathy the gymnast complained about the government, how they screwed the 1980 Olympic team by boycotting.

"Sounds like you all got a lot in common with Indians," Thomas said.

Nobody laughed.

After the plane landed in Phoenix and they had all found their way to the terminal, Cathy the gymnast smiled and waved good-bye.

"She was really nice," Thomas said.

"Yeah, but everybody talks to everybody on airplanes," Victor said. "It's too bad we can't always be that way."

"You always used to tell me I think too much," Thomas said. "Now it sounds like you do."

"Maybe I caught it from you."

"Yeah."

Thomas and Victor rode in a taxi to the trailer where Victor's father died.

"Listen," Victor said as they stopped in front of the trailer. "I never told you I was sorry for beating you up that time."

"Oh, it was nothing. We were just kids and you were drunk."

"Yeah, but I'm still sorry."

"That's all right."

Victor paid for the taxi and the two of them stood in the hot Phoenix summer. They could smell the trailer.

"This ain't going to be nice," Victor said. "You don't have to go in."

"You're going to need help."

Victor walked to the front door and opened it. The stink rolled out and made them both gag. Victor's father had lain in that trailer for a week in hundred-degree temperatures before anyone found him. And the only reason anyone found him was because of the smell. They needed dental records to identify him. That's exactly what the coroner said. They needed dental records.

"Oh, man," Victor said. "I don't know if I can do this."

"Well, then don't."

"But there might be something valuable in there."

"I thought his money was in the bank."

"It is. I was talking about pictures and letters and stuff like that."

"Oh," Thomas said as he held his breath and followed Victor into the trailer.

When Victor was twelve, he stepped into an underground wasp nest. His foot was caught in the hole, and no matter how hard he struggled, Victor couldn't pull free. He might have died there, stung a thousand times, if Thomas Builds-the-Fire had not come by.

"Run," Thomas yelled and pulled Victor's foot from the hole. They ran then, hard as they ever had, faster than Billy Mills, faster than Jim Thorpe,[2] faster than the wasps could fly.

2 **Billy Mills . . . Jim Thorpe:** Native American Olympic athletes. Both were gold medalists—Thorpe in 1912 and Mills in 1964.

Victor and Thomas ran until they couldn't breathe, ran until it was cold and dark outside, ran until they were lost and it took hours to find their way home. All the way back, Victor counted his stings.

"Seven," Victor said. "My lucky number."

Victor didn't find much to keep in the trailer. Only a photo album and a stereo. Everything else had that smell stuck in it or was useless anyway.

"I guess this is all," Victor said. "It ain't much."

"Better than nothing," Thomas said.

"Yeah, and I do have the pickup."

"Yeah," Thomas said. "It's in good shape."

"Dad was good about that stuff."

"Yeah, I remember your dad."

"Really?" Victor asked. "What do you remember?"

Thomas Builds-the-Fire closed his eyes and told this story: "I remember when I had this dream that told me to go to Spokane, to stand by the Falls in the middle of the city and wait for a sign. I knew I had to go there but I didn't have a car. Didn't have a license. I was only thirteen. So I walked all the way, took me all day, and I finally made it to the Falls. I stood there for an hour waiting. Then your dad came walking up. *What the hell are you doing here?* he asked me. I said, *Waiting for a vision.* Then your father said, *All you're going to get here is mugged.* So he drove me over to Denny's, bought me dinner, and then drove me home to the reservation. For a long time I was mad because I thought my dreams had lied to me. But they didn't. Your dad was my vision. *Take care of each other* is what my dreams were saying. *Take care of each other.*"

Victor was quiet for a long time. He searched his mind for memories of his father, found the good ones, found a few bad ones, added it all up, and smiled.

"My father never told me about finding you in Spokane," Victor said.

"He said he wouldn't tell anybody. Didn't want me to get in trouble. But he said I had to watch out for you as part of the deal."

"Really?"

"Really. Your father said you would need the help. He was right."

"That's why you came down here with me, isn't it?" Victor asked.

"I came because of your father."

Victor and Thomas climbed into the pickup, drove over to the bank, and claimed the three hundred dollars in the savings account.

Thomas Builds-the-Fire could fly.

Once, he jumped off the roof of the tribal school and flapped his arms like a crazy eagle. And he flew. For a second, he hovered, suspended above all the other Indian boys who were too smart or too scared to jump.

"He's flying," Junior yelled, and Seymour was busy looking for the trick wires or mirrors. But it was real. As real as the dirt when Thomas lost altitude and crashed to the ground.

He broke his arm in two places.

"He broke his wing," Victor chanted, and the other Indian boys joined in, made it a tribal song.

"He broke his wing, he broke his wing, he broke his wing," all the Indian boys chanted as they ran off, flapping their wings, wishing they could fly, too. They hated Thomas for his courage, his brief moment as a bird. Everybody has dreams about flying. Thomas flew.

One of his dreams came true for just a second, just enough to make it real.

Victor's father, his ashes, fit in one wooden box with enough left over to fill a cardboard box.

"He always was a big man," Thomas said.

Victor carried part of his father and Thomas carried the rest out to the pickup. They set him down carefully behind the seats, put a cowboy hat on the wooden box and a Dodgers cap on the cardboard box. That's the way it was supposed to be.

"Ready to head back home," Victor asked.

"It's going to be a long drive."

"Yeah, take a couple days, maybe."

"We can take turns," Thomas said.

"Okay," Victor said, but they didn't take turns. Victor drove for sixteen hours straight north, made it halfway up Nevada toward home before he finally pulled over.

"Hey, Thomas," Victor said. "You got to drive for a while."

"Okay."

Thomas Builds-the-Fire slid behind the wheel and started off down the road. All through Nevada, Thomas and Victor had been amazed at the lack of animal life, at the absence of water, of movement.

I can't believe this," Thomas said. "You drive for a thousand miles and there ain't even any bugs smashed on the windshield. I drive for ten seconds and kill the only living thing in Nevada."

"Where is everything?" Victor had asked more than once.

Now when Thomas was finally driving they saw the first animal, maybe the only animal in Nevada. It was a long-eared jackrabbit.

"Look," Victor yelled. "It's alive."

Thomas and Victor were busy congratulating themselves on their discovery when the jackrabbit darted out into the road and under the wheels of the pickup.

"Stop the damn car," Victor yelled and Thomas did stop, backed the pickup to the dead jackrabbit.

"Oh, man, he's dead," Victor said as he looked at the squashed animal.

"Really dead."

"The only thing alive in this whole state and we just killed it."

"I don't know," Thomas said. "I think it was suicide."

Victor looked around the desert, sniffed the air, felt the emptiness and loneliness, and nodded his head.

"Yeah," Victor said. "It had to be suicide."

"I can't believe this," Thomas said. "You drive for a thousand miles and there ain't even any bugs smashed on the windshield. I drive for ten seconds and kill the only living thing in Nevada."

"Yeah," Victor said. "Maybe I should drive."

"Maybe you should."

Thomas Builds-the-Fire walked through the corridors of the tribal school by himself. Nobody wanted to be anywhere near him because of all those stories. Story after story.

Thomas closed his eyes and this story came to him: "We are all given one thing by which our lives are measured, one determination. Mine are the stories which can change or not change the world. It doesn't matter which as long as I continue to tell the stories. My father, he died on Okinawa in World War II, died fighting for this country, which had tried to kill him for years. My mother, she died giving birth to me, died while I was still inside her. She pushed me out into the world with her last breath. I have no brothers or sisters. I have only my stories which came to me before I even had the words to speak. I learned a thousand stories before I took my first thousand steps. They are all I have. It's all I can do."

Thomas Builds-the-Fire told his stories to all those who would stop and listen. He kept telling them long after people had stopped listening.

Victor and Thomas made it back to the reservation just as the sun was rising. It was the beginning of a new day on earth.

"Good morning," Thomas said.

"Good morning."

The tribe was waking up, ready for work, eating breakfast, reading the newspaper, just like everybody else does. Willene LeBret was out in her garden wearing a bathrobe. She waved when Thomas and Victor drove by.

"Crazy Indians made it," she said to herself and went back to her roses.

Victor stopped the pickup in front of Thomas Builds-the-Fire's HUD[3] house. They both yawned, stretched a little, shook dust from their bodies.

"I'm tired," Victor said.

"Of everything," Thomas added.

They both searched for words to end the journey. Victor needed to thank Thomas for his help, for the money, and make the promise to pay it all back.

"Don't worry about the money," Thomas said. "It don't make any difference anyhow."

"Probably not, enit?"

"Nope."

Victor knew that Thomas would remain the crazy story teller who talked to dogs and cars, who listened to the wind and pine trees. Victor knew that he couldn't really be friends with Thomas, even after all that had happened. It was cruel but it was real. As real as the ashes, as Victor's father, sitting behind the seats.

"I know how it is," Thomas said. "I know you ain't going to treat me any better than you did before. I know your friends would give you too much trouble."

Victor was ashamed of himself. Whatever happened to the tribal ties, the sense of community? The only real thing he shared with anybody was a bottle and broken dreams. He owed Thomas something, anything.

---

3 **HUD:** Housing and Urban Development, the federal government department in charge of housing; here it means a house built with HUD funds

"Listen," Victor said and handed Thomas the cardboard box which contained half of his father. "I want you to have this."

Thomas took the ashes and smiled, closed his eyes, and told this story: "I'm going to travel to Spokane Falls one last time and toss these ashes into the water. And your father will rise like a salmon, leap over the bridge, over me, and find his way home. It will be beautiful. His teeth will shine like silver, like a rainbow. He will rise, Victor, he will rise."

Victor smiled.

"I was planning on doing the same thing with my half," Victor said. "But I didn't imagine my father looking anything like a salmon. I thought it'd be like cleaning the attic or something. Like letting things go after they've stopped having any use."

"Nothing stops, cousin," Thomas said. "Nothing stops."

Thomas Builds-the-Fire got out of the pickup and walked up his driveway. Victor started the pickup and began the drive home.

"Wait," Thomas yelled suddenly from his porch. "I just got to ask one favor."

Victor stopped the pickup, leaned out the window, and shouted back. "What do you want?"

"Just one time when I'm telling a story somewhere, why don't you stop and listen?" Thomas asked.

"Just once?"

"Just once."

Victor waved his arms to let Thomas know that the deal was good. It was a fair trade, and that was all Victor had ever wanted from his whole life. So Victor drove his father's pickup toward home while Thomas went into his house, closed the door behind him, and heard a new story come to him in the silence afterwards.

Responding to the Story

1. **LITERARY LENS** In what ways does this "story" break the rules of the traditional plot structure of exposition, rising action, climax, and resolution?

2. Do you think the relationship between Victor and Thomas will change after this trip? Support your answer with evidence from the text.

3. Critics often describe Alexie's writing as "energetic." What techniques help give this story its liveliness?

4. What is your response to the title?

5. In one sentence each, describe the relationship between Victor and his father, and between Thomas and Victor's father.

6. **THE AUTHOR'S STYLE** This story about a storyteller is made up of many shorter stories told by either the narrator or by Thomas Builds-the-Fire. Reread one of these shorter stories and explain how it fits into the overall meaning of the entire story.

Andre Dubus
1936–1999

About the Author

Born in Lake Charles, Louisiana, Andre Dubus entered the Marine Corps after finishing college. He left the military in his late twenties to pursue his career as a writer. "The Intruder," which you are about to read, is his first published story.

Dubus spent the last several years of his life in a wheelchair. When he was in his early fifties, he was struck by a car while helping a stranded motorist at the side of the road, and consequently lost a leg. His nonfiction book about that event and its aftermath, *Broken Vessels*, was a runner-up for the Pulitzer Prize in 1992. Known primarily as a writer of short stories, one of his most recognized works is the short story collection *Dancing After Hours*. His short story "In the Bedroom" was adapted into an Academy Award-nominated film in 2001.

Writer Richard Ravin wrote in the March 18, 1999, issue of *Salon*: "I always thought Andre's beauty as a writer was his patience with the line, playing out the sentence longer and longer, note after note like the scat singers he collected, Ella Fitzgerald or June Christie or Betty Carter."

****

The Author's Style

The writing of Dubus is candid and assertive. Dubus's stories, like Raymond Carver's, have uncomplicated plots involving unexceptional people who have to come to terms with their needs, fantasies, emotions, and questionable behavior. Like Katherine Anne Porter, Dubus pays close attention to the details of daily life in his realistic stories of compassion and understanding. He often uses third-person narrators, showing the emotions and points of view of his characters empathetically and without judging them.

Through almost conversational language, Dubus explores the moral problems of lonely middle-class people who struggle to move beyond their limitations. He is skilled at showing the often-contradictory nature of his characters, many of whom struggle with addictions.

A devout Catholic, Dubus has been called a spiritual writer, one who conveys a sense of mystery and a belief in the miraculous in everyday life. He shares this characteristic with such diverse fellow writers as Flannery O'Connor, Isaac Bashevis Singer, and Bernard Malamud.

In "The Intruder," the author's disclosure of the young man's personality from his own point of view—but not in his own words—helps remind the reader that events can always be judged from more than one perspective.

LITERARY LENS Look for the perspective in this story.

THE
INTRUDER

ANDRE DUBUS

ecause Kenneth Girard loved his parents and his sister and because he could not tell them why he went to the woods, his first moments there were always uncomfortable ones, as if he had left the house to commit a sin. But he was thirteen and he could not say that he was going to sit on a hill and wait for the silence and trees and sky to close in on him, wait until they all became a part of him and thought and memory ceased and the voices began. He could only say that he was going for a walk and, since there was so much more to say, he felt cowardly and deceitful and more lonely than before.

He could not say that on the hill he became great, that he had saved a beautiful girl from a river (the voice then had been gentle and serious and she had loved him), or that he had ridden into town, his clothes dusty, his black hat pulled low over his sunburned face, and an hour later had ridden away with four fresh notches on the butt of his six-gun, or that with the count of three-and-two and the bases loaded, he had driven the ball so far and high that the outfielders did not even move, or that he had waded through surf and sprinted over sand, firing his Tommy gun and shouting to his soldiers behind him.

Now he was capturing a farmhouse. In the late movie the night before, the farmhouse had been very important, though no one ever said why, and sitting there in the summer dusk, he watched the backs of his soldiers as they advanced through the woods below him and crossed the clear, shallow creek and climbed the hill that he faced. Occasionally, he lifted his twenty-two-caliber rifle and fired at a rusty tin can across the creek, the can becoming a Nazi face in a window as he squeezed the trigger and the voices filled him: *You got him, Captain. You got him.* For half an hour he sat and fired at the can, and anyone who might have seen him could never know that he was doing anything else, that he had been wounded in the shoulder and lost half his men but had captured the farmhouse.

Kenneth looked up through the trees, which were darker green now. While he had been watching his battle, the earth, too, had become darker, shadowed, with patches of late sun on the grass and brown fallen pine needles. He stood up, then looked down at the creek, and across it, at the hill on the other side. His soldiers were gone. He was hungry, and he turned and walked back through the woods.

Then he remembered that his mother and father were going to a party in town that night and he would be alone with Connie. He liked being alone, but, even more, he liked being alone with his sister. She was nearly seventeen; her skin was fair, her cheeks colored, and she had long black hair that came down to her shoulders; on the right side of her face, a wave of it reached the corner of her eye. She was the most beautiful girl he knew. She was also the only person with whom, for his entire life, he had been nearly perfectly at ease. He could be silent with her or he could say whatever occurred to him and he never had to think about it first to assure himself that it was not foolish or, worse, uninteresting.

Leaving the woods, he climbed the last gentle slope and entered the house. He leaned his rifle in the corner of his room, which faced the quiet blacktop road, and went to the bathroom and washed his hands. Standing at the lavatory, he looked into the mirror. He suddenly felt as if he had told a lie. He was looking at his face and, as he did several times each day, telling himself, without words, that it was a handsome face. His skin was fair, as Connie's was, and he had color in his cheeks; but his hair, carefully parted and combed, was more brown than black. He believed that Connie thought he was exactly like her, that he was talkative and well liked. But she never saw him with his classmates. He felt that he was deceiving her.

He left the house and went into the outdoor kitchen and sat on a bench at the long, uncovered table and folded his arms on it.

"Did you kill anything?" Connie asked.

"Tin cans."

His father turned from the stove with a skillet of white perch in his hand.

"They're good ones," he said.

"Mine are the best," Kenneth said.

"You didn't catch but two."

"They're the best."

His mother put a plate in front of him, then opened a can of beer and sat beside him. He sat quietly, watching his father at the stove. Then he looked at his mother's hand holding the beer can. There were veins and several freckles on the back of it. Farther up her forearm was a small yellow bruise; the flesh at her elbow was wrinkled. He looked at her face. People said that he and Connie looked like her, so he supposed it was true, but he could not see the resemblance.

"Daddy and I are going to the Gossetts' tonight," she said.

"I know."

"I wrote the phone number down," his father said. "It's under the phone."

"Okay."

His father was not tall either, but his shoulders were broad. Kenneth wondered if his would be like that when he grew older. His father was the only one in the family who tanned in the sun.

"And *please*, Connie," his mother said, "will you go to sleep at a reasonable hour? It's hard enough to get you up for Mass when you've had a good night's sleep."

"Why don't we go into town for the evening Mass?"

"No. I don't like it hanging over my head all day."

"All right. When will y'all be home?"

"About two. And that doesn't mean read in bed till then. You need your sleep."

"We'll go to bed early," Connie said.

His father served fried perch and hush puppies onto their plates and they had French bread and catsup and Tabasco sauce and iced tea. After dinner, his father read the newspaper and his mother read a *Reader's Digest* condensation, then they showered and dressed, and at seven-thirty, they left. He and Connie followed them to the door. Connie kissed them; then he did. His mother and father looked happy, and he felt good about that.

"We'll be back about two," his mother said. "Keep the doors locked."

"Definitely," Connie said. "And we'll bar the windows."

"Well, you never know. Y'all be good. G'night."

"Hold down the fort, son," his father said.

"I will."

Then they were gone, the screen door slamming behind them, and Connie left the sunporch, but he stood at the door, listening to the car starting and watching its headlights as it backed down the trail through the yard, then turned into the road and drove away. Still he did not move. He loved the nights at the camp when they were left alone. At home, there was a disturbing climate about their evenings alone, for distant voices of boys in the neighborhood reminded him that he was not alone entirely by choice. Here, there were no sounds.

He latched the screen and went into the living room. Connie was sitting in the rocking chair near the fireplace, smoking a cigarette. She looked at him, then flicked ashes into an ashtray on her lap.

"Now don't you tell on me."

"I didn't know you did that."

"Please don't tell. Daddy would skin me alive."

"I won't."

He could not watch her. He looked around the room for a book.

"Douglas is coming tonight," she said.

"Oh," He picked up the *Reader's Digest* book and pretended to look at it. "Y'all going to watch TV?" he said.

"Not if you want to."

"It doesn't matter."

"You watch it. You like Saturday nights."

She looked as if she had been smoking for a long time, all during the summer and possibly the school year, too, for months or even a year without his knowing it. He was hurt. He laid down the book.

"Think I'll go outside for a while," he said.

He went onto the sunporch and out the door and walked down the sloping car trail that led to the road. He stopped at the gate, which was open, and leaned on it. Forgetting Connie, he looked over his shoulder at the camp, thinking that he would never tire of it. They had been there for six weeks, since early June, his father coming on Friday evenings and leaving early Monday mornings, driving sixty miles to their home in southern Louisiana. Kenneth fished during the day, swam with Connie in the creeks, read novels about baseball, and watched the major league games on television. He thought winter at the camp was better, though. They came on weekends and hunted squirrels, and there was a fireplace.

He looked down the road. The closest camp was half a mile away, on the opposite side of the road, and he could see its yellow-lighted windows through the trees. *That's the house. Quiet now. We'll sneak through the woods and get the guard, then charge the house. Come on.* Leaning against the gate, he stared into the trees across the road and saw himself leading his soldiers through the woods. They reached the guard. His back was turned and Kenneth crawled close to him, then stood up and slapped a hand over the guard's mouth and stabbed him in the back. They rushed the house and Kenneth reached the door first and kicked it open. The general looked up from his desk, then tried to get his pistol from his holster. Kenneth shot him with his Tommy gun. *Grab those papers, men. Let's get out of here.* They got the papers and ran outside and Kenneth stopped to throw a hand grenade through the door. He reached the woods before it exploded.

> *That's the house. Quiet now. We'll sneak through the woods and get the guard, then charge the house. Come on.* Leaning against the gate, he stared into the trees across the road and saw himself leading his soldiers through the woods.

He turned from the gate and walked toward the house, looking around him at the dark pines. He entered the sunporch and latched the screen; then he smelled chocolate, and he went to the kitchen. Connie was stirring a pot of fudge on the stove. She had changed to a fresh pale blue shirt, the tails of it hanging almost to the bottom of her white shorts.

"It'll be a while," she said.

He nodded, watching her hand and the spoon. He thought of Douglas coming and began to feel nervous.

"What time's Douglas coming?"

"Any minute now. Let me know if you hear his car."

"All right."

He went to his room and picked up his rifle; then he saw the magazine on the chest of drawers and he leaned the rifle in the corner again. Suddenly his mouth was dry. He got the magazine and quickly turned the pages until he found her: she was stepping out of the surf on the French Riviera, laughing, as if the man with her had just said something funny. She was blond and very tan and she wore a bikini. The photograph was in color. For several moments he looked at it; then he got the rifle and cleaning kit and sat in the rocking chair in the living room, with the rifle across his lap. He put a patch on the cleaning rod and dipped it in bore cleaner and pushed it down the barrel, the handle of the rod clanging against the muzzle. He worked slowly, pausing often to listen for Douglas's car, because he wanted to be cleaning the rifle when Douglas came. Because Douglas was a tackle on the high school football team in the town, and Kenneth had never been on a football team, and never would be.

The football players made him more uncomfortable than the others. They walked into the living room and firmly shook his father's hand, then his hand, beginning to talk as soon as they entered, and they sat and waited for Connie, their talking never ceasing, their big chests and shoulders leaned forward, their faces slowly turning as they looked at each picture on the wall, at the designs on the rug, at the furniture, passing over Kenneth as if he were another chair, filling the room with a feeling of strength and self-confidence that defeated him, paralyzing his tongue and even his mind, so that he merely sat in thoughtless anxiety, hoping they would not speak to him, hoping especially that they would not ask: *You play football?* Two of them had, and he never forgot it. He had answered with a mute, affirming nod.

He had always been shy and, because of it, he had stayed on the periphery of sports for as long as he could remember. When his teachers forced him to play, he spent an anxious hour trying not to become involved, praying in right field that no balls would come his way, lingering on the outside of the huddle so that no one would look up and see his face and decide to throw him a pass on the next play.

But he found that there was one thing he could do and he did it alone, or with his father: he could shoot and he could hunt. He felt that shooting was the only thing that had ever been easy for him. Schoolwork was, too, but he considered that a curse.

He was not disturbed by the boys who were not athletes, unless, for some reason, they were confident anyway. While they sat and waited for Connie, he was cheerful and teasing, and they seemed to like him. The girls were best. He walked into the living room and they stopped their talking and laughing and all of them greeted him and sometimes they said: "Connie, he's so cute," or "I wish you were three years older," and he said: "Me, too," and tried to be witty and usually was.

He heard a car outside.

"Douglas is here," he called.

Connie came through the living room, one hand arranging the wave of hair near her right eye, and went into the sunporch. Slowly, Kenneth wiped the rifle with an oily rag. He heard Douglas's loud voice and laughter and heavy footsteps on the sunporch; then they came into the living room. Kenneth raised his face.

"Hi," he said.

"How's it going?"

"All right."

Douglas Bakewell was not tall. He had blond hair, cut so short on top that you could see his scalp, and a reddish face, and sunburned arms, covered with bleached hair. A polo shirt fit tightly over his chest and shoulders and biceps.

"Whatcha got there?" Douglas said.

"Twenty-two."

"Let's see."

"Better dry it."

He briskly wiped it with a dry cloth and handed it to Douglas. Quickly, Douglas worked the bolt, aimed at the ceiling, and pulled the trigger.

"Nice trigger," he said.

He held it in front of his waist and looked at it, then gave it to Kenneth.

"Well, girl," he said, turning to Connie, "where's the beer?"

"Sit down and I'll get you one."

She went to the kitchen. Douglas sat on the couch and Kenneth picked up his cleaning kit and, not looking at Douglas, walked into his bedroom.

He stayed there until Connie returned from the kitchen; then he went into the living room. They were sitting on the couch. Connie was smoking again. Kenneth kept walking toward the sunporch.

"I'll let you know when the fudge is ready," Connie said.

"All right."

On the sunporch, he turned on the television and sat in front of it. He watched ten minutes of a Western before he was relaxed again, before he settled in his chair, oblivious to the quiet talking in the living room, his mind beginning to wander happily as a gunfighter in dark clothes moved across the screen.

By the time the fudge was ready, he was watching a detective story, and when Connie called him, he said: "Okay, in a minute," but did not move, and finally she came to the sunporch with a saucer of fudge and set it on a small table beside his chair.

"When that's over, you better go to bed," she said.

"I'm not sleepy."

"You know what Mother said."

"*You're* staying up."

"Course I am. I'm also a little older than you."

"I want to see the late show."

"No!"

"Yes, I am."

"I'll tell Daddy."

"He doesn't care."

"I'll tell him you wouldn't listen to me."

"I'll tell him you smoke."

"Oh, I could *wring* your neck!"

She went to the living room. He tried to concentrate on the Western, but it was ruined. The late show came on and he had seen it several months before and did not want to see it again, but he would not go to bed. He watched absently. Then he had to urinate. He got up and went into the living room, walking quickly, only glancing at them once, but when he did, Connie smiled and, with her voice friendly again, said: "What is it?"

He stopped and looked at her.

"*Red River.*"

He smiled.

"I already saw it," he said.

"You watching it again?"

"Maybe so."

"Okay."

He went to the bathroom and when he came back, they were gone. He went to the sunporch. Connie and Douglas were standing near the back door. The television was turned off. Kenneth wondered if Connie had seen *Red River*. If she had not, he could tell her what had happened during the part she missed. Douglas was whispering to Connie, his face close to hers. Then he looked at Kenneth.

"Night," he said.

"G'night," Kenneth said.

He was gone. Kenneth picked up the saucer his fudge had been on and took it to the kitchen and put it in the sink. He heard Douglas's car backing down the trail, and he went to the sunporch, but Connie was not there, so he went to the bathroom door and said: "You seen *Red River*?"

"Yes."

"You taking a bath?"

"Just washing my face. I'm going to bed."

He stood quietly for a moment. Then he went into the living room and got a magazine and sat in the rocking chair, looking at the people in the advertisements. Connie came in, wearing a robe. She leaned over his chair and he looked up and she kissed him.

"Good night," she said.

"G'night."

"You going to bed soon?"

"In a minute."

She got her cigarettes and an ashtray from the coffee table and went to her room and closed the door. After a while, he heard her getting into bed.

He looked at half the magazine, then laid it on the floor. Being awake in the house where everyone else was sleeping made him lonely. He went to the sunporch and latched the screen, then closed the door and locked it. He left the light on but turned out the one in the living room. Then he went to his room and took off everything but his shorts. He was about to turn out the light when he looked at the chest of drawers and saw the magazine. He hesitated. Then he picked it up and found the girl and looked at the exposed tops of her breasts and at her navel and below it. Suddenly he closed the magazine and raised his eyes to the ceiling, then closed them and said three

Hail Mary's. Without looking at it, he picked up the magazine and took it to the living room, and went back to his bedroom and lay on his belly on the floor and started doing push-ups. He had no trouble with the first eight; then they became harder, and by the fifteenth he was breathing fast and his whole body was trembling as he pushed himself up from the floor. He did one more, then stood up and turned out the light and got into bed.

His room extended forward of the rest of the house, so that, from his bed, he could look through the window to his left and see the living room and Connie's bedroom. He rolled on his back and pulled the sheet up to his chest. He could hear crickets outside his window.

He flexed his right arm and felt the bicep. It seemed firmer than it had in June, when he started doing push-ups every night. He closed his eyes and began the Lord's Prayer and got as far as *Thy kingdom come* before he heard it.

Now it was not the crickets that he heard. He heard his own breathing and the bedsprings as his body tensed; then he heard it again, somewhere in front of the house: a cracking twig, a rustle of dried leaves, a foot on hard earth. Slowly, he rolled on his left side and looked out the windows. He waited to be sure, but he did not have to; then he waited to decide what he would do, and he did not have to wait for that either, because he already knew, and he looked at the far corner of the room where his rifle was, though he could not see it, and he looked out the window again, staring at the windows of the living room and Connie's room, forcing himself to keep his eyes there, as if it would be all right if the prowler did not come into his vision, did not come close to the house; but listening to the slow footsteps, Kenneth knew that he would.

Get up. Get up and get the rifle. If you don't do it now, he might come to this window and look in and then it'll be too late.

For a moment, he did not breathe. Then, slowly, stopping at each sound of the bedsprings, he rolled out of bed and crouched on the floor beneath the window. He did not move. He listened to his breathing, for there was no other sound, not even crickets, and he began to tremble, thinking the prowler might be standing above him, looking through his window at the empty bed. He held his breath. Then he heard the footsteps again, in front of the house, closer now, and he thought; *He's by the pines in front of Connie's room.* He crawled away from the window, thinking of a large, bearded man standing in the pine trees thirty yards from Connie's room, studying the house and deciding which window to use; then he stood up and walked on tiptoes to the chest of drawers and moved his hand over the top of it until he touched the handful of bullets, his fingers quickly closing on them, and he picked up the rifle and took out the magazine and loaded it, then inserted it again and laid the extra bullets on the chest of drawers. Now he had to work the bolt. He pulled it up and back and eased it forward again.

Staying close to the wall, he tiptoed back to the window, stopping at the edge of it, afraid to look out and see a face looking in. He heard nothing. He looked through the windows in the opposite wall, thinking that if the prowler had heard him getting the rifle, he could have run back to the road, back to wherever he had come from, or he could still be hiding in the pines, or he could have circled to the rear of the house to hide again and listen, but there was no way of knowing, and he would have to stand in the room, listening, until his father came home. He thought of going to wake Connie, but he was afraid to move. Then he heard him again, near the pines, coming toward the house. He kneeled and pressed his shoulder against the wall, moving his face slightly, just enough to look out the screen and see the prowler walking toward Connie's window, stopping there and looking over his shoulder at the front yard and the road, then reaching out and touching the screen.

Kenneth rose and moved away from the wall, standing close to his bed now; he aimed through the screen, found the side of the man's head, then fired. A scream filled the house, the yard, his mind, and he thought at first it was the prowler, who was lying on the ground now, but it was a high, shrieking scream; it was Connie, and he ran into the living room, but she was already on the sunporch, unlocking the back door, not screaming now, but crying, pulling open the wooden door and hitting the screen with both hands, then stopping to unlatch it, and he yelled: "Connie!"

She turned, her hair swinging around her cheek.

"Get away from me!"

Then she ran outside, the screen door slamming, the shriek starting again, a long, high wail, ending in front of the house with "*Douglas, Douglas, Douglas!*" Then he knew.

Afterward, it seemed that the events of a year had occurred in an hour, and, to Kenneth, even that hour seemed to have a quality of neither speed nor slowness, but a kind of suspension, as if time were not passing at all. He remembered somehow calling his father and crying into the phone: "I shot Douglas Bakewell," and because of the crying, his father kept saying: "What's that, son? What did you say?" and then he lay facedown on his bed and cried, thinking of Connie outside with Douglas, hearing her sometimes when his own sounds lulled, and sometimes thinking of Connie inside with Douglas, if he had not shot him. He remembered the siren when it was far away and their voices as they brought Connie into the house. The doctor had come first, then his mother and father, then the sheriff; but, remembering, it was as if they had all come at once, for there was always a soothing or questioning face over his bed. He remembered the footsteps and hushed voices as they carried the body past his window, while his mother sat on the bed and stroked his forehead and cheek. He would never forget that.

Now the doctor and sheriff were gone and it seemed terribly late, almost sunrise. His father came into the room, carrying a glass of water, and sat on the bed.

"Take this," he said. "It'll make you sleep."

Kenneth sat up and took the pill from his father's palm and placed it on his tongue, then drank the water. He lay on his back and looked at his father's face. Then he began to cry.

"I thought it was a prowler," he said.

"It was, son. A prowler. We've told you that."

"But Connie went out there and she stayed all that time and she kept saying '*Douglas*' over and over; I heard her–"

"She wasn't out there with *him*. She was just out in the yard. She was in shock. She meant she wanted Douglas to be there with her. To help."

"No, *no*. It was *him*."

"It was a prowler. You did right. There's no telling what he might have done."

Kenneth looked away.

"He was going to her room," he said. "That's why she went to bed early. So I'd go to bed."

"It was a prowler," her father said.

Now Kenneth was sleepy. He closed his eyes and the night ran together in his mind and he remembered the rifle in the corner and thought: *I'll throw it in the creek tomorrow. I never want to see it again.* He would be asleep soon. He saw himself standing on the hill and throwing his rifle into the creek; then the creek became an ocean, and he stood on a high cliff and for a moment he was a mighty angel, throwing all guns and cruelty and sex and tears into the sea.

Responding to the Story

1. **LITERARY LENS** In five words or less, describe Kenneth's main inner motives and concerns.

2. Look for evidence in the story that others do not find Kenneth as awkward and unappealing as he thinks he is. Why do you think he has a negative image of himself?

3. Why do you think his sister is the only person with whom Kenneth has ever felt at ease?

4. Why do you think Kenneth shoots the "prowler"?

5. **THE AUTHOR'S STYLE** Dubus is praised by critics for drawing characters that readers come to empathize with but that are otherwise troubled or troubling. In what ways does Kenneth match this character type?

Tobias Wolff
1945

About the Author

Born in Birmingham, Alabama, Tobias Wolff had a difficult childhood and adolescence. His father was a con man and his parents divorced when he was young, his mother taking him to raise and his father taking his brother. He traveled with his mother, who moved frequently, finally settling in Seattle where she remarried an abusive man. Wolff recalls those experiences in *This Boy's Life: A Memoir*, which was made into a film in 1993.

After serving in Vietnam, Wolff was educated at Oxford University and Stanford University. He is known primarily as a writer of short stories; his collections of them include *In the Garden* *of North American Martyrs* and *Back in the World*.

In *Passion and Craft*, Wolff is quoted as saying, "All my stories are in one way or another auto-biographical. Sometimes they're autobiographical in the actual events which they describe, sometimes more in their depiction of a particular character. In fact, you could say that all my characters are reflections of myself, in that I share their wish to count for something and their almost complete confusion as to how this is supposed to be done."

★★★★★★★★★★★

The Author's Style

Wolff has worked as a waiter, night watchman, high school teacher, and reporter. His fiction often involves ordinary people in everyday situations who make extraordinary discoveries about the role of morality in their lives. Wolff's stories are often character studies that turn on human impulse, weakness, loneliness, and betrayal—always with a sense that people's choices and actions have complex moral consequences, often unforeseen. In some stories the ending is inconclusive, suggesting that the full impact of events is yet to come. Lying and other forms of deception make up a consistent thematic thread in his fiction.

Wolff's writing is straightforward. His stories develop forcefully, but he is more interested in the circumstances and the complex consequences of people's actions than in using them to teach, warn, or judge. At times his stories reveal the flawed-but-funny aspects of experience that make us refer to life as the human comedy. The story you are about to read was inspired by an incident that occurred when Wolff was writing obituaries for the *Washington Post*.

LITERARY LENS Watch for the role that morality plays in this story.

MORTALS

TOBIAS WOLFF

T he metro editor called my name across the newsroom and beckoned to me. When I got to his office he was behind the desk. A man and a woman were there with him, the man nervous on his feet, the woman in a chair, bony-faced and vigilant, holding the straps of her bag with both hands. Her suit was the same bluish gray as her hair. There was something soldierly about her. The man was short, doughy, rounded off. The burst vessels in his cheeks gave him a merry look until he smiled.

"I didn't want to make a scene," he said. "We just thought you should know." He looked at his wife.

"You bet I should know," the metro editor said. "This is Mr. Givens," he said to me, "Mr. Ronald Givens. Name ring a bell?"

"Vaguely."

"I'll give you a hint. He's not dead."

"Okay," I said. "I've got it."

"Another hint," the metro editor said. Then he read aloud, from that morning's paper, the obituary I had written announcing Mr. Givens's death. I'd written a whole slew of obits the day before, over twenty of them, and I

HARD AND SOFT FIGURES, Saul Steinburg, 1952

didn't remember much of it, but I did remember the part about him working for the IRS for thirty years. I'd recently had problems with the IRS, so that
stuck in my mind.

As Givens listened to his obituary he looked from one to the other of us.
He wasn't as short as I'd first thought. It was an impression he created by
hunching his shoulders and thrusting his neck forward like a turtle. His eyes
were soft, restless. He used them like a peasant, in swift measuring glances
with his face averted.

He laughed when the metro editor was
through. "Well, it's accurate," he said. "I'll give
you that."

"Except for one thing." The woman was
staring at me.

"I owe you an apology," I told Givens. "It
looks like somebody pulled the wool over my
eyes."

*He wasn't as short as
I'd first thought. It was an
impression he created
by hunching his shoulders
and thrusting his neck
forward like a turtle.*

"Apology accepted!" Givens said. He
rubbed his hands together as if we'd all just
signed something. "You have to see the humor,
Dolly. What was it Mark Twain said? 'The
reports of my death—'"

"So what happened?" the metro editor said to me.

"I wish I knew."

"That's not good enough," the woman said.

"Dolly's pretty upset," Givens said.

"She has every right to be upset," the metro editor said. "Who called in
the notice?" he asked me.

"To tell the truth, I don't remember. I suppose it was somebody from the
funeral home."

"You call them back?"

"I don't believe I did, no."

"Check with the family?"

"He most certainly did not," Mrs. Givens said.

"No," I said.

The metro editor said, "What do we do before we run an obituary?"

"Check back with the funeral home and the family."

"But you didn't do that."

"No, sir. I guess I didn't."

"Why not?"

I made a helpless gesture with my hands and tried to appear properly stricken, but I had no answer. The truth was, I never followed those procedures. People were dying all the time. I hadn't seen the point in asking their families if they were really dead, or calling funeral parlors back to make sure the funeral parlors had just called me. All this procedural stuff was a waste of time, I'd decided; it didn't seem possible that anyone could amuse himself by concocting phony death notices and impersonating undertakers. Now I saw that this was foolish of me, and showed a radical failure of appreciation for the varieties of human pleasure.

But there was more to it than that. Since I was still on the bottom rung in metro, I wrote a lot of obituaries. Some days they gave me a choice between that and marriage bulletins, but most of the time obits were all I did, one after another, morning to night. After four months of this duty I was full of the consciousness of death. It soured me. It puffed me up with morbid snobbery, the feeling that I knew a secret nobody else had even begun to suspect. It made me wearily philosophical about the value of faith and passion and hard work, at a time when my life required all of these. It got me down.

I should have quit, but I didn't want to go back to the kind of jobs I'd had before a friend's father fixed me up with this one—waiting on tables, mostly, pulling night security in apartment buildings, anything that would leave my days free for writing. I'd lived like this for three years, and what did I have to show for it? A few stories in literary journals that nobody read, including me. I began to lose my nerve. I'd given up a lot for my writing, and it wasn't giving anything back—not respectability, nor money, nor love. So when this job came up I took it. I hated it and did it badly, but I meant to keep it. Someday I'd move over to the police beat. Things would get better.

I was hoping that the metro editor would take his pound of flesh and let me go, but he kept after me with questions, probably showing off for Givens and his wife, letting them see a real newshound at work. In the end I was forced to admit that I hadn't called any other families or funeral homes that day, nor, in actual fact, for a good long time.

Now that he had his answer, the metro editor didn't seem to know what to do with it. It seemed to be more than he'd bargained for. At first he just sat there. Then he said, "Let me get this straight. Just how long has this paper been running unconfirmed obituaries?"

"About three months," I said. And as I made this admission I felt a smile on my lips, already there before I could fight it back or dissemble it. It was the **rictus** of panic, the same smile I'd given my mother when she told me my father had died. But of course the metro editor didn't know that.

rictus:
gaping grin

He leaned forward in his chair and gave his head a little shake, the way a horse will, and said, "Clean out your desk." I don't think he'd meant to fire me; he looked surprised by his own words. But he didn't take them back.

Givens looked from one to the other of us. "Now hold on here," he said. "Let's not blow this all out of proportion. This is a live-and-learn situation. This isn't something a man should lose his job over."

"He wouldn't have," Mrs. Givens said, "if he'd done it right."

Which was a truth beyond argument.

I cleaned out my desk. As I left the building I saw Givens by the newsstand, watching the door. I didn't see his wife. He walked up to me, raised his hands, and said, "What can I say? I'm at a loss for words."

"Don't worry about it," I told him.

"I sure as heck didn't mean to get you fired. It wasn't even my idea to come in, if you want to know the truth."

"Forget it. It was my own fault." I was carrying a box full of notepads and files, several books. It was heavy. I shifted it under my other arm.

"Look," Givens said, "how about I treat you to lunch. What do you say? It's the least I can do."

I looked up and down the street.

"Dolly's gone on home," he said. "How about it?"

I didn't especially want to eat lunch with Givens, but it seemed to mean a lot to him, and I didn't feel ready to go home yet. What would I do there? Sure, I said, lunch sounded fine. Givens asked me if I knew anyplace reasonable nearby. There was a Chinese joint a few doors down, but it was always full of reporters. I didn't want to watch them try to conjure up sympathy over my situation, which they'd laugh about anyway the minute I left, not that I blamed them. I suggested Tad's Steakhouse over by the cable car turnaround. You could get a six-ounce sirloin, salad, and baked potato for a buck twenty-nine. This was 1974.

"I'm not that short," Givens said. But he didn't argue, and that's where we went.

Givens picked at his food, then pushed the plate away and contemplated mine. When I asked if his steak was okay, he said he didn't have much appetite.

"So," I said, "who do you think called it in?"

His head was bent. He looked up at me from under his eyebrows. "Boy, you've got me there. It's a mystery."

"You must have some idea."

"Nope. Not a one."

"Think it could've been someone you worked with?"

"Nah." He shook a toothpick out of the dispenser. His hands were pale and **sinewy**.

sinewy:
tough; stringy

"It had to be somebody who knows you. You have friends, right?"

"Sure."

"Maybe you had an argument, something like that. Somebody's mad at you."

He kept his mouth covered with one hand while he worked the toothpick with the other. "You think so? I had it figured for more of a joke."

"Well, it's a pretty serious joke, calling in a death notice on someone. Pretty threatening. I'd sure feel threatened, if it was me."

Givens inspected the toothpick, then dropped it in the ashtray. "I hadn't thought of it like that," he said. "Maybe you're right."

"You're sure it isn't one of your friends," I said. "It could be a little thing. You played cards, landed some big ones, then folded early before he had a chance to recoup."

I could see he didn't believe it for a second—didn't understand what had happened. The words of death had been pronounced on him, and now his life would be lived in relation to those words, in failing opposition to them, until they overpowered him and became true. Someone had put a contract out on Givens, with words as the torpedoes. Or so it appeared to me.

"You're sure it isn't one of your friends," I said. "It could be a little thing. You played cards, landed some big ones, then folded early before he had a chance to recoup."

"I don't play cards," Givens said.

"How about your wife? Any problems in that department?"

"Nope."

"Everything smooth as silk, huh?"

He shrugged. "Same as ever."

"How come you call her Dolly? That wasn't the name in the obit."

"No reason. I've always called her that. Everybody does."

"I don't feature her as a Dolly," I said.

He didn't answer. He was watching me.

"Let's say Dolly gets mad at you, really mad . . . She wants to send you a message—something outside normal channels."

"Not a chance." Givens said this without **bristling**. He didn't try to convince me, so I figured he was probably right.

bristling:
becoming angry

"You're survived by a daughter, right? What's her name again?"

"Tina," he said, with some tenderness.

"That's it, Tina. How are things with Tina?"

"We've had our problems. But I can guarantee you, it wasn't her."

"Well, hell's bells," I said. "Somebody did it."

I finished my steak, watching the show outside: winos, evangelists, outpatients, whores, fake hippies selling oregano to tourists in white shoes. Pure theater, even down to the smell of popcorn billowing out of Woolworth's. Richard Brautigan often came here. Tall and owlish, he stooped to his food and ate slowly, ruminating over every bite, his eyes on the street. Some funny things happened here, and some appalling things. Brautigan took it all in and never stopped eating.

I told Givens that we were sitting at the same table where Richard Brautigan sometimes sat.

"Sorry?"

"Richard Brautigan, the writer."

Givens shook his head.

I was ready to go home. "Okay," I said, "you tell me. Who wants you dead?"

"No one wants me dead."

"Somebody's imagining you dead. Thinking about it. The wish is father to the deed."

"Nobody wants me dead. Your problem is, you think everything has to mean something."

That was one of my problems, I couldn't deny it.

"Just out of curiosity," he said, "what did you think of it?"

"Think of what?"

"My obituary." He leaned forward and started fooling with the salt and pepper shakers, tapping them together and sliding them around like partners in a square dance. "I mean, did you get any feeling for who I was? The kind of person I am?"

I shook my head.

"Nothing stood out?"

I said no.

"I see. Maybe you wouldn't mind telling me, what exactly does it take for you to remember someone?"

"Look," I said, "you write obituaries all day, they sort of blur into each other."

"Yes, but you must remember some of them."

"Some of them—sure."

"Which ones?"

"Writers I like. Great baseball players. Movie stars I've been in love with."

"Celebrities, in other words."

"Some of them, yes. Not all."

"You can lead a good life without being a celebrity," he said. "People with big names aren't always big people."

"That's true," I said, "but it's sort of a little person's truth."

"Is that so? And what does that make you?"

> *I*f the only thing that impresses you is having a big name, then you must be a regular midget. At least that's the way I see it." He gave me a hard look and gripped the salt and pepper shakers like a machine gunner about to let off a burst.

I didn't answer.

"If the only thing that impresses you is having a big name, then you must be a regular midget. At least that's the way I see it." He gave me a hard look and gripped the salt and pepper shakers like a machine gunner about to let off a burst.

"That's not the only thing that impresses me."

"Oh yeah? What else, then?"

I let the question settle. "Moral distinction," I said.

He repeated the words. They sounded **pompous**.

pompous:
self-important

"You know what I mean," I said.

"Correct me if I'm wrong," he said, "but I have a feeling that's not your department, moral distinction."

I didn't argue.

"And you're obviously not a celebrity."

"Obviously."

"So where does that leave you?" When I didn't answer, he said, "Think you'd remember your own obituary?"

"Probably not."

"No probably about it! You wouldn't even give it a second thought."

"Okay, definitely not."

"You wouldn't even give it a second thought. And you'd be wrong. Because you probably have other qualities that would stand out if you were looking closely. Good qualities. Everybody has something. What do you pride yourself on?"

"I'm a survivor," I said. But I didn't think that claim would carry much weight in an obituary.

Givens said, "With me it's loyalty. Loyalty is a very clear pattern in my life. You would've noticed that if you'd had your eyes open. When you read that a man has served his country in time of war, stayed married to the same woman for forty-two years, worked at the same job, by God, that should tell you something. That should give you a certain picture."

He stopped to nod at his own words. "And it hasn't always been easy," he said.

I had to laugh, mostly at myself for being such a dim bulb. "It was you," I said. "You did it."

"Did what?"

"Called in the obit."

"Why would I do that?"

"You tell me."

"That would be saying I did it." Givens couldn't help smiling, proud of what a slyboots he was.

I said, "You're out of your ever-loving mind," but I didn't mean it. There was nothing in what Givens had done that I couldn't make sense of or even, in spite of myself, admire. He had dreamed up a way of going to his own funeral. He'd tried on his last suit, so to speak, seen himself rouged up and laid out, and listened to his own eulogy. And the best part was, he resurrected afterward. That was the real point, even if he thought he was doing it to throw a scare into Dolly or put his virtues on display. Resurrection was what it was all about, and this tax collector had gotten himself a taste of it. It was biblical.

"You're a caution, Mr. Givens. You're a definite caution."

"I didn't come here to be insulted."

"Relax," I told him. "I'm not mad."

He scraped his chair back and stood up. "I've got better things to do than sit here and listen to accusations."

I followed him outside. I wasn't ready to let him go. He had to give me something first. "Admit you did it," I said.

He turned away and started up Powell.

"Just admit it," I said. "I won't hold it against you."

He kept walking, head stuck forward in that turtlish way, navigating the crowd. He was slippery and fast. Finally I took his arm and pulled him into a doorway. His muscles bunched under my fingers. He almost jerked free, but I tightened my grip and we stood there frozen in contention.

"Admit it."

He shook his head.

"I'll break your neck if I have to," I told him.

"Let go," he said.

"If something happened to you right now, your obituary would be solid news. Then I could get my job back."

He tried to pull away again but I held him there.

"It'd make a hell of a story," I said.

I felt his arm go slack. Then he said, almost inaudibly, "Yes." Just that one word.

This was the best I was going to get out of him. It had to be enough. When I let go of his arm he turned and ducked his head and took his place in the stream of people walking past. I started back to Tad's for my box. Just ahead of me a mime was following a young swell in a three-piece suit, catching to the life his leading-man's assurance, the **supercilious** tilt of his chin. A girl laughed raucously. The swell looked back and the mime froze. He was still holding his pose as I came by. I slipped him a quarter, hoping he'd let me pass.

supercilious:
arrogant

522   Tobias Wolff

Responding to the Story

1. LITERARY LENS A morality play—a once-popular kind of drama—
   is a stage piece in which characters are named for, and personify,
   moral or abstract qualities such as Charity, Greed, Death, and
   Youth. Do you think you could recast "Mortals" as a morality play?
   If so, what titles would you assign the narrator and Givens?

2. Givens comments, "People with big names aren't always big people."
   The narrator concedes the point, adding "but it's a little person's
   truth." What do you think he means by "a little person's truth"?

3. "Everybody has something," Givens insists at one point, meaning
   something to pride oneself on. Do you agree? Explain.

4. What do you think the title "Mortals" means?

5. Reread the last paragraph of the story. What are some of the layers
   of meaning in the narrator's wish that the mime let him pass?

6. THE AUTHOR'S STYLE Consider the quotation from Wolff below.
   In what way does "Mortals" "open people up to scrutiny"?

Opening Up

*There's no form you can prescribe for a short story. I would say that the
stories that have stayed with me over the years are stories that make some
unexpected use of the form, that open people up to scrutiny in a way that
I haven't quite seen. I go case by case. Not why are stories good, but why
is this story good.*

—Tobias Wolff, *Stanford Today Online*

Paul Theroux
1941

About the Author

Born in Massachusetts to a large family, Paul Theroux had this to say about his childhood in the book *The Powells.com Interviews*: "My earliest thought, long before I was in high school, was just to go away, get out of my house, get out of my city. I went to Medford High School, but even in grade school and junior high, I fantasized about leaving . . . . So I had the idea of being a traveler, of going to some exotic place, before I wanted to be a writer. Then the idea of writing began to absorb me."

Theroux has written travelogues, essays, and novels based on his travels, sometimes blurring the line between fact and fiction. After hearing claims that his 1989 novel, *My Secret History*, was a thinly disguised autobiography, he turned the tables by writing a novel, *My Other Life*, and calling it an autobiography. "It is a pack of lies that looks like it amounts to a sort of truth," he says. His best-known work includes the travel book *The Great Railway Bazaar*, and two novels which have been adapted for the screen, *St. Jack* and *The Mosquito Coast*.

★★★★★★★★★★★

The Author's Style

Theroux is widely known as a nonfiction travel writer, but he has also written much fiction based on the experiences of visiting and living in other countries. His life of travel began in 1963, when he was an English teacher and Peace Corps volunteer in Africa. A consistent theme of his writing is that of the stranger who experiences discomfort in an unfamiliar situation. Theroux develops characters by having them make discoveries and gain understanding through their relationships with others in "foreign" places.

Since individuals reveal their character when they are under pressure, Theroux chooses his narrators carefully. He enjoys using point of view to reveal the significance of experiences and events. The narrator of his stories that are set in the London Embassy, a consul named Savage, tells stories in precise diplomatic language that conveys information in a safe, protected way.

The cultural contrasts in Theroux's stories create ironic situations, but he treats them with sympathetic humor as well as satirical criticism. Conflicts that arise from characters' responses to new places and unconventional people are intriguing and challenging—even threatening—and for this reason make for interesting stories.

LITERARY LENS Watch for the most frequently used metaphor in this story.

★★

CHARLIE HOGLE'S EARRING

PAUL THEROUX

There is something athletic, something physical, in the way the most successful people reach decisions. The businessmen who plot take-overs, the upstarts who become board chairmen, the masterminds of conglomerates—they are often jocks who regard more thoughtful men as cookie-pushers, and who shoulder their way into offices and hug their allies and muscle in on deals. They move like swaggerers and snatchers, using their elbows when their money fails. And when they are in command they are puppetmasters.

Everett Horton, our number two, prized his football photograph (Yale '51) as much as he did his autographed portrait of the President. Here was another of him, posed with a Russian diplomat, each in white shorts, holding a tennis racket and shaking hands across a tennis net. And others: Horton golfing, Horton fishing,

Horton sailing. Horton had interesting ears—slightly swollen, and gristlier than the average, and they did not match: "Wrestling," someone said. It seemed innocent vanity that Horton thought of himself as a man of action. I suppose he was a man of action. He worked hard. He succeeded where Ambassador Noyes often failed.

Erroll Jeeps used to say: "Watch out for Horton's body English."

He could have sent me a memo, or phoned me, or we might have had lunch. But he had not become minister by sending memos. He was a hugger, a hand-shaker, a back-slapper—body English—and when something important came up he tore downstairs and interrupted whatever I was doing and said, "You're the only one around here who can straighten this out. You've been in the Far East, not in Washington, among the cookie-pushers!"

Today he hugged me. His sweet-whiskey fragrance of aftershave lotion stung my eyes. A file folder was tucked under his arm.

"Is that the problem?"

"That's his file," Horton said.

I tried to catch a glimpse of the name, but he tossed the file onto a chair and kicked my office door shut.

"Let me tell you about it. That'll be quicker than reading this crap." He sat on the edge of my desk and swung one heavy thigh over the other.

"Do you know Charlie Hogle from C and R?"

"I saw him once at your house—that reception you gave for me. I don't go down to the telex room."

"You let your *pyoon* do it, eh?" It was the Malay word for office lackey, and he was mocking me with it. He said, "You should get around more—you'd be amazed at some of the things you find."

"In the telex room?"

"Especially there," Horton said. "This fellow Hogle—very gifted, they say, if you can describe a telex operator in that way. Very personable. Highly efficient, if a bit invisible. He's been here almost three years. No trouble, no scandal, nothing." Horton stopped talking. He stared at me. "I was down there this morning. What do I find?" Horton watched me again, giving me the same dramatic scrutiny as before. He wanted my full attention and a little pause.

I said, "I give up—what did you find?"

"Hogle. With an earring." Horton sighed, slid off the desktop, and threw himself into a chair. He was remarkably **agile** for such a big man.

agile:
nimble; graceful

I said, "An earring?"

"Right. One of those gold . . . loops? Don't make me describe it." Horton suddenly seemed cross. "I don't know anything about earrings."

"Was he wearing it?"

"What a dumb question! Of course he was."

"I thought you were going to tell me that he stole it—that you found it on him."

"He's got a hole in his ear for it."

I said, "So he's had his ear pierced."

"Can you imagine? A special hole in his ear!"

I said, "What exactly is wrong, coach?"

He had encouraged us to use this ridiculous word for him. I had so far refrained from it, and though I felt like a jackass using it today, it seemed to have the right effect. It calmed him. He smiled at me.

"Let's put it at its simplest. Let's be charitable. Let's not mock him," Horton said. "An earring is against regulations."

"Which ones?"

"Dress regulations. The book. It's as if he's wearing a skirt."

"But he's not wearing a skirt. It's jewelry. Is there a subsection for that?"

"Sure! In Muslim countries, Third World countries—"

"This is England, coach."

"And he's a guy! And he's got this thing hanging off his ear!"

"You're not going to get him on a technicality," I said. "All you can do is ask him to remove it. 'Would you mind taking off that earring, Mr. Hogle?'"

Horton did not smile. He began lecturing me. He said, "You act as if there's nothing wrong. Did you know there's no law against lesbianism in this country? Do you know why? Because Queen Victoria refused to believe that women indulged in that sort of behavior!"

"Hogle's earring is hardly in that category," I said.

"Bull! It's precisely in that category. That's how serious a violation it is. It's unthinkable for a man to turn up at work wearing an earring, so there's no legislation, nothing in the rulebook for earrings *per se*. But there's a paragraph on Improper Dress—"

"That covers lewd or suggestive clothes."

"What about Inappropriate Accessories?"

"Religious or racial taboos. Cowhide presents in Hindu countries, pigskin suitcases in Muslim countries, the New York Philharmonic touring Israel and playing Wagner."

"What has Wagner got to do with Accessories?"

"You know what I mean. Earrings don't figure."

"There's something," Horton said. He came over to me and jerked my shoulder, giving me a hug. "It doesn't matter." He grinned. He was a big man. He hugged me sideways as we stood shoulder to shoulder. "There's always something—just find it."

"Why me?" I said. "You could do it more easily."

His eyes became narrow and dark as he said, "I'll tell you why I can't." He looked at the door suspiciously, as if he were about to bark at it. Then he made an ugly disgusted face and whispered, "When I saw Hogle with that thing in his ear, and the hole, and the implications, I felt sick to my stomach." He glanced darkly at the door again. "He's a nice clean-cut guy. I'd lay into him—I'd lose my temper. I know I would, and I want to spare him that. You'll be more rational. You know about these nutty customs. You've been in the Far East."

"Doesn't Hogle have a personnel officer?"

Horton gave me a disdainful look. His expression said I was letting him down, I was a coward, a weakling.

He said, "You don't want to do this, do you?"

"What I want is of no importance," I said. "I do what I'm told."

"Excellent!" he said. Horton stood up straight. The muddy green was gone from his eyes; he was smiling. "Now get down there and tell Hogle to **divest** himself."

divest:
get rid of
something

I said, "That's his file, right?"

"Ignore the file for now. When you've settled this problem, stick a memo in here and hand it back to me. I also want to know why he's wearing it— that's important. And, by the way, this is strictly confidential, this whole matter—everything I've said."

I made a move toward the file.

"You don't really need that," he said.

"Maybe not," I said. "But I think I'll take it home and blow on it."

had a thought, *Why me?* But of course Horton was testing me as much as he was gunning for Hogle. He was trying to discover where my sympathies were: Would I give him an argument, or would I obey? Perhaps I was a latent earring-wearer? Horton's own reaction seemed to me extraordinary. He felt sick to his stomach. That may have been an exaggeration, but the fear that he would lose his temper was almost unbelievable in someone whose temper was always in check. Everett Horton—he wanted to be called 'coach'!—was a man of action. I could not understand his **reticence** now, unless I was right in assuming that I was the real subject of the inquiry.

I was new here—less than four months on the job. I had to play ball. And I must admit I was curious.

The file was thin. Charlie Hogle had come to us from the Army under a program we called Lateral Entry. He had been in the communications unit of the Signal Corps, running a C and R office in Frankfurt. He was twenty-nine, not married, a graduate—German major—of the University of Northern Iowa in Cedar Falls. He had been born and raised in nearby Waterloo, Iowa. His annual job evaluations from the State Department fault-finders were very good. In fact, one suggested—as a black mark—that Hogle had experienced "no negative situations." In other words, he was such a happy fellow he might prove to be a problem. I did not buy that naive analysis. Hogle was a well-adjusted, middle-level technician with a good record, and after looking through this worthy man's file I regretted what I had been ordered to do.

> $\mathcal{H}$ogle was a well-adjusted, middle-level technician with a good record, and after looking through this worthy man's file I regretted what I had been ordered to do.

reticence: restraint; hesitancy

Lunch with him was out: it was both too businesslike and too friendly. Anyway, I hated lunch as unnecessary and time-wasting. Lunch is the ritual meal that makes fat people fat. And dinner was out—too formal. I kept telling myself that this was a small matter. I could send for him. I pictured poor Hogle, clutching his silly earring, cowering in my office, awkward in his chair.

There was only one possibility left—a drink after work. That made it less official, less intimidating, and if I got bored I could plead a previous engagement and go home.

I met him at a large overdecorated pub called the Audley, on the corner of Mount and Audley Streets, not far from the Embassy. Hogle, whom I spotted as American from fifty feet away, was tall even by the generous standards of the Midwest. He was good-looking, with a smooth polite face and clear blue eyes. His blond eyelashes made him look completely frank and unsecretive. His hands were nervous, but his face was innocent and still. His voice had the plain splintery **cadences** of an Iowa Lutheran being truthful. I took him to be a muscular Christian.

cadences:
rhythms

"I kind of like these English beers," he was saying now. (Earlier we had talked about his Sunday school teaching.) "They're a little flat, but they don't swell you up or make you drunk, like lager. Back home—"

As he spoke, I glanced at his earring. It was a small gold hoop, as Horton had said, but Horton had made it seem like junk jewelry, rather vulgar and obvious—and embarrassing to the onlooker. I was surprised to find it a lovely earring. And it was hardly noticeable—too small to be a pirate's, too simple for a transvestite. I thought it suited him. It was the sort of detail that makes some paintings remarkable; it gave his face position and focus—and an undeniable beauty. It was the size, and it had the charm, of Shakespeare's **raffish** earring in the painting in the National Portrait Gallery.

raffish:
carelessly
unconventional

Charlie Hogle was still talking about beer. His favorite was the Colorado Coors brand, because it was made from—

This was ridiculous. We were getting nowhere. I said, "Is that an earring you're wearing?"

His fingers went for it. "Yes," he said. "What do you think of it?"

"Very nice," I said. He smiled. I said, "And unusual."

"It cost me twenty-two pounds. That's almost fifty bucks, but it included getting my ear pierced. I figure it was worth it, don't you?"

Was he trying to draw me?

"You've just," I said, "got the one?"

"One earring's enough!"

I said, "I'm not sure—"

"You think I should have *two*? Don't you think that'd be pushing it a little?"

"Actually," I said, and hated my tone of voice and dreaded what was coming, "I was wondering whether one earring might be pushing it, never mind two."

"You said it was nice." He looked at me closely, and sniffed. He was an honest fellow for whom a contradiction was a bad smell. "What do you mean, 'One earring might be pushing it'?"

"It *is* very nice," I said. "And so are those split skirts the secretaries have started to wear. But I wouldn't be very happy about your wearing a split skirt, Mr. Hogle."

He smiled. He was not threatened: he saw a joke where I had intended a warning. He said, "I'm not wearing a split skirt, sir."

"Yes," I said. "But you are wearing an earring."

"Is that the same as wearing a skirt?"

"Not exactly, but it's the same *kind* of thing."

"What—illegal?"

"Inappropriate," I said. This was Horton's line, and its illogicality was hideously apparent to me as I parroted it. "Like coming to work in your bathing suit, or dyeing your hair green, or—"

I couldn't go on. Hogle was, quite rightly, smiling at the stupidity of my argument. And now I saw that Horton's objection was really a form of abuse.

Hogle said, "I know those things are silly and inappropriate. I wouldn't come to work dressed like a slob. I'm no punk. I don't have green hair."

"Yes, I know."

"I've got a pretty clean record, sir. I got a commendation from the Consul in Frankfurt for hanging on and keeping the telex room open during a Red Army Faction riot. I'm not bragging, sir. I'm just saying I take my job seriously."

"Yes, it's mentioned in your file. I know about it."

"You've been looking in my file," he said. His face became sad, and his attention slackened. He had let go of his earring. "I get it—my ass is in a crack."

"Not yet."

"Sir, I could have bought a cheaper earring—one of those silver dangly ones. Instead I saved up. I bought a nice one. You said so yourself."

"I also said it's rather unusual."

"There's nothing wrong with 'unusual,' is there?"

"Some people think so."

He looked at me, with his lips compressed. He had now seen the purpose of this innocent drink. I had led him here on false pretext; I had deceived him. His eyes went cold.

He said, "Mr. Horton, the minister. It's him, isn't it?"

"It's the regulations," I said lamely.

"He was staring at me the other day, like the second louies used to stare at me when I was in the Army. Even though he was about fifty feet away I could feel his eyes pressing on my neck. You can tell when something's wrong." Hogle shook his head in a heavy rueful way. "I thought he used to like me. Now he's yanked my file and sent you to nail me down."

Hogle was completely correct. But I could not admit it without putting Horton into a vulnerable position and exposing him as petty and spiteful. After all, Horton's was the only objection to the earring. But Horton was boss.

I said, "Everyone thinks that it would be better if you dispensed with your earring."

"I still don't understand why."

"It's contrary to dress regulations. Isn't that obvious?"

He touched the earring, as if for luck. He said, "Maybe they should change the regulations."

"Do you think it's likely they will?"

He made a glum face and said no.

Not any more than your tie clip is a symbol. You don't see many tie clips these days—and I think yours is neat. I think this earring is neat. That's the only reason. Don't you think that's a pretty good reason?"

"Be a sport," I said. "I'm telling you this for your own good. Get rid of that thing and save yourself a headache."

Hogle had been staring at his glass of beer. Without moving his head, he turned his eyes on me and said, "I don't want to seem uncooperative, sir, but I paid good money for this earring. And I had a hole punched in my ear. And I like it, and it's not hurting anyone. So—no way am I going to get rid of it."

"What if we take disciplinary action?"

"That's up to you, sir."

"You could be suspended on half-pay. What do you say to that?"

"I wouldn't like it much," Hogle said.

"Mr. Hogle," I said, "does that earring represent anything? I mean, is it a sort of symbol?"

"Not any more than your tie clip is a symbol. You don't see many tie clips these days—and I think yours is neat. I think this earring is neat. That's the only reason. Don't you think that's a pretty good reason?"

TRACK JACKET, Alex Katz, 1956

I wished he would not ask me these questions. They were traps; they **incriminated** me; they tore me in two. I said, "What I think doesn't matter. I'm an employee. So are you. What you think doesn't matter either. There is nothing personal about this; there's no question about opinion or tolerance or flexibility. It's strictly regulations."

Hogle replied in a sort of wounded whisper. "I'd like to see the regulations, sir," he said. "I'd like to see in black and white which rule I've broken."

"It's a very general regulation concerning appropriate dress," I said. "And we can make it stick. We're going to give you a few days to decide which is more important to you—your earring or your job."

incriminated: proved guilty

officious:
prying;
interfering

I had lapsed into "we"—it is hard to use it and not seem cold and bullying; it can be a terrifying pronoun. And yet I had hoped this meeting would be friendly. It was, from my point of view, disastrously cold. His resentment made me **officious**; my officiousness made him stubborn. In the end I had simply pulled rank on him, used the scowling "we," and given him a crude choice. Then I left him. He looked isolated and lonely at the table in the pub, and that saddened me, because he was handsome and intelligent and young and a very hard worker. His earring distinguished him and made him look like a prince.

The next day I went to Horton's office. Seeing me, he rushed out and gave me a playful shove. He then helped me into the office with a hug, all the while saying, "Get in here and tell me what a great success you've been in the telex room."

I hated this fooling. I said, "I've had a talk with Hogle."

"With what result?"

"He's thinking about it."

"You mean, it's not settled? You let him *think* about it?"

I freed myself from his grasp. I said, "Yes."

"It's not a thinking matter," Horton said. "It's an order—didn't you tell him that?"

"I didn't want to throw my weight around. You said yourself there's no point making an issue out of it if it can be settled quietly."

Horton gaped at this. He became theatrical, imitating shock and incredulity with his exaggerated squint, and there was something of an actressy whine in his voice when he said, "So he's still down there, wearing that *thing* on his ear?"

I let him rant a bit more. Then I said, "I didn't want to put pressure on him. If he hasn't got the sense to see that our displeasure matters, then he's hardly any use to us."

"That's a point—I don't want any passengers in this Embassy, and I certainly won't put up with freaks." Horton's phone was ringing; it had the effect of sobering him and making him snappish. "I'll expect that file back by the end of the week—and I want a happy conclusion. Remember, if you can't get this chappie"—Horton wiggled his head on the word—"to remove his earring, you can hardly expect me to have much faith in your powers of persuasion."

"I'd like to drop the whole damned thing," I said.

Horton paused, and he peered at me with interest in spite of his nagging phone. "And why is that?"

"I don't see the importance of it," I said.

"It is very important," he said. "And of course I'm interested in your technique. You see, in this Embassy one is constantly trying to point out that there is a sensible, productive way of doing things—and there is the British way. Tactful persuasion is such an asset, whether one is dealing with a misunderstood aspect of NATO[1] or an infraction of the dress regulations by a serving officer—I mean, Hogle's earring. I hate even the word."

"I'll do it," I said. "But my heart isn't in it."

"That is precisely why I want you to do it," Horton said. "If nothing else, this should teach you that feelings have nothing to do with this job. Now, please, get it over with. It's starting to make me sick."

I chose the pub carefully. It was in Earl's Court and notoriously male; but at six-thirty it was empty and could easily have been mistaken for the haunt of darts players and polite locals with wives and dogs. Hogle was late. Waiting there, I thought that he might not turn up at all, just to teach me a lesson. But he came with an excuse and an apology. He had been telexing an urgent cable. Only he had clearance to work with classified material after hours, and the duty officer—Yorty, a newcomer—had no idea how to use a telex machine. So Hogle had worked late. As an ex-Army man he understood many of the military cables, and he had security clearance, and he was willing; I knew from his file that he didn't make mistakes. His obedience had never been questioned—that is, until Horton spotted the earring. I began to see why this detail worried Horton so much: Hogle, in such a ticklish job, had to be absolutely reliable.

He said, "I've been thinking over what you told me."

He looked tired—paler than he had three days ago. It was not the extra work, I was sure—he was worrying, not sleeping well. Perhaps he had already decided to resign on a point of principle, for in spite of his wilted posture and ashen skin, his expression was full of **tenacity**. I suppose it was his eyes. They were narrow, as though wounded, and hot, and seemed to say *No surrender*.

tenacity: perseverance; stubbornness

I said, "Don't say anything."

He had been staring into the middle distance. Now he looked closely at me. He winced, but he kept his gaze on me.

I said, "I've managed to prevail. I took it to the highest possible level. I think everyone understands now."

---

1 **NATO:** North Atlantic Treaty Organization

"What do you mean, 'understands'?" There was a hint of anxiety in his voice.

"Your earring," I said.

"What's there to understand?"

"You've got nothing to worry about. We don't persecute people for their beliefs anymore. If that were the case I wouldn't be in the Foreign Service."

"Wearing an earring," Hogle said. "Is that a belief?"

"It depends on how naïve you are," I said. "But be glad it doesn't matter. Be glad you live in a free society, where you can dress any way you like, and where you can choose your friends, whether they're British or American, white or black, female or male—"

Hogle became very attentive.

I said, "I'm grateful to you. It's people like you who break down barriers and increase our self-awareness."

"I don't want to break down any barriers," he said. "I'm not even sure what self-awareness is all about."

"It's about earrings," I said. "The other day I told you your earring was nice. I was being insincere. May I call you Charlie?"

"Sure."

"Charlie, I think your earring is fantastic."

His hand went to his ear. He looked wary. He did not let go of the earring or his earlobe. He sat fixedly with his fingers making this plucking gesture on his ear.

"It's a very handsome accessory," I said. His fingers tightened. "A real enhancement." They moved again. "An elegant statement—"

I thought he was going to yank his ear off. His hand was trembling, still covering the earring. He said, "I'm not making a statement."

"Take it easy," I said, giving him the sort of blanket assurance of no danger that convinces people—and rightly—that they're in a tight spot. "You've got absolutely nothing to worry about!" He looked very worried. "You can relax with me." I ordered him a drink and told him there was no point in discussing the earring.

"To be perfectly honest," I said, "I rather like your earring."

"I'm certainly not making any kind of statement," Hogle said. The word worried him. It had implications of being unerasable and hinted of hot water. "I got the idea from one of the delivery men—an English guy. He wasn't making a statement. It looked neat, that's all."

"It looks more than neat," I said. "It has a certain mystery. I think that's its real charm."

He winced at this, and how he was pinching his earlobe. He lowered his eyes. He did not look up again.

"I feel funny," he said.

"Be glad you work with people who say yes instead of no."

I gave him a friendly punch on the shoulder, the sort of body English Horton would have approved. It made me feel uncomfortable and mannered and overhearty. It amazed me then to realize that Horton was always punching and hugging and digging in the ribs. Hogle was unresponsive, not to say wooden. His eyes darted sideways.

The night's clients had started to arrive in the pub—men in leather jackets, with close-cropped hair, and heavy chains around their necks, and tattooed thumbs, and sunglasses. Some were bald, some devilishly bearded; one wore crimson shoes; another had an enormous black dog on a leather strap. All of them wore earrings.

"Have another drink," I said.

Hogle stood up. "I have to go."

"What's the hurry?"

He was breathing hard. A man encased in tight black leather was hovering near us and staring at Hogle. The man had silver chains with thick links looped around his boots and they clanked as he came closer.

"No hurry," Hogle said. Now he was reassuring me in the way that I had reassured him earlier, giving me hollow guarantees as he backed away. "Hey, I had a good time." He stepped past the clanking man, whose leather, I swear, oinked and squeaked. "No kidding. It's just that"—he looked around—"I told this friend of mine, this girl I know, that I'd—I don't know, I'd give her a call." He looked desperate. "Hey, thanks a lot. I really appreciate everything you've done!"

Then he left, and then I removed my earring. That was easy enough to do—just a matter of unscrewing the little plunger and putting the foolish thing into my pocket. And I hurried out of the pub, hearing just behind me clanks and squeaks of **reproach**.

reproach: disappointment; blame

In my report for Charlie Hogle's file I recorded the earring incident as a minor infraction—Inappropriate Dress. I left it vague. What was the point in explaining? I noted the two meetings; I described Hogle as "compliant" and "reasonable." There was no **innuendo** in my report. I spared him any indignity. It sounded no worse than if he had come to work without a necktie.

innuendo:
subtle implication

Indeed, it was no worse than if he had come to work without a necktie. I had had no objection to the earring, nor had any of Hogle's co-workers in the telex room. Horton had made it an issue; Horton was minister, so Horton was obeyed. And Hogle did not wear his earring again.

"It's for his own good," Horton said later, and he squeezed my arm. I was the team member who had just played well; he was the coach. He was proud of me and pleased with himself. He was beaming. "I feel a thousand times better, too! That really annoyed me—that kid's earring. I used to go down to the telex room a lot. I realized I was staying away—couldn't stand to look at it!"

"Aren't you being a little melodramatic?"

"I'm completely serious," he said. "That situation was making me sick. I mean sick. I got so mad the first time I saw that thing on his ear"—Horton turned away and paused—"I got so mad I actually threw up. Puked! That's how angry I was."

"You must have been very angry," I said.

"Couldn't help it. We can't have that sort of thing—" He didn't finish the sentence. He shook his head from side to side and then said, "You were too easy on him in your report. That kid had a problem. Incredible. I took him for a clean, stand-up guy!"

I said, "He may have feelings of which he's unaware. It's not that uncommon."

"No," Horton said. "I'll keep an eye on him."

"Fine," I said. "Anyway, everyone's safe now, coach."

He smiled and smacked my arm and sent me back to my office.

In the following weeks I saw scores of young men Hogle's age wearing earrings. They were English, and all sorts, and I was ashamed that I had been a success. It was not merely that I had succeeded by deceiving Hogle, but that I had made him think there was something dangerous and deviant in this trinket decorating his ear. And he never knew just how handsome that trinket made him. Hogle would be all right. But after what he had told me, I was not so sure about Horton.

Paul Theroux

Responding to the Story

1. **LITERARY LENS** Horton is fond of sports metaphors. What does this say about his character?

2. One black mark in Charlie Hogle's file states that he never experienced "negative situations." How can his never having been in a "negative situation" be considered a black mark?

3. On several occasions in the story, the narrator is disgusted by his own actions. What do you think most bothers him about what he has been asked to do and how he does it?

4. At one point the narrator says, "I had lapsed into 'we'—it is hard to use it and not seem cold and bullying; it can be a terrifying pronoun." In what ways can "we" be "a terrifying pronoun"?

5. **THE AUTHOR'S STYLE** Often, Theroux's fiction involves characters who are under pressure. The threats they face help them reveal their character. What does the earring incident reveal about the characters of Horton, Hogle, and the narrator?

RESPONDING TO UNIT FOUR

Experiencing

1. A moral is a short statement that summarizes the main message of a fable or tale. For example, "Slow and steady wins the race" is an example of a moral statement. Select two of the stories in this unit and write moral statements for each. Be prepared to explain your response.

2. It might be said that "This Is What It Means to Say Phoenix, Arizona" is a collage of stories. As a reader, what response do you have to this episodic style?

Interpreting

3. The voices in "Ladies and Gentlemen:" and "Top of the Food Chain" are similar in some ways. Compare and contrast the two stories to find what different results the voices achieve.

4. Consider the story "The Intruder," written in the third person point of view, and "Mortals," written in first person. What do you think the advantages of each point of view are in making readers feel empathy for the main characters?

Evaluating

5. Some critics complain that contemporary fiction lacks moral standards and depicts a gloomy vision of an amoral society. Do you agree or disagree with these critics? Use the fiction in this unit to support your position.

6. Although short stories are labeled fiction, many are based on actual people and events. Consider Paul Theroux's response below to readers who want to know if the events in his fiction actually happened. In your own writing or your reading, do you agree with him that it doesn't matter if a story actually happened or not?

> It's a 'What if?' life. The question is not, 'Did it happen?' It is, 'Did it convince you? Did it hold you until the end? Did you like it?' Rather than, 'Is it true?' If all the other things happen—if you read it, like it, remember it, dream about it—in a way it doesn't matter if it's true or not.
>
> —Paul Theroux

WRITING ABOUT THE LITERATURE

Staying Power

Some of the relatively recent stories in this unit may be ignored by future readers and others may gain staying power and appear over and over in anthologies like this one. Select the one that you think will last and one that, in your opinion, will be soon forgotten. Explain your choices in a short essay.

WRITING WITH STYLE

Choose one of the following writing activities.

Found Story

Robert Olen Butler has been known to find inspiration for his stories in unusual places. For example, he wrote a story titled "*Titantic* Victim Speaks Through Waterbed" based on a headline of a supermarket tabloid. Develop a story line using a "found" object (a soft drink can, a piece of clothing—whatever you decide) or a "found" story (such as a newspaper account).

From Story to Film

While trying to find a studio to finance a movie version of "This Is What It Means to Say Phoenix, Arizona," Sherman Alexie was urged to use white actors for the two main characters. The movie *Smoke Signals* was finally produced using Native Americans. Refer to passages in "This Is What It Means to Say Phoenix, Arizona" that use dialogue, such as the exchanges on page 490. Now take a shot at Alexie's style by making up a scene in dialogue, in which Alexie meets with a white producer to discuss making the film.

IN YOUR OWN STYLE

Several of the stories in this unit involve a moral dilemma: whether to persuade Charlie Hogle to give up his earring in "Charlie Hogle's Earring," for example, or how Victor should treat Thomas in "This Is What It Means to Say Phoenix, Arizona." Now it's your turn. Try writing about any moral dilemma of your choosing—whether it actually happened or not—in your own style. Instinctive or deliberate, the choices you make about dialogue, point of view, and tone will help to shape your style.

GLOSSARY OF LITERARY TERMS

absurdism	writing that reflects the idea that the universe is irrational and meaningless
allegory	a literary work in which characters, objects, and events stand for abstract qualities outside the story such as goodness, pleasure, or evil
allusion	a reference to an historical or literary figure or event
analogy	a description of an unfamiliar thing through comparing it to something more well-known
anecdote	a short incident or story that illustrates a point; anecdotal stories usually have an informal storyteller's **tone**
anti-hero	a **protagonist** who displays traits opposite to the qualities usually associated with the traditional hero
archetype	an image, character, **symbol**, **plot**, or other literary device that appears frequently enough in **myths**, **folktales**, and other literary works so as to become an important part of a culture
characterization	the manner in which an author creates and develops a character utilizing **exposition**, **dialogue**, and **action**
climax	the high point of a **plot**; sometimes coincides with the *turning point* or *defining moment*; some stories do not have a clear climax
colloquialism	a local or regional expression
concrete universal	a universal concern (one that applies to everyone, everywhere) addressed through a concrete, or local, setting
conflict	the struggle between opposing forces; *external conflict* involves an outer force such as nature or another character while *internal conflict* exists inside a person, say between a hero's sense of duty and desire for freedom
denouement	literally "the untying;" the part of a plot in which the **conflict** is "untied" or resolved; usually follows the **climax**
dialogue	conversation between characters in a literary work
epiphany	an event, sometimes **mystical** in nature, in which a character changes in profound ways due to the revelation of a simple yet powerful truth; also sometimes called a *defining moment*, *moment of clarity*, or *moment of truth*
exposition	information or background that is directly conveyed or explained, usually by the **narrator**

fable	a short story or tale that demonstrates a moral or truth; frequently contains **fantasy** elements such as talking animal characters
falling action	the events of a **plot** that follow the **climax;** also referred to as the **denouement** or **resolution**
fantasy	stories that contain characters, settings, and objects that could not exist, such as dragons or magic swords; often heroic in nature and sometimes based on **myths** and legends
figurative language	any of several techniques such as **imagery**, **metaphor**, or **analogy** that describe an object or character through comparison to something else
figure of speech	an expression that conveys meaning or increases an effect, usually through **figurative language**
first person point of view	see **point of view**
flashback	an interruption of the normal chronological order of a **plot** to narrate events that happened earlier
folktale	a narrative, usually originating in an **oral tradition**, with a timeless and placeless **setting** and **archetypal plot** elements and characters; may contain elements of **fantasy** as well
foreshadowing	use of hints or clues about what will happen later in a **plot**
frame narrator	a **narrator** of a story in which other narrators may appear to tell stories within the story
genre	a distinctive type or category of literature, such as the epic, comedy, tragedy, short story, novel, science fiction, or mystery
gothic	a type of writing that focuses on the macabre, grotesque, mysterious, and/or violent; *Southern Gothic* refers to stories that have these elements and are set in the American South
idiom	an expression that is peculiar to a group or community; often difficult to translate
imagery	vivid and striking descriptions of objects and details in a literary work, often through **figurative language**
in media res	literally, "in the midst of things;" refers to a type of **plot** that begins at a high point of the action and fills in **exposition** later
interior monologue	the presentation in a literary work of the unspoken thoughts and feelings of a character
interpretation	an explanation of the meaning of a piece of literature, dependent in part on the perspective of the reader

irony	a recognition and heightening of the difference between appearance and reality; *situational irony* occurs when events turn out differently than expected; *dramatic irony* occurs when the audience has important knowledge that a main character lacks
juxtaposition	two or more things placed side by side, generally in an unexpected combination
local color movement	a style of writing that developed just after the Civil War and that strives to reveal the peculiarities of a particular place and the people who live there
metafiction	fiction that contains within it a comment about the process of writing fiction
metaphor	a **figure of speech** that implies a similarity between two unlike things
minimalist	a spare, pared down style of writing made popular in the 1970s
morality play	a play in which the characters personify moral or abstract qualities such as Charity or Death
motivation	the reasons or forces that cause characters to act as they do
mysticism	the belief that knowledge of God, truth, or reality can be gained through intuition or insight
myth	a traditional story, often one that explains a belief or natural phenomenon
narrator	a teller of a story; an *unreliable narrator* makes incorrect conclusions and biased assumptions; a *naïve narrator* doesn't fully understand the events he or she narrates
neologism	a newly coined word
oral tradition	legends, folktales, and stories that were initially told orally
pathos	an element of literature that evokes pity or compassion
plot	the events of a story
point of view	the perspective from which a story is narrated: in *first person point of view* the narrator is a character in the story and uses the personal pronoun "I"; in *third person limited point of view*, the narrator is outside the story but presents the story through the thoughts and feelings of one character; in *third person omniscient point of view*, the narrator is outside the story and knows the thoughts and feelings of all characters and can comment on any part of the story
protagonist	the main character of a story
realistic fiction	fiction that attempts to describe the world in a realistic fashion
regionalism	literature with an emphasis on locale or other local characteristics such as dialect
repartee	quick, witty exchanges of **dialogue**
resolution	the point at which the chief **conflict** or complication is worked out
rising action	the events leading up to the **climax** of a **plot**

satire	writing that uses humor or ridicule to point out human shortcomings and follies
scenario	a plot outline; one of many ways in which a story could be worked out
setting	the time and place of the action of a story
simile	a comparason of one thing to another that uses "like" or "as"
stream of consciousness	the flow of various impressions—visual, auditory, psychological, intuitive—that represent the mind and heart of a character
subtext	a hidden meaning, often **symbolic** or **metaphorical**, that must be inferred from the text given
surrealism	a literary and artistic movement emphasizing the expression of the subconscious through dreamlike **imagery**
symbol	an object that stands for or represents a more abstract concept, such as an eagle for freedom or a rose for love
tale	a series of facts or events either told or written
theme	the underlying meaning or message of a literary work
third person limited point of view	see **point of view**
third person omniscient point of view	see **point of view**
tone	the author or narrator's attitude toward the subject of a work; an author might have an ironic, humorous, sarcastic, serious, or deadpan tone, to name a few
universality	the quality of having feelings, thoughts, emotions, themes, or problems that cross all times and cultures
voice	an author or character's distinctive way of expressing himself or herself
world view	the background, attitudes, and values of a society or individual

INDEX OF TITLES AND AUTHORS

A & P   259

Alexie, Sherman   472

American Horse   355

Angel Levine   207

Babylon Revisited   43

Banks, Russell   382

Barn Burning   185

Black Ball, The   115

Boyle, T. Coraghessan   454

Bradbury, Ray   168

Butler, Robert Olen   462

Capote, Truman   146

Carver, Raymond   326

Charlie Hogle's Earring   529

Cheever, John   220

Chrysanthemums, The   85

Detroit Skyline, 1949   335

Doctorow, E. L.   368

Dubus, Andre   502

Ellison, Ralph   114

Erdrich, Louise   354

Everything Stuck to Him   327

Everything That Rises
    Must Converge   241

Far and the Near, The   67

Faulkner, William   184

Fault Lines   443

Fish, The   383

Fitzgerald, F. Scott   42

Flowers, The   313

Gaines, Ernest J.   268

Harrison Bergeron   231

He   29

Hemingway, Ernest   20

In Another Country   21

Intruder, The   503

Jackson, Shirley   134

Keillor, Garrison   392

Key, The   301

Kingsolver, Barbara   442

Ladies and Gentlemen: 433

Letters from My Father   463

Lottery, The   135

Malamud, Bernard   **206**

Mason, Bobbie Ann   **334**

McCullers, Carson   **72**

Miriam   **147**

Mortals   **517**

Oates, Joyce Carol   **432**

O'Brien, Tim   **316**

O'Connor, Flannery   **240**

Petrakis, Harry Mark   **298**

Porter, Katherine Anne   **28**

Rules of the Game   **401**

Secret Life of Walter Mitty, The   **127**

Singer, Isaac Bashevis   **300**

Sky Is Gray, The   **269**

Steinbeck, John   **84**

Sucker   **73**

Tan, Amy   **400**

Theroux, Paul   **528**

*This Is What It Means to
    Say Phoenix, Arizona*   **473**

Thurber, James   **126**

Top of the Food Chain   **455**

Truckstop   **393**

Updike, John   **258**

Veldt, The   **169**

Vonnegut, Kurt   **230**

Walker, Alice   **312**

Welty, Eudora   **98**

*Where Have You Gone,
    Charming Billy?*   **317**

Why I Live at the P.O.   **99**

Wolfe, Thomas   **66**

Wolff, Tobias   **516**

Wooing of Ariadne, The   **299**

Writer in the Family, The   **369**

Wrysons, The   **221**

★★★

ACKNOWLEDGMENTS

Text Credits

"A & P" by John Updike from *Pigeon Feathers and Other Stories*. Copyright © 1962, renewed 1990 by John Updike. Used by permission of Alfred A. Knopf, a division of Random House, Inc.

"American Horse" by Louise Erdrich. Copyright © 1983 by Louise Erdrich. Reprinted by permission of The Wylie Agency, Inc.

"Angel Levine" by Bernard Malamud from *The Magic Barrel*. Copyright © 1950, 1958, renewed 1977, 1986 by Bernard Malamud. Reprinted by permission of Farrar, Straus & Giroux, LLC.

"Babylon Revisited" by F. Scott Fitzgerald from *The Short Stories of F. Scott Fitzgerald*. Copyright 1931 by Curtis Publishing Company, renewed © 1959 by Frances Scott Fitzgerald Lanahan. Reprinted with permission of Scribner, a division of Simon & Schuster, Inc.

"Barn Burning" by William Faulkner from *Collected Stories of William Faulkner*. Copyright © 1950 by Random House, renewed 1977 by Jill Faulkner Summers. Used by permission of Random House, Inc.

"The Black Ball" by Ralph Ellison from *Flying Home and Other Stories*. Copyright © 1996 by Fanny Ellison; Introduction copyright © 1996 by John F. Callahan. Used by permission of Random House, Inc.

"Charlie Hogle's Earring" by Paul Theroux from *Collected Stories of Paul Theroux*. Copyright © 1969, 1970, 1971, 1972, 1975, 1977 by Paul Theroux, Copyright © 1980, 1982, 1983, 1996, 1997 by Cape Cod Scriveners. Used by permission of Viking Penguin, a division of Penguin Putnam Inc.

"The Chrysanthemums" by John Steinbeck. Copyright 1937, renewed © 1965 by John Steinbeck. Used by permission of Viking Penguin, a division of Penguin Putnam Inc.

"Detroit Skyline, 1949" by Bobbie Ann Mason from *Shiloh & Other Stories*. Copyright © 1982 by Bobbie Ann Mason. Reprinted by permission of International Creative Management.

"Everything Stuck to Him" by Raymond Carver from *What We Talk About When We Talk About Love*. Copyright © 1981 by Raymond Carver. Reprinted by permission of International Creative Management.

Photo and Art Credits

Page 16: TL and page 18, J. C. Leyendecker, Arrow Color Advertisement, The Granger Collection; Insert and page 19, Robert Capa/Magnum Photos; TR and page 19, ©Hulton-Deutsch Collection/CORBIS; BL and page 18, Copyright the Dorothea Lange Collection, Oakland Museum of California, City of Oakland. Gift of Paul S. Taylor; BR and page 19, CORBIS. Page 17: T and page 19, Arthur Rothstein/CORBIS; BL and page 18, Margaret Bourke-White/TimePix; BR and page 19, Joe Rosenthal/CORBIS. PAGE 20: ©The Nobel Foundation. Page 23: ©CORBIS. Page 28: Papers of Katherine Anne Porter, Special Collections, University of Maryland Libraries. Page 30: ©Horace Bristol/CORBIS. Pages 38 and 39: Andrew Wyeth, *Public Sale*, 1943. Tempera, 22 × 48 in. The Philadelphia Museum of Art. Page 47: Florine Stettheimer, *The Cathedrals of Broadway*, 1929. Oil on canvas, 60 1/8 × 50 1/8. The Metropolitan Museum of Art, gift of Ettie Stettheimer, 1953. Page 69: Thomas Hart Benton, *Train on the Desert*, 1926-28. Oil on canvas, 13 1/4 × 19 1/4 in. ©T. H. Benton and R. P. Benton Testamentary Trusts/Licensed by VAGA, New York. Page 72: United Press International. Page 81: Andrew Wyeth, *Winter*, 1946. Tempera on board, 31 3/8 × 48 in. The North Carolina Museum of Art, Raleigh. Purchased with funds from the State of North Carolina. Page 84: ©The Nobel Foundation. Page 94: Rinaldo Cuneo, *Earth Patterns*, c. 1932. Oil on canvas, 30 × 36 in. Gift of Howard E. Johnson, Oakland Museum of California. Page 98: Gil Ford Photography. Page 109: Walker Evans, *Interior of Negro Preacher's House, Florida*, 1934. ©Walker Evans Archive, The Metropolitan Museum of Art, 1994. (1994.258.326). Page 111: Walker Evans, *Frame Houses in Virginia*, 1936. ©Walker Evans Archive, The Metropolitan Museum of Art, 1994. (1994.258.311). Page 114: AP Photo. Page 118 and TOC: Ruth Marten. Page 126: United Press International. Page 128 and TOC: Roy Lichtenstein, *Blam*, 1962. Oil on canvas, 5 ft. 8 in. × 6 ft. 8 in. Yale University Art Gallery. Gift of Richard Brown Baker, B.A. 1935. Page 134: Courtesy of Laurence J. Hyman. Page 137: Grant Wood, *Stone City, Iowa*, 1930. Oil on wood panel, 30 1/4 × 40 in. Joslyn Art Museum, Omaha, NE. Page 146: ©Hulton-Deutsch Collection/CORBIS. Page 151 and TOC: Fairfield Porter, *Katie in an Armchair*, 1954. Used with permission. Page 164: T and page 167: Bernie Boston Photography; Insert and page 166, ©Christie's Images/CORBIS/Arists Rights Society (ARS) New York; B and page 167, ©James H. Karales/Peter Arnold Inc.; Inset and page 167, Hulton/Archive by Getty Images. Page 165: T and page 166: NASA/CORBIS; B and page 167, Larry Burrows/TimePix; Insert and page 166, Toni Frissell /Magnum Photos. Page 168: Christine Rose Photography. Page 184: J. R. Colfield. Pages 186 and 187: Andrew Wyeth, *Hay Ledge*, 1957. Tempera on panel, 21 1/2 × 45 1/4. Greenville County Museum of Art, museum purchase in honor of Greenville philanthropists, Holly and Arthur Magill with major funding from the Museum Association, Inc. Page 206: ©David Lees/CORBIS. Page 214: Archibald Motley, Jr., *Blues*, 1929. Oil on canvas, 36 × 42 in. Collection of Archie Motley and Valerie Gerrard Browne. Page 220: ©David Lees/CORBIS. Page 223: Fairfield Porter, *Jane and Elizabeth*, 1967. Oil on canvas. 55 1/8 × 48 1/8 in. The Parrish Art Museum. Southhampton. NY. Gift of Jan Freilicher. (1979.13.2). Page 230: United Press International. Page 237: Jonathan Borofsky, *Stick Man*. ©1983, Jonathan Borofsky and Gemini G.E.L., Los Angeles. Page 240: AP Photo. Page 242: Daphne Confar, *Morality Was Her Own*. Oil on copper, 6 × 4.5 in. Courtesy Pepper Gallery, Boston. Page 258: United Press International. Page 261 and TOC: Victor Maldonado, *Measure*, 2001. Acrylic, xerography, wax, 12 × 12 in. Courtesy of Froelick Gallery, Portland, OR. Page 268: Brad Kemp/AP Photo. Page 279: Romare Bearden, *Sunday Morning Breakfast*, 1967. Collage on masonite, 44 × 56 in. ©Bearden Foundation/Licensed by VAGA, New York. Page 298: Courtesy of Ivan R. Dee Publishing, Inc. Page 302 and TOC: Timothy Harney, *The Painter of Tbilisi*, 1989. Acrylic and mixed media, collage/paper, 40 × 30 in. Private Collection. Page 312: O. Louis Guglielmi, *Wedding in South Street*, 1936. Oil on canvas, 30× 24 in. Copyright The Museum of Modern Art/Licensed by SCALA/Art Resource, New York. Page 316: T and page 318, Star Black, *Hey, Yuppie, Search Your Heart*; Inset and page 318, ©Ellis Richard/CORBIS SYGMA; B and page 319, Wally McNamee/CORBIS; Inset and page 319, ©Bettmann/CORBIS. Page 317: T and page 319 ©1989 Alexandra Avakian/Contact Press Images; B and page 319, ©Reuters NewMedia Inc./CORBIS; Inset and page 318, ©Roger Ressmeyer/CORBIS. Page 320: Kathy Willens/AP Photo. Page 332: Noah Berger/AP Photo. Page 336: Jerry Bauer. Page 339 and TOC: Michael Brostowitz, *Come a Little Closer*, 1997. Oil on board, 15 1/4 × 19 3/4 in. The National Vietnam Veterans Art Museum. Page 345: Charlie Shobe, *On the Road to Con Thien*, 1980. Oil on canvas,

24 x 18 in. National Vietnam Veterans Art Museum. Page 348: Chester Higgins/The New York Times. Page 356: Roger Rawlings. Page 362: Charles Sheeler, *American Landscape,* 1930. Oil on canvas, 24 x 31 in. Gift of Abby Aldrich Rockefeller (166.1934). The Museum of Modern Art, New York. Copyright The Museum of Modern Art/Licensed by SCALA/Art Resource, New York. Page 376: ©Marc Norberg/The Wylie Agency. Page 390: ©Bettmann/CORBIS. Page 393: Maynard Dixon, *Southern Arizona,* 1941. Pen and ink, 14 x 12 1/2 in. Private Collection. Page 403 and TOC: Maynard Dixon, *Central Nevada,* 1941. Pen and ink, 14 x 12 1/2 in. Private Collection. Page 406: ©Nathan Farb. Page 411: Joseph Raffael, *Return to the Beginning, In Memory of Ginger,* 1981. Watercolor on paper, 33 1/2 x 41 in. Private collection. Photo courtesy of Nancy Hoffman Gallery, New York. Page 416: B. Paul Burnett/AP Photo. Page 418 and TOC: Ralph Goings, *Burger Chef,* 1970. Oil on canvas, 40 x 56 in. Photo courtesy of O. K. Harris Works of Art, New York. Page 424: ©Reuters NewMedia, Inc./CORBIS. Page 427: Mary Heussenstamm, *Girl with Bangs.* Watercolor. Page 436: Martin Wong, *Grant Avenue, San Francisco,* 1992. Acrylic on linen, 108 x 42 in. Private Collection. Photo courtesy Pilkington Olsoff Fine Arts, Inc., New York. Page 440: T and page 442, Peter Turnley/CORBIS; Inset R, CORBIS SYGMA; Inset L and page 442, Charles H. Porter IV/CORBIS SYGMA; BL and page 442, ©Touhig Sion/CORBIS SYGMA; BR and Page 443, Jim Bourg/Reuters/TimePix; Page 441: T and page 443, Peter Turnley/CORBIS; Inset R and page 443, CORBIS; B and page 443, Joseph Sohm/CORBIS; Inset BL and page 443, ©Chauvel Patrick/CORBIS SYGMA; Page 444: AP Photo. Page 450: Charles Burchfield, *The Sphinx and the Milky Way,* c. 1946. Watercolor, 52 5/8 x 44 3/4 in. Munson-Williams-Proctor Arts Institute, Museum of Art, Utica, NY (48.45). Page 454: ©2000 Steven L. Hopp. Courtesy of HarperCollins. Page 456: Wayne Thiebaud, *San Francisco Landscape,* 1976. Oil on canvas, 12 x 14 in. ©Wayne Thiebaud/Licensed by VAGA, New York. Page 466: Jim Cooper/AP Photo. Page 472: Caty Bartholomew. Page 474: ©Philip Gould/CORBIS. Page 481 and TOC: Larry Yung, *Separation.* Latex, acrylic, plaster, chalk on plywood, 89 x 84 in. Page 484: Jim Cooper/AP Photo. Page 498: Marion Ettlinger/AP Photo. Page 512: Dagmar Logie. Page 514: Saul Steinberg, *Hard and Soft Figures,* 1952. ©2002 The Saul Steinberg Foundation/Artists Rights Society (ARS) New York. The New Yorker magazine original source of publication. Page 524: ©Jonathan Torgovinik/CORBIS SYGMA. Page 533 and TOC: Alex Katz, *Track Jacket,* 1956. Oil on masonite, 24 x 18 in. Colby College Museum of Art, gift of the artist. (1995.062) ©Alex Katz/Licensed by VAGA, New York.